QA
691
B4

Introduction to
Hilbert Space

UNIVERSITY TEXTS IN THE MATHEMATICAL SCIENCES

Introduction to Hilbert Space

STERLING K. BERBERIAN

State University of Iowa

New York   OXFORD UNIVERSITY PRESS   1961

To Jean Arnold

Preface

This textbook has evolved from a set of lecture notes which I prepared for a semester course in Hilbert space at the State University of Iowa. In both the course and the book, I have in mind first- or second-year graduate students in Mathematics and related fields such as Physics.

It is necessary for the reader to have a foundation in advanced calculus which includes familiarity with: least upper bound (LUB) and greatest lower bound (GLB), the concept of function, ϵ's and their companion δ's, and basic properties of sequences of real and complex numbers (convergence, Cauchy's criterion, the Weierstrass-Bolzano theorem). It is *not* presupposed that the reader is acquainted with vector spaces (which are discussed in Chapter I), matrices (which are mentioned only in a few exercises), or determinants (which are mentioned nowhere else in the book). In keeping with these prerequisites, I have refrained from using set-theoretic notation in the first two chapters; some of the notations and terminology of set theory are gradually introduced thereafter. Occasionally I have inserted remarks and exercises, not essential to the exposition, which call for considerably more background than the general level of the text. Such statements can be recognized by the phrase "it can be shown"; they are likely to be out of reach of the reader's technique, but not out of reach of his curiosity.

There are over four hundred exercises, most of them easy. Some of these describe generalizations of material in the text. Others provide examples and counter-examples for the definitions and theorems of the text. Any of them may be used for practice in the construction of proofs. Hints for solution, and references to other sources, will be found in the Appendix. Exercises in the "it can be shown" category are marked with a *. The reader who prefers to vault over the exercises may do so without breaking the continuity of the exposition.

The "spectral theorem" presented here is confined to completely continuous normal operators, the most elementary infinite case. This is not enough for many applications, but it is about as far as one can get without sophisticated techniques. Many beautiful expositions of advanced spectral theory are available to the interested and prepared reader (a few of these are listed in the Appendix).

It is my hope that this book, aside from being an exposition of certain basic material on Hilbert space, may also serve as an introduction to other areas of functional analysis. It seems to me that Hilbert space, fortified with the experience and geometrical intuition developed in two- and three-dimensional cases, is an excellent vehicle for introducing topics such as vector spaces, metric spaces, Banach spaces, Banach algebras, and so on. Such opportunities are exploited frequently in the text and in the exercises.

The system of bookkeeping I have used is as follows. Each chapter is organized into sections (§). Within each §, *Definitions, Examples, Theorems,* and *Exercises* are numbered starting at 1. For example: *Theorem VI.8.1* is the first theorem in § 8 of Chapter VI; within a chapter, *Theorem 3.2* refers to the second theorem in § 3 of that chapter; within a §, *Theorem 3* refers to the third theorem in that §. The end of a proof is indicated by the Halmos finality symbol ▌; I have also used this symbol in a few other places to indicate a pause before a new train of ideas begins. ▌

I am grateful to my colleagues Lloyd A. Knowler and William T. Reid, and to the staff of the Oxford University Press, for encouraging me to bring forth this book.

S. K. B.

September 1961
Iowa City

Contents

Chapter VIII. COMPLETELY CONTINUOUS OPERATORS

Introduction to
Hilbert Space

Vector Spaces

§ 1. COMPLEX VECTOR SPACES

Underlying every Hilbert space, there is a vector space; the present chapter contains preparatory material on vector spaces. The reader who is already acquainted with the basic theory of vector spaces can pass directly to Chapter II, for there is nothing in the present chapter which is particularly oriented toward Hilbert space.

In the sequel, complex numbers will also be referred to as **scalars**.

Definition 1. *A* **vector space** $\mathcal{V}$ *is a set of objects* $x, y, z, \cdots$ *called* **vectors.** *One vector is distinguished, called the* **zero vector,** *and denoted* θ. *For each vector* x, *there is distinguished a vector* $-x$, *called the* **negative** *of* x. *The following axioms are assumed to hold.*

(A) *For each pair of vectors* x, y, *there is determined a vector called the* **sum** *of* x *and* y, *denoted* $x + y$ *(read "x plus y"). The "addition" of vectors is subject to these rules:*

    (A1) $x + y = y + x$ *(commutative law)*

    (A2) $x + (y + z) = (x + y) + z$ *(associative law)*

    (A3) $x + \theta = x$

    (A4) $x + (-x) = \theta.$

(M)   *For each scalar* λ, *and each vector x, there is determined a vector called the* **multiple** *of x by* λ (*or the* **product** *of* λ *and x*), *denoted* λx. *The "multiplication" of vectors by scalars is subject to these rules:*

(M1) $\lambda(x + y) = \lambda x + \lambda y$ ⎤

(M2) $(\lambda + \mu)x = \lambda x + \mu x$ ⎦   (*distributive laws*)

(M3) $(\lambda\mu)x = \lambda(\mu x)$ (*associative law*)

(M4) $1x = x.$

The reader will observe that in (M2), the symbol $+$ is used in two senses: for the sum of scalars, and the sum of vectors. In (M3), the juxtaposition of letters has two meanings: the product of two scalars, or the product of a scalar and a vector.

Examples

1. Given a fixed positive integer n. Let $\mathcal{V}$ be the set of all symbols $x = (\lambda_1, \cdots, \lambda_n)$, called *$n$-ples*, where $\lambda_1, \cdots, \lambda_n$ are scalars. If $x = (\lambda_1, \cdots, \lambda_n)$ and $y = (\mu_1, \cdots, \mu_n)$, write $x = y$ in case $\lambda_k = \mu_k$ for $k = 1, \cdots, n$; λ_k is called the k'th *component* of x. Define $\theta = (0, \cdots, 0)$, $-x = (-\lambda_1, \cdots, -\lambda_n)$, $x + y = (\lambda_1 + \mu_1, \cdots, \lambda_n + \mu_n)$, and $\lambda x = (\lambda\lambda_1, \cdots, \lambda\lambda_n)$. The axioms (A) and (M) are verified by using the given criterion for equality, and the analogous properties of sums and products of scalars. For instance, if $x = (\lambda_1, \cdots, \lambda_n)$ and $y = (\mu_1, \cdots, \mu_n)$, the relations $\lambda_k + \mu_k = \mu_k + \lambda_k$ $(k = 1, \cdots, n)$ yield $x + y = y + x$. In the sequel, this example will be referred to as *the vector space of n-ples*.

2. Let $\mathcal{V}$ be the set of all functions x defined on a set $\mathfrak{I}$, having scalar values. Write $x = y$ in case $x(t) = y(t)$ for all t in $\mathfrak{I}$. Define the functions θ, $-x$, $x + y$, and λx by the formulas

$$\theta(t) = 0$$

$$(-x)(t) = -x(t)$$

$$(x + y)(t) = x(t) + y(t)$$

$$(\lambda x)(t) = \lambda x(t).$$

This example will be referred to as *the vector space of scalar-valued functions on* $\mathfrak{I}$.

One can obtain *Example 1* as a special case: take for $\mathfrak{I}$ the set of integers $1,\cdots,n$, and interpret $x = (\lambda_1,\cdots,\lambda_n)$ as the function on $\mathfrak{I}$ such that $x(k) = \lambda_k$. If $\mathfrak{I}$ is the set of all positive integers $1,2,3,\cdots$, then $\mathfrak{V}$ can be interpreted as the set of all sequences $x = (\lambda_k)$ with scalar terms λ_k $(k = 1,2,3,\cdots)$; in this context, two sequences are considered to be equal if they are equal term by term.

3. Let $\mathfrak{V}$ be the set of all scalar-valued functions x defined, and continuous, on the closed interval $[a,b]$. Write $x = y$ in case $x(t) = y(t)$ for all t, $a \leq t \leq b$. Define θ, $-x$, $x + y$, and λx as in *Example 2*; these functions are continuous by elementary calculus. This example will be referred to as *the vector space of continuous functions on* $[a,b]$.

4. Let $\mathfrak{V}$ be the set of all polynomial functions, with complex coefficients, defined on the closed interval $[a,b]$. Equality, zero, negatives, sums, and scalar multiples are defined as in *Example 3*. The sum of two polynomial functions, and a scalar multiple of a polynomial function, are themselves polynomial functions. This example will be referred to as *the vector space of polynomial functions on* $[a,b]$.

5. Given a fixed positive integer n. Let $\mathfrak{V}$ be the set of all polynomial functions, with complex coefficients, of degree $<n$, defined on the interval $[a,b]$. Sums and scalar multiples are defined as in *Example 4*.

6. Let $\mathfrak{V}$ be the set of all sequences $x = (\lambda_k)$ of scalars, all of whose terms, from some index onward, are 0 (the particular index may vary from sequence to sequence). Write $(\lambda_k) = (\mu_k)$ in case $\lambda_k = \mu_k$ for all $k = 1,2,3,\cdots$. Define $\theta = (0)$, $-(\lambda_k) = (-\lambda_k)$, $(\lambda_k) + (\mu_k) = (\lambda_k + \mu_k)$, and $\lambda(\lambda_k) = (\lambda\lambda_k)$. See the discussion in *Example 2*. This example will be referred to as *the vector space of finitely non-zero sequences*.

7. Let $\mathfrak{V}$ be the set of all scalar-valued functions x defined on a set $\mathfrak{I}$, such that $x(t) = 0$ except for at most a finite number of points t. Define θ, $-x$, $x + y$, and λx as in *Example 2*. One obtains *Example 6* by taking, in the place of $\mathfrak{I}$, the set of all positive integers. If $\mathfrak{I}$ contains only finitely many points, say n of them, one obtains *Example 1* (see the discussion in *Example 2*). This example will be referred to as *the vector space of finitely non-zero functions on* $\mathfrak{I}$.

8. The set $\mathfrak{C}$ of all complex numbers μ is a vector space, with $\mu + \nu$ and $\lambda\mu$ defined as usual. This is essentially *Example 1* with $n = 1$.

Exercises

1. Fill in the details in the above examples.

2. Given a vector space $\mathcal{W}$, let $\mathcal{U}$ be the set of all functions x defined on a set $\mathfrak{I}$, taking values in $\mathcal{W}$. With suitable definitions, $\mathcal{U}$ is a vector space.

3. Same as *Exercise 2*, except that x has values $\neq \theta$ for at most finitely many points t.

§ 2. FIRST PROPERTIES OF VECTOR SPACES

Several immediate consequences of the axioms for a vector space are developed in this section.

Theorem 1. *In any vector space:*

(1)   *The vector equation $x + y = z$ has one and only one solution x, the vectors y and z being given in advance.*

(2)   *If $z + z = z$, necessarily $z = \theta$.*

(3)   *$\lambda\theta = \theta$, for every scalar λ.*

(4)   *$0x = \theta$, for every vector x.*

(5)   *If $\lambda x = \theta$, then either $\lambda = 0$ or $x = \theta$.*

Proof.

(1): Given vectors y and z. Set $x = z + (-y)$; one has $x + y = [z + (-y)] + y = z + [(-y) + y] = z + \theta = z$. This proves that a solution exists. Suppose x_1 and x_2 are solutions: $x_1 + y = z = x_2 + y$. Then, $(x_1 + y) + (-y) = (x_2 + y) + (-y)$, $x_1 + [y + (-y)] = x_2 + [y + (-y)]$, $x_1 + \theta = x_2 + \theta$, $x_1 = x_2$. Thus, only one solution exists.

(2): Suppose $z + z = z$. Since also $\theta + z = z$, $z = \theta$ follows from the uniqueness of solutions.

(3): $\lambda\theta = \lambda(\theta + \theta) = \lambda\theta + \lambda\theta$, hence $\lambda\theta = \theta$ by part (2).

(4): $0x = (0 + 0)x = 0x + 0x$, hence $0x = \theta$.

(5): Suppose $\lambda x = \theta$, and $\lambda \neq 0$. If μ is the reciprocal of λ, $\theta = \mu\theta = \mu(\lambda x) = (\mu\lambda)x = 1x = x$. ∎

It follows that in axiom (A3), no other vector can play the role of θ; that is, the distinguished vector θ is *unique*. Furthermore, given any vector x, the equation $x + y = \theta$ has exactly one solution y, namely $y = -x$; thus, the only vector that can fulfill axiom (A4) is $-x$. Briefly: the zero vector is unique, and each vector has a unique negative.

Definition 1. *Given two vectors x and y, the vector $x + (-y)$ is called the* **difference** *of x and y, and is denoted $x - y$ (read "x minus y").*

Thus, in part (1) of *Theorem 1*, the unique solution x of $x + y = z$ is $x = z - y$.

Corollary. *In any vector space,*

(6) $(-\lambda)x = \lambda(-x) = -(\lambda x)$

(7) $\lambda(x - y) = \lambda x - \lambda y$

(8) $(\lambda - \mu)x = \lambda x - \mu x.$

Proof.

(6): One has $\theta = 0x = [\lambda + (-\lambda)]x = \lambda x + (-\lambda)x$, hence $(-\lambda)x = -(\lambda x)$ by the uniqueness of negatives. Similarly, $\theta = \lambda\theta = \lambda[x + (-x)] = \lambda x + \lambda(-x)$, hence $\lambda(-x) = -(\lambda x)$. The reader can easily supply the proofs of (7) and (8). ∎

In particular, $(-1)x = -x$.

Exercises

1. In any vector space, $-(-x) = x$, $-\theta = \theta$, $-(x + y) = -x - y$, $x - (y + z) = (x - y) - z$, $-(x - y) = y - x$.

§3. FINITE SUMS OF VECTORS

Throughout this section, all vectors are taken from an arbitrary vector space $\mathcal{V}$.

If x_1, x_2, x_3 are vectors, one has $x_1 + (x_2 + x_3) = (x_1 + x_2) + x_3$ by the associative law; one writes simply $x_1 + x_2 + x_3$. Strictly according to the axioms, vector sums are performed with two vectors at a time; the symbol $x_1 + x_2 + x_3$ is nevertheless unambiguous, since the result is the same whichever $+$ sign is given priority. Another commonly used symbol for this vector is $\sum_{k=1}^{3} x_k$. In general:

Definition 1. *If $x_1, \cdots, x_n$ are vectors $(n > 1)$, the symbol $\sum_{k=1}^{n} x_k$ denotes the vector defined inductively as follows:*

$$\sum_{k=1}^{2} x_k = x_1 + x_2$$

$$\sum_{k=1}^{n} x_k = \left(\sum_{k=1}^{n-1} x_k\right) + x_n, \quad (n > 2).$$

Other notations: $x_1 + \cdots + x_n$, $\sum_{1}^{n} x_k$, $\sum_{k} x_k$.

More generally, if $m < n$, and vectors $x_m, \cdots, x_n$ are given, $\sum_{m}^{n} x_k$ denotes the vector defined inductively by the formulas

$$\sum_{m}^{m+1} x_k = x_m + x_{m+1}$$

$$\sum_{m}^{n} x_k = \left(\sum_{m}^{n-1} x_k\right) + x_n, \quad (n > m + 1).$$

It is also convenient to define $\sum_{n}^{n} x_k = x_n$, and $\sum_{m}^{n} x_k = \theta$ when $m > n$. For example, $\sum_{3}^{3} x_k = x_3$, and $\sum_{3}^{2} x_k = \theta$.

Given vectors x_1, x_2, x_3, x_4, consider the vector $y = x_1 + x_2 + x_3 + x_4$. Officially this is $[(x_1 + x_2) + x_3] + x_4$, the $+$ signs being given priority from left to right. It follows from the associative law that all other ways of assigning priority produce the same vector y:

$$(x_1 + x_2) + (x_3 + x_4) = [(x_1 + x_2) + x_3] + x_4 = y$$

$$[x_1 + (x_2 + x_3)] + x_4 = [(x_1 + x_2) + x_3] + x_4 = y$$

$$x_1 + [(x_2 + x_3) + x_4] = [x_1 + (x_2 + x_3)] + x_4 = y$$

$$x_1 + [x_2 + (x_3 + x_4)] = x_1 + [(x_2 + x_3) + x_4] = y.$$

This principle holds for a sum of n vectors:

Theorem 1. (Generalized associative law) *Given vectors $x_1, \cdots, x_n$. Suppose $0 = n_0 < n_1 < n_2 < \cdots < n_{r-1} < n_r = n$. Define*

$$y_1 = \sum_1^{n_1} x_k$$

$$y_2 = \sum_{n_1+1}^{n_2} x_k$$

$$\cdots$$

$$y_j = \sum_{n_{j-1}+1}^{n_j} x_k$$

$$\cdots$$

$$y_r = \sum_{n_{r-1}+1}^{n} x_k.$$

Then, $\sum_1^r y_j = \sum_1^n x_k.$

Proof.

The proof is by complete induction on n. If $n = 2$, either (i) $r = 2$, in which case $n_1 = 1$ and $n_2 = 2$, or (ii) $r = 1$, in which case $n_1 = 2$. In case (i), $y_1 = x_1$ and $y_2 = x_2$, thus $\sum_1^2 y_j = \sum_1^2 x_k$. In case (ii), $y_1 = x_1 + x_2$, thus $\sum_1^1 y_j = \sum_1^2 x_k$.

Assume inductively that the conclusion holds whenever the number of given vectors x_k is $< n$. Suppose $x_1, \cdots, x_n$ given, $n \geq 3$. Let us consider three cases.

Case 1. $r = 1$

Necessarily $n_1 = n$, thus $\sum_1^r y_j = \sum_1^1 y_j = y_1 = \sum_1^{n_1} x_k = \sum_1^n x_k$. Assume, for the remainder of the proof, that $r > 1$. Then $\sum_1^r y_j = \sum_1^{r-1} y_j + y_r = \sum_1^{n_{r-1}} x_k + y_r$, by the inductive assumption.

Case 2. $n_{r-1} = n - 1$

Then, $y_r = \sum_n^n x_k = x_n$, thus $\sum_1^r y_j = \sum_1^{n_r \ 1} x_k + y_r = \sum_1^{n-1} x_k + x_n = \sum_1^n x_k$.

Case 3. $n_{r-1} < n - 1$

In this case, the sum $y_r = \sum_{n_{r-1}+1}^{n} x_k$ has at least two terms, hence $y_r = \sum_{n_{r-1}+1}^{n-1} x_k + x_n$. Then, $\sum_1^r y_j = \sum_1^{n_{r-1}} x_k + y_r = \sum_1^{n_{r-1}} x_k + \left(\sum_{n_{r-1}+1}^{n-1} x_k + x_n \right) = \left(\sum_1^{n_{r-1}} x_k + \sum_{n_{r-1}+1}^{n-1} x_k \right) + x_n;$

the latter is equal, by the inductive assumption, to $\left(\sum_1^{n-1} x_k\right) + x_n$ $= \sum_1^n x_k$. ∎

The sum of n vectors is also independent of the order in which the terms are written. For example, $x_2 + x_3 + x_1 = (x_2 + x_3) + x_1 = x_1 + (x_2 + x_3) = (x_1 + x_2) + x_3 = x_1 + x_2 + x_3$. In general:

Theorem 2. (Generalized commutative law) *Given vectors* $x_1, \cdots, x_n$. *Let* $1', \cdots, n'$ *be any rearrangement of the indices* $1, \cdots, n$, *and set* $y_k = x_{k'}(k = 1, \cdots, n)$. *Then,* $\sum_1^n y_k = \sum_1^n x_k$.

Proof.
For $n = 1$, the assertion is trivial. Assume the conclusion holds when the number of given vectors is $< n$.

Case 1. If $n' = n$, then $y_n = x_n$. Also, $1', \cdots, (n-1)'$ is a rearrangement of $1, \cdots, n-1$. Then, $\sum_1^n y_k = \sum_1^{n-1} y_k + y_n = \sum_1^{n-1} x_k + x_n$ by the inductive assumption.

Case 2. If $n' < n$, then $n = m'$ for some index $m < n$. Consider the rearrangement $1^*, \cdots, n^*$ of $1, \cdots, n$ defined as follows: $m^* = n'$, $n^* = m' = n$, and $k^* = k'$ for all remaining k; in other words, in the arrangement $1', \cdots, n'$, interchange m' and n'. Set $z_k = x_{k*}$ $(k = 1, \cdots, n)$; since $n^* = n$, one has $\sum_1^n z_k = \sum_1^n x_k$ by case 1. Using *Theorem 1* and axiom (A1) at the appropriate steps, $\sum_1^n x_k =$

$$\sum_1^n z_k = \left(\sum_1^{m-1} z_k + z_m\right) + \left(\sum_{m+1}^{n-1} z_k + z_n\right)$$

$$= \left(\sum_1^{m-1} z_k + z_n\right) + \left(\sum_{m+1}^{n-1} z_k + z_m\right)$$

$$= \left(\sum_1^{m-1} x_{k'} + x_{m'}\right) + \left(\sum_{m+1}^{n-1} x_{k'} + x_{n'}\right)$$

$$= \left(\sum_1^{m-1} y_k + y_m\right) + \left(\sum_{m+1}^{n-1} y_k + y_n\right) = \sum_1^n y_k. \quad ∎$$

Exercises

1. Show directly that $x_{1'} + x_{2'} + x_{3'} = x_1 + x_2 + x_3$ for every rearrangement $1', 2', 3'$ of $1, 2, 3$. [There are six arrangements, also called *permutations*.]

2. If $x_k = \theta$ for all k, then $\sum_1^n x_k = \theta$.

3. $-\left(\sum_1^n x_k\right) = \sum_1^n (-x_k)$.

4. $\sum_1^n x_k + \sum_1^n y_k = \sum_1^n (x_k + y_k)$.

5. If $x_k = x$ for all k, then $\sum_1^n x_k = nx$.

6. Given vectors $x_{jk}(j = 1, \cdots, m; k = 1, \cdots, n)$. For each j, define $y_j = \sum_k x_{jk}$, and for each k, define $z_k = \sum_j x_{jk}$. Then $\sum_j y_j = \sum_k z_k$. That is,

$$\sum_j \left(\sum_k x_{jk}\right) = \sum_k \left(\sum_j x_{jk}\right).$$

§4. LINEAR COMBINATIONS OF VECTORS

In the vector space of n-ples (*Example 1.1*), consider a vector $x = (\lambda_1, \cdots, \lambda_n)$. Let e_k denote the vector whose k'th component is 1, all others 0. Then, $x = (\lambda_1, 0, \cdots, 0) + (0, \lambda_2, 0, \cdots, 0) + \cdots + (0, \cdots, 0, \lambda_n) = \lambda_1 e_1 + \lambda_2 e_2 + \cdots + \lambda_n e_n$. This is an instance of the following:

Definition 1. *In any vector space, a vector x is said to be a* **linear combination** *of the vectors $x_1, \cdots, x_n$, with scalar* **coefficients** $\lambda_1, \cdots, \lambda_n$, *in case $x = \sum_1^n \lambda_k x_k$.*

For example, in the vector space of 2-ples, let $x = (2, 3)$, $x_1 = (1, 0)$, $x_2 = (0, 1)$, $x_3 = (1, 1)$. Then, $x = 2x_1 + 3x_2 + 0x_3 = 0x_1 + 1x_2 + 2x_3 = (-1)x_1 + 0x_2 + 3x_3 = 1x_1 + 2x_2 + 1x_3$, etc. . . .

A number of useful facts about linear combinations are collected in the following theorem. These are easily deduced from the results of the preceding section; the proofs are left to the reader:

Theorem 1. *In any vector space:*

(1) $\sum_1^n \lambda_k x_k + \sum_1^n \mu_k x_k = \sum_1^n (\lambda_k + \mu_k) x_k$

(2) $\lambda \left(\sum_1^n x_k \right) = \sum_1^n \lambda x_k$

(3) $\left(\sum_1^m \lambda_j \right) x = \sum_1^m \lambda_j x$

(4) $\left(\sum_1^m \lambda_j \right) \left(\sum_1^n x_k \right) = \sum_{j=1}^m \left(\sum_{k=1}^n \lambda_j x_k \right)$

$\qquad\qquad = \sum_{k=1}^n \left(\sum_{j=1}^m \lambda_j x_k \right).$

(5) θ *is a linear combination of* $x_1, \cdots, x_n$.

(6) x *is a linear combination of* x.

(7) *Given vectors* $x, x_1, \cdots, x_n$. *If* $m < n$, *and* x *is a linear combination of* $x_1, \cdots, x_m$, *then* x *is also a linear combination of* $x_1, \cdots, x_n$.

(8) *Suppose* x *is a linear combination of* $x_1, \cdots, x_n$; *if* $1', \cdots, n'$ *is any rearrangement of* $1, \cdots, n$, *and* $y_k = x_{k'}$, *then* x *is a linear combination of* $y_1, \cdots, y_n$.

(9) *If* x *is a linear combination of* $y_1, \cdots, y_m$, *and each* y_j *is a linear combination of* $x_1, \cdots, x_n$, *then* x *is a linear combination of* $x_1, \cdots, x_n$.

Exercises

1. In the space of 4-ples, express $x = (\lambda_1, \lambda_2, \lambda_3, \lambda_4)$ as a linear combination of $x_1 = (1,0,0,0)$, $x_2 = (1,1,0,0)$, $x_3 = (1,1,1,0)$, $x_4 = (1,1,1,1)$.

2. In the space of 3-ples, can $x = (1,0,1)$ be expressed as a linear combination of $x_1 = (1,1,0)$, $x_2 = (0,1,1)$, $x_3 = (1,2,1)$?

3. If x and y are linear combinations of $x_1, \cdots, x_n$, so are $x + y$ and λx.

4. In the space of m-ples, given vectors $x, x_1, \cdots, x_n$. The problem of expressing x as a linear combination of $x_1, \cdots, x_n$ is equivalent to

the problem of solving a certain system of m linear equations in n unknowns. This system is homogeneous if and only if $x = \theta$.

§ 5. LINEAR SUBSPACES, LINEAR DEPENDENCE

Consider, in the vector space of n-ples, the totality of all vectors x whose first component is 0, that is, $x = (0, \lambda_2, \cdots, \lambda_n)$. If x and y are two such vectors, so are $x + y$ and λx. Evidently, this set of vectors is a vector space in its own right. This is a special case of the following:

Definition 1. *Let $\mathcal{V}$ be a vector space. A* **linear subspace** *of $\mathcal{V}$ is a set $\mathfrak{N}$ of vectors belonging to $\mathcal{V}$, such that:* (i) $\mathfrak{N}$ *contains the vector θ,* (ii) *if x and y are vectors in $\mathfrak{N}$, the vector $x + y$ is in $\mathfrak{N}$, and* (iii) *if x is a vector in $\mathfrak{N}$, and λ is any scalar, the vector λx is in $\mathfrak{N}$.*

Briefly, a linear subspace contains sums and scalar multiples of its vectors. If $\mathfrak{N}$ is a linear subspace of $\mathcal{V}$, and x is a vector in $\mathfrak{N}$, the relation $-x = (-1)x$ shows that $-x$ is in $\mathfrak{N}$; since the vectors in $\mathfrak{N}$ satisfy all the identities in the axioms for $\mathcal{V}$, clearly $\mathfrak{N}$ is itself a vector space.

The purpose of condition (i) is to ensure that $\mathfrak{N}$ is not the empty set of vectors, that is, contains at least one vector z; $\mathfrak{N}$ will then contain $\theta = 0z$ by condition (iii).

Examples

1. In any vector space, the set $\mathfrak{N}$ containing just the vector θ is a linear subspace; this is shown by the relations $\theta + \theta = \theta$ and $\lambda\theta = \theta$.

2. $\mathcal{V}$ is itself a linear subspace of the vector space $\mathcal{V}$.

3. If $\mathcal{V}$ is a vector space, and z is a fixed vector in $\mathcal{V}$, the set $\mathfrak{N}$ of all scalar multiples μz of z is a linear subspace. This results from the relations $\theta = 0z$, $\mu z + \nu z = (\mu + \nu)z$, and $\lambda(\mu z) = (\lambda\mu)z$.

4. Let $\mathcal{V}$ be the vector space of scalar-valued functions defined on a set $\mathfrak{J}$ (*Example 1.2*). If t_0 is a fixed point of $\mathfrak{J}$, the set $\mathfrak{N}$ of all functions x such that $x(t_0) = 0$ is a linear subspace of $\mathcal{V}$.

5. Let $\mathcal{V}$ be the vector space of all scalar-valued functions x defined on the interval $[a,b]$. The following is a series of linear subspaces (getting smaller):

(i) $\mathfrak{N}_1$ the set of functions x which are continuous at a fixed point t_0 of $[a,b]$.

(ii) $\mathfrak{N}_2$ the set of functions x which are continuous at every point of $[a,b]$ (this is *Example 1.3*).

(iii) $\mathfrak{N}_3$ the set of all polynomial functions x with complex coefficients (this is *Example 1.4*).

(iv) $\mathfrak{N}_4$ the set of all polynomial functions, with complex coefficients, of degree $<n$, where n is a fixed positive integer (this is *Example 1.5*).

6. Let $\mathcal{V}$ be the vector space of continuous functions x on $[a,b]$ (*Example 1.3*). The set $\mathfrak{N}$ of all x which are differentiable on $[a,b]$ is a linear subspace.

7. Let $\mathcal{V}$ be the set of all twice-differentiable functions x defined on $[a,b]$, and $\mathfrak{N}$ the set of those functions x which satisfy the differential equation $x'' + x = 0$. Then, $\mathcal{V}$ is a vector space, and $\mathfrak{N}$ is a linear subspace of $\mathcal{V}$.

Theorem 1. *If $\mathfrak{M}$ and $\mathfrak{N}$ are linear subspaces of $\mathcal{V}$, the set of all vectors of the form $y + z$, with y in $\mathfrak{M}$ and z in $\mathfrak{N}$, is a linear subspace of $\mathcal{V}$.*

Proof.

$\theta = \theta + \theta$, $(y_1 + z_1) + (y_2 + z_2) = (y_1 + y_2) + (z_1 + z_2)$, and $\lambda(y + z) = \lambda y + \lambda z$. ∎

Definition 2. *The linear subspace described in Theorem 1 is called the* **sum** *of $\mathfrak{M}$ and $\mathfrak{N}$, and is denoted $\mathfrak{M} + \mathfrak{N}$.*

Examples of such sums will be found in the exercises.

Lemma. *If $\mathfrak{M}$ is a linear subspace of $\mathcal{V}$, and $x_1, \cdots, x_n$ are vectors in $\mathfrak{M}$, then every linear combination of $x_1, \cdots, x_n$ belongs to $\mathfrak{M}$.*

Proof.

$\sum_1^n \lambda_k x_k$ is the same vector, whether formed in the vector space $\mathcal{V}$ or in the vector space $\mathfrak{M}$. ∎

Theorem 2. *Let $\mathcal{S}$ be any set of vectors in a space $\mathcal{V}$, and let $\mathfrak{N}$ be the set of all vectors in $\mathcal{V}$ which can be expressed as a linear combination of vectors in $\mathcal{S}$. Then,*

(1) *$\mathfrak{N}$ is a linear subspace of $\mathcal{V}$;*

(2) *every vector of $\mathcal{S}$ belongs to $\mathfrak{N}$.*

Moreover, $\mathfrak{N}$ is the smallest such linear subspace, in the following sense:

(3)   *if $\mathfrak{M}$ is a linear subspace which contains every vector of $\mathcal{S}$, necessarily $\mathfrak{M}$ contains every vector of $\mathfrak{N}$.*

Proof.

(1): If $\mathcal{S}$ is the empty set of vectors (i.e. contains no vectors at all), the convention is that $\mathfrak{N}$ consists of just the vector θ.

Otherwise, if the vector z belongs to $\mathcal{S}$, $\mathfrak{N}$ contains θ via the relation $\theta = 0z$. Suppose x and y are vectors in $\mathfrak{N}$, say $x = \sum_1^n \lambda_k x_k$ and $y = \sum_1^m \mu_j y_j$, where the x_k and y_j are in $\mathcal{S}$. Then, $x + y$ is a linear combination of the vectors $x_1, \cdots, x_n, y_1, \cdots, y_m$ of $\mathcal{S}$ (see *Theorem 3.1*), hence $x + y$ belongs to $\mathfrak{N}$. Also, $\lambda x = \sum_1^n (\lambda\lambda_k)x_k$ shows that λx belongs to $\mathfrak{N}$. Thus, $\mathfrak{N}$ is a linear subspace.

(2): If z is in $\mathcal{S}$, $z = 1z$ shows that z belongs to $\mathfrak{N}$.

(3): Suppose $\mathfrak{M}$ is a linear subspace which contains every vector of $\mathcal{S}$. Then, $\mathfrak{M}$ contains every vector of $\mathfrak{N}$ by the *Lemma*.   ∎

Definition 3. *If $\mathcal{S}$ is a set of vectors in the space $\mathcal{V}$, the linear subspace described in Theorem 2 is denoted [$\mathcal{S}$], and is called the linear subspace* **generated** *by $\mathcal{S}$.*

Evidently, [$\mathcal{V}$] coincides with $\mathcal{V}$. If $\mathcal{V}$ is the vector space of n-ples, and $\mathcal{S}$ is the set of vectors $e_1, \cdots, e_n$ described in § 4, then [$\mathcal{S}$] coincides with $\mathcal{V}$ since every vector in $\mathcal{V}$ can be expressed as a linear combination of the e_k. Thus, different sets of vectors may generate the same linear subspace.

Definition 4. *Let $\mathfrak{N}$ be a linear subspace of $\mathcal{V}$. A set $\mathcal{S}$ of vectors is called a* **system of generators** *for $\mathfrak{N}$ in case the linear subspace [$\mathcal{S}$] coincides with $\mathfrak{N}$. Briefly, $\mathcal{S}$* **generates** *$\mathfrak{N}$.*

Another way of expressing what is going on in *Theorem 2* is as follows:

Definition 5. *Let $\mathcal{S}$ be a set of vectors in a space $\mathcal{V}$. A vector x is said to be* **linearly dependent on** *$\mathcal{S}$ in case there exist vectors $x_1, \cdots, x_n$ in $\mathcal{S}$ such that x is a linear combination of the x_k. Briefly: x* **depends on** *$\mathcal{S}$.*

The convention is that only the vector θ depends on the empty set of vectors. Comparing *Definitions 3 and 5*:

Theorem 3. *If* S *is any set of vectors in the space* $\mathcal{V}$, *then the linear subspace* [S] *generated by* S *is precisely the set of all vectors which are linearly dependent on* S.

If x depends on S, evidently x depends on any set of vectors which includes S. If $\mathfrak{N}$ is a linear subspace, every vector dependent on $\mathfrak{N}$ actually belongs to $\mathfrak{N}$.

Exercises

1. Let $\mathcal{V}$ be the vector space of n-ples, and let $\alpha_1, \cdots, \alpha_n$ be fixed scalars. The set $\mathfrak{N}$ of all vectors $x = (\lambda_1, \cdots, \lambda_n)$ such that $\sum_1^n \alpha_k \lambda_k = 0$ is a linear subspace of $\mathcal{V}$.

2. Let $\mathcal{V}$ be the vector space of n-ples, and let (α_{jk}) be a system of fixed scalars $(j = 1, \cdots, m;\ k = 1, \cdots, n)$. The set $\mathfrak{N}$ of all vectors $x = (\lambda_1, \cdots, \lambda_n)$ such that $\sum_{k=1}^n \alpha_{jk} \lambda_k = 0$ for $j = 1, \cdots, m$, is a linear subspace of $\mathcal{V}$. [It is the set of all "solutions of a system of m homogeneous linear equations in n unknowns."]

3. Let $\mathcal{V}$ be the vector space of scalar-valued functions x defined on a set $\mathfrak{I}$ (*Example 1.2*). The following are linear subspaces of $\mathcal{V}$:
   (i) $\mathfrak{N}$ the set of all finitely non-zero functions x, described in *Example 1.7*.
   (ii) Fix a set S of points of $\mathfrak{I}$, and let $\mathfrak{N}$ be the set of all functions x which are 0 at every point of S.

4. If $\mathfrak{M}$ and $\mathfrak{N}$ are linear subspaces of $\mathcal{V}$, the set of vectors common to $\mathfrak{M}$ and $\mathfrak{N}$ is a linear subspace of $\mathcal{V}$. [This subspace is called the *intersection* of $\mathfrak{M}$ and $\mathfrak{N}$.]

5. Let $\mathcal{V}$ be the vector space of 3-ples.
   (i) If $\mathfrak{M}$ is the set of all vectors $y = (\lambda, 0, 0)$, and $\mathfrak{N}$ is the set of all vectors $z = (\mu, \mu, 0)$, describe $\mathfrak{M} + \mathfrak{N}$.
   (ii) If $\mathfrak{M}$ is the set of all vectors $y = (\alpha, \beta, 0)$, and $\mathfrak{N}$ is the set of all vectors $z = (0, \lambda, \mu)$, describe $\mathfrak{M} + \mathfrak{N}$.

6. Let $\mathcal{V}$ be the vector space of scalar-valued functions x defined on the symmetric interval $[-a, a]$. Call x *even* if $x(-t) = x(t)$ for all t, and *odd* if $x(-t) = -x(t)$ for all t. The set $\mathfrak{M}$ of all even functions is a linear subspace of $\mathcal{V}$; so is the set $\mathfrak{N}$ of all odd functions. Describe $\mathfrak{M} + \mathfrak{N}$.

7. Let $\mathfrak{M}$, $\mathfrak{N}$ be linear subspaces of $\mathcal{V}$, and suppose θ is the only vector common to $\mathfrak{M}$ and $\mathfrak{N}$. Then, the representation of a vector x of $\mathfrak{M} + \mathfrak{N}$ in the form $x = y + z$, where y is in $\mathfrak{M}$ and z is in $\mathfrak{N}$, is unique. That is, if $y_1 + z_1 = y_2 + z_2$, necessarily $y_1 = y_2$ and $z_1 = z_2$. Apply this result to *Exercise 6*.

8. Let $\mathfrak{M}$ and $\mathfrak{N}$ be linear subspaces of $\mathcal{V}$, and let $\mathcal{S}$ be the set of all vectors x which belong either to $\mathfrak{M}$ or to $\mathfrak{N}$ (or to both). Then, $[\mathcal{S}]$ is the linear subspace $\mathfrak{M} + \mathfrak{N}$.

9. Let $\mathcal{V}$ be the vector space of n-ples, $\mathcal{S}$ the set of vectors $x_1 = (1,0,\cdots,0)$, $x_2 = (1,1,0,\cdots,0),\cdots$, $x_n = (1,1,\cdots,1)$. Describe $[\mathcal{S}]$.

10. Let $\mathcal{V}$ be the vector space of polynomial functions on $[a,b]$ (*Example 1.4*), and let $\mathcal{S}$ be the set of polynomials $1,t,t^2,\cdots,t^n$. Describe $[\mathcal{S}]$.

11. Let $\mathcal{V}$ be the vector space of twice-differentiable functions on $[a,b]$, and let $\mathcal{S}$ be the set consisting of the two functions $\sin t$, $\cos t$. Then $[\mathcal{S}]$ is the vector space of solutions of the differential equation $x'' + x = 0$.

12. If $\mathfrak{N}$ is a linear subspace of $\mathcal{V}$, then $[\mathfrak{N}]$ is precisely $\mathfrak{N}$.

13. $\mathcal{S}$ and $\mathfrak{I}$ generate the same linear subspace $\mathfrak{N}$ if and only if: every vector of $\mathcal{S}$ is a linear combination of vectors in $\mathfrak{I}$, and vice versa.

14. In the vector space $\mathcal{V}$ of n-ples, the following sets $\mathcal{S}$ are systems of generators for $\mathcal{V}$:
   (i) $\mathcal{S}$ consists of the n vectors $e_1 = (1,0,\cdots,0),\cdots$, $e_n = (0,\cdots,0,1)$.
   (ii) $\mathcal{S}$ consists of the n vectors $x_1 = (1,0,\cdots,0)$, $x_2 = (1,1,0,\cdots,0)$, $\cdots$, $x_n = (1,1,\cdots,1)$.
   (iii) $\mathcal{S}$ consists of $x_1,\cdots,x_n$, as in (ii), together with $x = (1,2,3,0,\cdots,0)$ and $y = (-1,0,5,0,\cdots,0)$.

§6. LINEAR INDEPENDENCE

In the space of 3-ples, the vector $e_3 = (0,0,1)$ cannot be expressed as a linear combination of the vectors $e_1 = (1,0,0)$ and $e_2 = (0,1,0)$; for, any linear combination $\lambda_1 e_1 + \lambda_2 e_2$ necessarily has 0 for its third component. One expresses this inexpressibility by saying that e_3 is linearly independent of e_1,e_2. In general:

Definition 1. *Let* S *be a set of vectors in the space* $\mho$*. A vector* x *is said to be* **linearly independent of** S *if it cannot be expressed as a linear combination of vectors in* S*. Briefly:* x *is* **independent of** S*.*

Thus, x is independent of S precisely when it does not depend on S in the sense of *Definition 5.5*. Clearly x is independent of S precisely when it does not belong to the linear subspace [S] generated by S; in particular, $x \neq \theta$. The convention is that every non-zero vector is independent of the empty set of vectors. If x is independent of S, it is also independent of every set of vectors which is included in S. If $\mathfrak{N}$ is a linear subspace of $\mho$, the vectors independent of $\mathfrak{N}$ are precisely those which are excluded by $\mathfrak{N}$.

Consider, in the space of 3-ples, the vectors e_1, e_2, e_3 discussed earlier. It was noted that e_3 is independent of e_1, e_2. It is equally clear that e_2 is independent of e_1, e_3, and e_1 is independent of e_2, e_3. Briefly, one says that e_1, e_2, e_3 are independent. In general:

Definition 2. *A set* S *of vectors is said to be* **linearly independent** *in case: each vector in* S *is independent of the remaining vectors of* S*; that is, no vector of* S *can be expressed as a linear combination of* **other** *vectors of* S*. Briefly:* S *is an* **independent** *set of vectors.*

The convention is that the empty set of vectors is independent; otherwise, independent sets contain only non-zero vectors. The set S consisting of a single non-zero vector x is independent.

It is clear from *Definition 2* that a set S is independent, if and only if every finite set of vectors $x_1, \cdots, x_n$ in S is independent. In practice, it is useful to have several reformulations of the condition for the independence of $x_1, \cdots, x_n$:

Theorem 1. *The following conditions on the set of vectors* $x_1, \cdots, x_n$ *imply one another:*

(a) $x_1, \cdots, x_n$ *are   independent.*

(b) x_k *is independent of* $x_1, \cdots, x_{k-1}$*, for* $k = 1, \cdots, n$*.*

(c)   *If* $\sum_1^n \lambda_k x_k = \theta$*, necessarily* $\lambda_k = 0$ *for all* k*.*

(d)   *If* $\sum_1^n \lambda_k x_k = \sum_1^n \mu_k x_k$*, necessarily* $\lambda_k = \mu_k$ *for all* k*.*

Proof.

The equivalence of these four conditions will be established by proving the following propositions: (a) implies (b), (b) implies (c), (c) implies (d), and (d) implies (a). The assertion in (b) for $k = 1$ means simply that $x_1 \neq \theta$, in view of the conventions about the empty set of vectors.

(a) *implies* (b): This is clear from *Definition 2*.

(b) *implies* (c): Assume to the contrary that a relation $\sum_1^n \lambda_k x_k = \theta$ exists in which not all the λ_k are 0. If r is the largest subscript for which $\lambda_r \neq 0$, then $\sum_1^r \lambda_k x_k = \sum_1^n \lambda_k x_k = \theta$. Since $x_1 \neq \theta$ by the hypothesis (b), necessarily $r > 1$ (see part (5) of *Theorem 2.1*). Then, $x_r = \sum_1^{r-1} (-\lambda_r^{-1}\lambda_k)x_k$; but this contradicts (b).

(c) *implies* (d): If $\sum_1^n \lambda_k x_k = \sum^n \mu_k x_k$, then $\sum_1^n (\lambda_k - \mu_k)x_k = \theta$, hence $\lambda_k - \mu_k = 0$ for all k, by the hypothesis (c).

(d) *implies* (a): Assume to the contrary that for some index j, x_j can be expressed as a linear combination of the remaining x_k, say $x_j = \sum_{k \neq j} \lambda_k x_k$. Defining $\lambda_j = -1$, one has $\sum_1^n \lambda_k x_k = \theta$. Since also $\theta = \sum_1^n 0x_k$, the hypothesis (d) yields $\lambda_k = 0$ for all k; this is absurd for $k = j$. ∎

Condition (d) can be interpreted as follows: when a vector is expressible as a linear combination of independent vectors $x_1,\cdots,x_n$, the coefficients are *unique*.

Suppose now that $\mathfrak{N}$ is the linear subspace generated by a set $\mathcal{S}$ of vectors. This means that $\mathfrak{N}$ is the set of all vectors which can be expressed as a linear combination of vectors in $\mathcal{S}$. At times, unique expressibility may be desirable; this requires not merely a system of generators for $\mathfrak{N}$, but an *independent* system of generators. It can be proved that every system of generators $\mathcal{S}$ includes an independent system of generators $\mathcal{J}$; so to speak, one obtains $\mathcal{J}$ by suppressing certain vectors of $\mathcal{S}$, each suppressed vector being one which is still expressible as a linear combination of the vectors of $\mathcal{S}$ which remain. The translation of this idea into a formal proof requires some form of "transfinite induction"; however, for our purposes, the following special case will suffice:

Theorem 2. *Suppose the linear subspace $\mathfrak{N}$ of $\mathcal{V}$ is generated by a* **sequence** *(finite or infinite) of vectors $x_1, x_2, x_3, \cdots$. Then, there exists a subsequence $x_{k_1}, x_{k_2}, x_{k_3}, \cdots$ which* (i) *generates $\mathfrak{N}$, and* (ii) *is linearly independent.*

Proof. (after a fashion)

If all the x_k are θ, one takes the "empty subsequence" having no terms. Otherwise, let x_{k_1} be the first non-zero x_k; then, for $k < k_1$, $x_k = \theta = 0x_{k_1}$.

If all the x_k for $k > k_1$ are scalar multiples of x_{k_1}, the proof halts. Otherwise, let x_{k_2} be the first x_k which is not a multiple of x_{k_1}; then, for $k < k_2$, x_k is a multiple of x_{k_1}.

If all the x_k for $k > k_2$ are expressible as linear combinations of x_{k_1}, x_{k_2}, the proof halts. Otherwise, let x_{k_3} be the first x_k which is independent of x_{k_1}, x_{k_2}; then, for $k < k_3$, x_k is a linear combination of x_{k_1}, x_{k_2}.

The proof continues (or halts) inductively. Since $k_1 < k_2 < k_3 < \cdots$, the x_{k_j} are a subsequence of the x_k. Given any vector x in $\mathfrak{N}$, say $x = \sum_1^n \lambda_k x_k$. Since each of $x_1, \cdots, x_n$ is a linear combination of $x_{k_1}, \cdots, x_{k_m}$, provided m is taken large enough, x is itself a linear combination of $x_{k_1}, \cdots, x_{k_m}$; thus, the subsequence x_{k_j} generates $\mathfrak{N}$. By construction, each x_{k_n} is independent of $x_{k_1}, \cdots, x_{k_{n-1}}$, hence the subsequence x_{k_j} is independent by *Theorem 1*. ∎

Exercises

1. In the vector space of n-ples, the following vectors are independent: $x_1 = (1,0,\cdots,0)$, $x_2 = (1,1,0,\cdots,0), \cdots$, $x_n = (1,1,\cdots,1)$.

2. In the vector space of finitely non-zero sequences (*Example 1.6*), let x_k be the sequence whose first k terms are $=1$, all other terms $=0$. Every vector is uniquely expressible as a linear combination of the x_k.

3. In the vector space of continuous functions on $[a,b]$, $a < b$:
  (i)   The functions $\sin t$, $\cos t$ are independent.
  (ii) The functions $\sin t$, $\sin ct$ are independent, provided $c^2 \neq 1$.
  (iii) If x is any polynomial function, the functions $x(t), e^t, \sin t$ are independent.

4. In the vector space of polynomial functions on $[a,b]$, where $a < b$, the functions $1, t, t^2, \cdots, t^n$ are independent.

5. In the vector space of 2-ples:
  (i) Vectors $x = (\alpha, \beta)$, $y = (\gamma, \delta)$ are independent if and only if $\alpha\delta - \beta\gamma \neq 0$.

(ii) If x,y are independent, every vector z can be expressed as a linear combination of x,y.

(iii) It is not possible to have three independent vectors.

§7. BASIS, DIMENSION

The problem of finding an independent generating system is easily solved for the following class of vector spaces:

Definition 1. *A vector space* $\mathcal{V}$ *is said to be* **finitely generated** *if there exists a finite set of vectors* $x_1, \cdots, x_n$ *which generate* $\mathcal{V}$ *in the sense of Definition 5.4.*

Definition 2. *A set* $\mathfrak{I}$ *of vectors is said to be a* **basis** *for a vector space* $\mathcal{V}$ *in case* (i) $\mathfrak{I}$ *generates* $\mathcal{V}$, *and* (ii) $\mathfrak{I}$ *is independent.*

Theorem 1. *Every finitely generated vector space has a basis.*

Proof.

By assumption, $\mathcal{V}$ has a finite system of generators $x_1, \cdots, x_n$; suppressing x's as necessary, we may suppose by *Theorem 6.2* that the x_k are also independent. Then, the x_k are a basis. ∎

Examples

1. In the vector space of n-ples, the vectors $e_1 = (1,0,\cdots,0)$, $e_2 = (0,1,0,\cdots,0), \cdots, e_n = (0,\cdots,0,1)$ are a basis. In the sequel, this will be referred to as the *canonical basis* for the space of n-ples.

2. In the vector space of finitely non-zero sequences (*Example 1.6*), the vectors $e_1 = (1,0,\cdots)$, $e_2 = (0,1,0,\cdots)$, $e_3 = (0,0,1,0,\cdots)$, $\cdots$ are a basis, called the *canonical basis*. This vector space is not finitely generated. For, if $x_1,\cdots,x_n$ is any finite set of vectors, there is a fixed index N such that the k'th component of any linear combination of $x_1,\cdots,x_n$ is 0 for all $k \geq N$.

3. In the vector space of polynomial functions on $[a,b]$ (*Example 1.4*), where $a < b$, the functions $1,t,t^2,\cdots$ are a basis (see *Exercise 6.4*). This space is not finitely generated, since the linear combinations of a fixed finite set of polynomials are of bounded degree. ∎

If $\mathcal{V}$ is a finitely generated vector space, the number of vectors in any basis is the same; this is a consequence of the following theorem, known as *Steinitz's exchange theorem*:

Theorem 2. *Suppose* $x_1, \cdots, x_n$ *is a system of generators for the vector space* $\mathcal{V}$. *Let* $y_1, \cdots, y_m$ *be linearly independent vectors, with* $m \leq n$. *Then, there exists a rearrangement* $1', \cdots, n'$ *of* $1, \cdots, n$, *such that the vectors* $y_1, \cdots, y_m$, $x_{(m+1)'}, \cdots, x_{n'}$ *generate* $\mathcal{V}$. *In other words, after a suitable rearrangement, the first* m *x's may be replaced by the y's, in such a way that the resulting set of vectors generates* $\mathcal{V}$.

Proof. (by induction on m)

If $m = 1$, one is simply assuming $y_1 \neq \theta$. Suppose $y_1 = \sum_1^n \lambda_k x_k$. Since $y_1 \neq \theta$, not every λ_k can be 0. Rearranging the x's, let us suppose $\lambda_1 \neq 0$; then, one can solve for x_1 as a linear combination of $y_1, x_2, \cdots, x_n$, say

$$(*) \qquad x_1 = \mu_1 y_1 + \sum_2^n \mu_k x_k.$$

It will be shown that the vectors $y_1, x_2, \cdots, x_n$ generate $\mathcal{V}$. Let x be any vector of $\mathcal{V}$, and suppose $x = \sum_1^n \nu_k x_k$. Replacing x_1 by the formula (*), x is expressed as a linear combination of $y_1, x_2, \cdots, x_n$.

Assume the theorem true for $m - 1$, and let independent vectors $y_1, \cdots, y_m$ be given. The vectors $y_1, \cdots, y_{m-1}$ are also independent; rearranging the x's, we may suppose, by the inductive assumption, that the vectors $y_1, \cdots, y_{m-1}, x_m, \cdots, x_n$ generate $\mathcal{V}$. In particular, $y_m = \sum_1^{m-1} \lambda_j y_j + \sum_m^n \mu_k x_k$, for suitable coefficients. Since y_m is independent of $y_1, \cdots, y_{m-1}$, not every μ_k can be 0. Rearranging $x_m, \cdots, x_n$, we may suppose $\mu_m \neq 0$. Then, x_m can be solved for as a linear combination of $y_1, \cdots, y_{m-1}, y_m, x_{m+1}, \cdots, x_n$; the concluding details are left to the reader. ∎

Corollary 1. *If* $\mathcal{V}$ *is generated by* $x_1, \cdots, x_n$, *no independent set can contain more than* n *vectors.*

Proof.

Assume to the contrary that $y_1, \cdots, y_n, y_{n+1}$ are independent vectors. Applying *Theorem 2* to $x_1, \cdots, x_n$ and $y_1, \cdots, y_n$, we conclude that $y_1, \cdots, y_n$ generate $\mathcal{V}$. In particular, y_{n+1} depends on $y_1, \cdots, y_n$, a contradiction. ∎

Corollary 2. *If* $x_1, \cdots, x_n$ *and* $y_1, \cdots, y_m$ *are bases for* $\mathcal{V}$, *necessarily* $m = n$.

Proof.

Since $x_1, \cdots, x_n$ generate $\mathcal{V}$, and $y_1, \cdots, y_m$ are independent, $m \leq n$ by *Corollary 1*; reversing the role of x's and y's, $n \leq m$. ∎

Definition 3. *If $\mathcal{V}$ is a finitely generated vector space, the (unique) number of vectors in any basis is called the* **dimension** *of $\mathcal{V}$; in this case, $\mathcal{V}$ is said to be* **finite-dimensional.** *If $\mathcal{V}$ is not finitely generated, it is said to be* **infinite-dimensional.**

As remarked in § 6, it can be shown that every vector space has a basis (what is needed, of course, is a proof for the infinite-dimensional case). For our purposes, the following aspect of infinite-dimensionality will suffice:

Theorem 3. *In any infinite-dimensional vector space $\mathcal{V}$, there exists an infinite sequence of linearly independent vectors $x_1, x_2, x_3, \cdots$.*

Proof.

Let x_1 be any non-zero vector; let x_2 be any vector independent of x_1; let x_3 be any vector independent of x_1, x_2. Inductively, let x_{n+1} be any vector independent of $x_1, \cdots, x_n$; such a vector must exist, otherwise $x_1, \cdots, x_n$ would generate $\mathcal{V}$. The x_k are independent by criterion (b) in *Theorem 6.1*. ∎

<h3 align="center">Exercises</h3>

1. In the vector space of n-ples, the vectors $x_1 = (1,0,\cdots,0)$, $x_2 = (1,1,0,\cdots,0), \cdots, x_n = (1,1,\cdots,1)$ are a basis.

2. In the vector space of finitely non-zero sequences, the vectors $x_1 = (1,0,0,\cdots)$, $x_2 = (1,1,0,\cdots)$, $x_3 = (1,1,1,0,\cdots), \cdots$ are a basis.

3. Let $\mathcal{V}$ be a vector space of finite dimension n. Then:
(i)   Every independent set of n vectors is generating.
(ii) Every generating set of n vectors is independent.
(iii) If $\mathcal{R}$ is a linear subspace of $\mathcal{V}$, then $\mathcal{R}$ has finite dimension m, with $m \leq n$; any basis for $\mathcal{R}$ can be augmented to a basis of $\mathcal{V}$; $m = n$ if and only if $\mathcal{R}$ is all of $\mathcal{V}$.

4. Let $\mathcal{V}$ be the vector space of finitely non-zero functions x defined on a set $\mathcal{S}$ (*Example 1.7*). For each point s of $\mathcal{S}$, let x_s denote that function whose value at s is 1, and which vanishes at every other point of $\mathcal{S}$. Then, the vectors x_s form a basis for $\mathcal{V}$.

5. If $\mathcal{V}$ is generated by a sequence of vectors $x_1, x_2, x_3, \cdots$, show that $\mathcal{V}$ has a basis.

*6. Every vector space has a basis.

§ 8. CODA

On looking over the foregoing definitions and theorems, it will be apparent to the reader that no use has been made of any particularly characteristic property of the system of complex scalars (such as the "fundamental theorem of algebra," real and imaginary parts, complex conjugation). The definitions and theorems make sense, and are valid, for other systems of scalars; for example, real scalars, or rational scalars, or Gaussian-rational scalars (complex numbers of the form $\alpha + i\beta$, where α and β are rational). More generally, the scalars may be drawn from an algebraic system known as a *field* (see any book on abstract algebra). Thus, one speaks of *complex vector spaces*, *real vector spaces*, and so on, in conformity with the system of scalars which is employed.

In the sequel, only complex vector spaces will be considered, and the terms **vector space** *and* **complex vector space** *will be used interchangeably.*

Exercises

1. (i) Every complex vector space can be regarded also as a real vector space.

(ii) The complex numbers form a one-dimensional complex vector space (*Example 1.8*), and a two-dimensional real vector space.

(iii) If $\mathcal{U}$ is an n-dimensional complex vector space, it is a $2n$-dimensional real vector space.

*2. View the real numbers as a rational vector space in the obvious way. Then 1, $\sqrt{2}$ are independent. So are 1, π. So are 1, $\sqrt{2}$, π. What is the dimension?

Hilbert Spaces

§ 1. PRE-HILBERT SPACES

The *conjugate* of a complex number λ will be denoted λ^*. Thus, if $\lambda = \alpha + i\beta$, where α and β are real numbers, then $\lambda^* = \alpha - i\beta$. The familiar properties of conjugation are as follows: $(\lambda^*)^* = \lambda$, $(\lambda + \mu)^* = \lambda^* + \mu^*$, $(\lambda\mu)^* = \lambda^*\mu^*$, $|\lambda| = \sqrt{\lambda^*\lambda}$, and $\lambda^* = \lambda$ if and only if λ is real.

Definition 1. *A* **pre-Hilbert space** *is a complex vector space $\mathcal{P}$. For each pair of vectors x,y of $\mathcal{P}$, there is determined a complex number called the* **scalar product** *of x and y, denoted $(x|y)$. Scalar products are assumed to obey these rules:*

(P1) $(y|x) = (x|y)^*$

(P2) $(x + y|z) = (x|z) + (y|z)$

(P3) $(\lambda x|y) = \lambda(x|y)$

(P4) $(x|x) > 0$ *when* $x \neq \theta$.

A convenient verbalization of $(x|y)$ is "x scalar y." The reason for the term *pre*-Hilbert space is that one can pass, by the procedure of "completion," from a pre-Hilbert space to a Hilbert space (see *Theorem V.2.1*).

Examples

1. Let $\mathcal{P}$ be the vector space of n-ples (*Example I.1.1*). If $x = (\lambda_1, \cdots, \lambda_n)$ and $y = (\mu_1, \cdots, \mu_n)$, define

$$(x \mid y) = \sum_1^n \lambda_k \mu_k^*.$$

The axioms (P1)–(P4) are easily verified. This example is known as n-dimensional *unitary space*, and will be denoted $\mathcal{C}^n$.

2. Let $\mathcal{P}$ be the vector space of continuous functions on $[a,b]$ (*Example I.1.3*), where $a < b$. Define

$$(x \mid y) = \int_a^b x(t) y(t)^* \, dt.$$

This example will be referred to as *the pre-Hilbert space of continuous functions on* $[a,b]$.

3. Let $\mathcal{P}$ be the vector space of finitely non-zero sequences (*Example I.1.6*). If $x = (\lambda_k)$ and $y = (\mu_k)$, define

$$(x \mid y) = \sum_1^\infty \lambda_k \mu_k^*.$$

Since this is essentially a finite sum, convergence is not an issue here. This example will be referred to as *the pre-Hilbert space of finitely non-zero sequences*.

4. If $\mathcal{P}$ is any pre-Hilbert space, and $\mathfrak{N}$ is a linear subspace of $\mathcal{P}$, obviously $\mathfrak{N}$ is itself a pre-Hilbert space.

Exercises

1. Fill in the details in the above examples (especially *Example 2*, for which the verification of (P4) is non-trivial).

2. The vector space $\mathcal{C}$ of complex numbers (*Example I.1.8*) is a pre-Hilbert space, via $(\lambda \mid \mu) = \lambda \mu^*$. [This is essentially the unitary space $\mathcal{C}^1$ of *Example 1*.]

3. Let $\mathcal{P}$ be the vector space of finitely non-zero functions defined on a set $\mathfrak{I}$ (*Example I.1.7*). Define

$$(x|y) = \sum_t x(t)y(t)^*,$$

the sum being extended over all t in $\mathfrak{I}$. Then, $\mathcal{P}$ is a pre-Hilbert space.

4. Let $\mathcal{P}$ be any vector space of finite dimension n, and $x_1, \cdots, x_n$ any basis of $\mathcal{P}$. If $x = \sum_1^n \lambda_k x_k$ and $y = \sum_1^n \mu_k x_k$, define $(x|y) = \sum_1^n \lambda_k \mu_k^*$. Then, $\mathcal{P}$ is a pre-Hilbert space.

§2. FIRST PROPERTIES OF PRE-HILBERT SPACES

Axioms (P2) and (P3) for a pre-Hilbert space can be expressed as follows: the scalar product $(x|y)$ is "additive" and "homogeneous" in the first factor. The first two statements of *Theorem 1* assert that $(x|y)$ is "additive" and "conjugate-homogeneous" in the second factor:

Theorem 1. *In any pre-Hilbert space:*

  (1) $(x|y + z) = (x|y) + (x|z)$

  (2) $(x|\lambda y) = \lambda^*(x|y)$

  (3) $(\theta|y) = (x|\theta) = 0$

  (4) $(x - y|z) = (x|z) - (y|z)$

        $(x|y - z) = (x|y) - (x|z)$

  (5)   *If* $(x|z) = (y|z)$ *for all z, necessarily* $x = y$.

Proof.

(1): Using axioms (P1) and (P2), $(x|y + z) = (y + z|x)^* = [(y|x) + (z|x)]^* = (y|x)^* + (z|x)^* = (x|y) + (x|z)$.

(2): Using axioms (P1) and (P3), $(x|\lambda y) = (\lambda y|x)^* = [\lambda(y|x)]^* = \lambda^*(y|x)^* = \lambda^*(x|y)$.

(3): $(\theta|y) = (\theta + \theta|y) = (\theta|y) + (\theta|y)$, hence $(\theta|y) = 0$. Similarly, $(x|\theta) = 0$.

(4): $(x - y|z) = (x + (-y)|z) = (x|z) + (-y|z) = (x|z) + ((-1)y|z) = (x|z) + (-1)(y|z) = (x|z) - (y|z)$. Similarly for the second relation.

(5): Suppose $(x\,|\,z) = (y\,|\,z)$ for all z. Then, $(x - y\,|\,z) = (x\,|\,z) - (y\,|\,z) = 0$ for all z; in particular, $(x - y\,|\,x - y) = 0$, hence $x - y = \theta$ by axiom (P4).   ∎

Exercises

1. In any pre-Hilbert space,

$$\left(\textstyle\sum_1^n \lambda_k x_k \,\big|\, y\right) = \sum_1^n \lambda_k (x_k \,|\, y)$$

$$\left(x \,\big|\, \textstyle\sum_1^m \mu_j y_j\right) = \sum_1^m \mu_j{}^*(x \,|\, y_j)$$

$$\left(\textstyle\sum_1^n \lambda_k x_k \,\big|\, \sum_1^m \mu_j y_j\right) = \sum_{k,j} \lambda_k \mu_j{}^*(x_k \,|\, y_j).$$

§3. THE NORM OF A VECTOR

Definition 1. *In a pre-Hilbert space, the* **norm** *(or "length") of a vector x, denoted $\|\,x\,\|$, is the non-negative real number defined by the formula $\|\,x\,\| = \sqrt{(x\,|\,x)}$.*

Suggested verbalization of $\|\,x\,\|$: "norm x."

Theorem 1. *In a pre-Hilbert space:*

(1) $\|\,\lambda x\,\| = |\lambda|\,\|\,x\,\|.$

(2) $\|\,x\,\| > 0$ *when* $x \neq \theta$; $\|\,x\,\| = 0$ *if and only if* $x = \theta$.

Proof.

(1): $\|\,\lambda x\,\|^2 = (\lambda x\,|\,\lambda x) = \lambda \lambda^*(x\,|\,x) = |\lambda|^2 \|\,x\,\|^2.$

(2): This is immediate from axiom (P4), and the relation $(\theta\,|\,\theta) = 0$.   ∎

In particular, $\|-x\,\| = \|\,x\,\|$ and $\|\,ix\,\| = \|\,x\,\|$. If $x \neq \theta$, the vector $\|\,x\,\|^{-1}\,x$ has norm 1.

Examples

1. In the unitary space $\mathbb{C}^n$ (*Example 1.1*), if $x = (\lambda_k)$,

$$\|\,x\,\| = \left(\sum_1^n |\lambda_k|^2\right)^{\!1/2}.$$

2. In the pre-Hilbert space of continuous functions on $[a,b]$ (*Example 1.2*),

$$\| x \| = \left(\int_a^b |x(t)|^2 \, dt \right)^{\frac{1}{2}}.$$

3. In the pre-Hilbert space of finitely non-zero sequences (*Example 1.3*), if $x = (\lambda_k)$,

$$\| x \| = \left(\sum_1^\infty |\lambda_k|^2 \right)^{\frac{1}{2}}. \quad \blacksquare$$

The additivity of the scalar product yields an identity expressible simply in terms of norms:

Theorem 2. (Parallelogram law) *In a pre-Hilbert space,*

$$\| x + y \|^2 + \| x - y \|^2 = 2 \| x \|^2 + 2 \| y \|^2.$$

Proof.
One has $\| x + y \|^2 = (x+y|x+y) = (x|x) + (x|y) + (y|x) + (y|y) = \| x \|^2 + \| y \|^2 + (x|y) + (y|x)$. Replacing y by $-y$, $\| x - y \|^2 = \| x \|^2 + \| y \|^2 - (x|y) - (y|x)$. $\quad \blacksquare$

The norm of a vector is expressed, by definition, in terms of the scalar product. There is a useful formula which expresses the scalar product in terms of norms:

Theorem 3. (Polarization identity) *In a pre-Hilbert space*, $(x|y) = \frac{1}{4}\{ \| x + y \|^2 - \| x - y \|^2 + i \| x + iy \|^2 - i \| x - iy \|^2 \}$.

Proof.
In the identity

(a) $\| x + y \|^2 = \| x \|^2 + \| y \|^2 + (x|y) + (y|x),$

replace y by $-y$, iy, and $-iy$:

$$\| x - y \|^2 = \| x \|^2 + \| y \|^2 - (x|y) - (y|x)$$

$$\| x + iy \|^2 = \| x \|^2 + \| y \|^2 - i(x|y) + i(y|x)$$

$$\| x - iy \|^2 = \| x \|^2 + \| y \|^2 + i(x|y) - i(y|x).$$

It follows that

(b) $- \parallel x - y \parallel^2 = - \parallel x \parallel^2 - \parallel y \parallel^2 + (x|y) + (y|x)$

(c) $i \parallel x + iy \parallel^2 = i \parallel x \parallel^2 + i \parallel y \parallel^2 + (x|y) - (y|x)$

(d) $-i \parallel x - iy \parallel^2 = -i \parallel x \parallel^2 - i \parallel y \parallel^2 + (x|y) - (y|x).$

Adding (a)–(d), the right hand side reduces to $4(x|y)$.   ∎

From the definition of norm, $(x|x) = \parallel x \parallel \parallel x \parallel$. In general, $|(x|y)|$ is dominated by the product of $\parallel x \parallel$ and $\parallel y \parallel$:

Theorem 4. (Cauchy-Schwarz inequality) *In a pre-Hilbert space,* $|(x|y)| \leq \parallel x \parallel \parallel y \parallel$.

Proof.

If $x = \theta$ or $y = \theta$, then $(x|y) = 0$, and the conclusion is clear.

Suppose, for instance, that $y \neq \theta$. Dividing through the desired inequality by $\parallel y \parallel$, the problem is to show that $|(x|z)| \leq \parallel x \parallel$ when $\parallel z \parallel = 1$. For every complex number λ,

$$\parallel x - \lambda z \parallel^2 = \parallel x \parallel^2 - \lambda^*(x|z) - \lambda(z|x) + \lambda\lambda^* \parallel z \parallel^2$$

$$= \parallel x \parallel^2 - (x|z)\lambda^* - \lambda(x|z)^* + \lambda\lambda^*$$

$$= \parallel x \parallel^2 - (x|z)(x|z)^*$$

$$+ (x|z)(x|z)^* - (x|z)\lambda^* - \lambda(x|z)^* + \lambda\lambda^*$$

$$= \parallel x \parallel^2 - |(x|z)|^2 + [(x|z) - \lambda][(x|z) - \lambda]^*$$

$$= \parallel x \parallel^2 - |(x|z)|^2 + |(x|z) - \lambda|^2.$$

In particular, for $\lambda_0 = (x|z)$, $0 \leq \parallel x - \lambda_0 z \parallel^2 = \parallel x \parallel^2 - |(x|z)|^2$.   ∎

Applying *Theorem 4* in the unitary space $\mathbb{C}^n$ (see *Example 1*),

Corollary. *If* $\lambda_1, \cdots, \lambda_n$ *and* $\mu_1, \cdots, \mu_n$ *are complex numbers,*

$$\left| \sum_1^n \lambda_k \mu_k^* \right| \leq \left(\sum_1^n |\lambda_k|^2 \right)^{1/2} \left(\sum_1^n |\mu_k|^2 \right)^{1/2}.$$

The Cauchy-Schwarz inequality leads to an inequality involving only norms:

Theorem 5. (Triangle inequality) *In a pre-Hilbert space, one has* $\parallel x + y \parallel \leq \parallel x \parallel + \parallel y \parallel$.

Proof.

Denote by $\rho\{\lambda\}$ the real part of the complex number λ; obviously $|\rho\{\lambda\}| \leq |\lambda|$. Applying the Cauchy-Schwarz inequality at the appropriate step, $\| x + y \|^2 = \| x \|^2 + \| y \|^2 + (x|y) + (x|y)^* = \| x \|^2 + \| y \|^2 + 2\rho \{(x|y)\} \leq \| x \|^2 + \| y \|^2 + 2|(x|y)| \leq \| x \|^2 + \| y \|^2 + 2 \| x \| \| y \| = (\| x \| + \| y \|)^2.$ ∎

Consider, for example, the unitary space $\mathbb{C}^2$. A vector $x = (\alpha_1,\alpha_2)$ with *real* components may be interpreted, in the Cartesian plane, as the "arrow" from the origin $(0,0)$ to the point (α_1,α_2). Then, $\| x \|$ is the familiar formula for the distance from $(0,0)$ to (α_1,α_2). If also $y = (\beta_1,\beta_2)$, with real components, $x + y$ represents the *resolvent* of the arrows x and y:

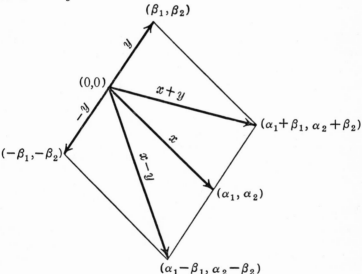

The triangle inequality and parallelogram law can now be given the obvious geometrical interpretations from which their name is drawn.

It is customary to carry over this geometrical language to pre-Hilbert spaces of arbitrary dimension:

Definition 2. *In a pre-Hilbert space,* $\| x - y \|$ *is called the* **distance** *from x to y.*

Certain properties of the norm have natural formulations in terms of distance:

Theorem 6. *In a pre-Hilbert space,*

   (1) $\| x - y \| \geq 0; \; \| x - y \| = 0$ *if and only if* $x = y$.

   (2) $\| x - y \| = \| y - x \|$

   (3) $\| x - z \| \leq \| x - y \| + \| y - z \|$.

Proof.

   (1) and (2) are clear from *Theorem 1*, and the relation $y - x = -(x - y)$.

   (3) results from the relation $x - z = (x - y) + (y - z)$, and *Theorem 5.* ∎

Exercises

   1. If x and y are continuous complex-valued functions on $[a,b]$, then

$$\left| \int_a^b x(t) y(t)^* \, dt \right|^2 \leq \int_a^b |x(t)|^2 \, dt \cdot \int_a^b |y(t)|^2 \, dt,$$

and

$$\left(\int_a^b |x(t) + y(t)|^2 \, dt \right)^{1/2} \leq \left(\int_a^b |x(t)|^2 \, dt \right)^{1/2} + \left(\int_a^b |y(t)|^2 \, dt \right)^{1/2}.$$

   2. Let x and y be vectors in a pre-Hilbert space. If $x = \theta$ or $y = \theta$, the Cauchy-Schwarz inequality reduces to $0 = 0$. Assuming $x \neq \theta$ and $y \neq \theta$, show that $|(x|y)| = \| x \| \, \| y \|$ if and only if x and y are "proportional" (i.e. $y = \lambda x$ for suitable λ).

   3. In a pre-Hilbert space, $| \, \| x \| - \| y \| \, | \leq \| x - y \|$.

   4. Let x and y be non-zero vectors in a pre-Hilbert space. The relation $\| x + y \| = \| x \| + \| y \|$ holds if and only if $y = \alpha x$ for some real number $\alpha > 0$.

   5. Let x,y,z be vectors in a pre-Hilbert space. The relation $\| x - z \| = \| x - y \| + \| y - z \|$ holds if and only if there exists a real number α, $0 \leq \alpha \leq 1$, such that $y = \alpha x + (1 - \alpha)z$.

   6. Let x and y be non-zero vectors in a pre-Hilbert space. The relation $\| x - y \| = | \, \| x \| - \| y \| \, |$ holds if and only if $y = \alpha x$ for some real number $\alpha > 0$.

7. In view of *Exercises 4* and *6*, one has $\| x + y \| = \| x \| + \| y \|$ if and only if $\| x - y \| = |\ \| x \| - \| y \|\ |$. This is also an immediate consequence of the parallelogram law.

8. Deduce another proof of the Cauchy-Schwarz inequality, using the polarization identity and the parallelogram law.

§ 4. METRIC SPACES

At the close of the preceding section, a notion of *distance* between vectors in a pre-Hilbert space was introduced. The role of this concept is clarified by abstracting certain essentials:

Definition 1. *A* **metric space** *is a set* $\mathfrak{X}$, *composed of objects called the* **points** *of the space. It is assumed that* $\mathfrak{X}$ *is non-empty (that is, contains at least one point). For each pair of points x and y of the space, there is determined a non-negative real number* $d(x,y)$, *called the* **distance** *from x to y, subject to the following axioms:*

(M1) $d(x,y) > 0$ *when* $x \neq y$;

            $d(x,y) = 0$ *if and only if* $x = y$

(M2) $d(x,y) = d(y,x)$

(M3) $d(x,z) \leq d(x,y) + d(y,z)$.

In words, distance is *strictly positive, symmetric*, and satisfies the *triangle inequality*.

Examples

1. Every pre-Hilbert space $\mathcal{P}$ is a metric space, with $d(x,y) = \| x - y \|$ (see *Theorem 3.6*).

2. A non-empty set $\mathfrak{X}$ of complex numbers is a metric space, with $d(\lambda,\mu) = |\lambda - \mu|$.

3. Let $\mathfrak{X}$ be any non-empty set. Define $d(x,y) = 1$ when $x \neq y$, and $d(x,x) = 0$ for all x. It is easy to see that $\mathfrak{X}$ is a metric space; such metric spaces are called *discrete*.

4. If $\mathfrak{X}$ is a metric space, and $\mathcal{S}$ is a non-empty set of points of $\mathfrak{X}$, then $\mathcal{S}$ is itself a metric space (distances in $\mathcal{S}$ being measured as they already are in $\mathfrak{X}$).

5. Let $\mathfrak{X}$ be the vector space of continuous functions defined on $[a,b]$ (*Example I.1.3*), where $a < b$. Define $d(x,y) = \text{LUB}\ \{\,|x(t) - y(t)| : a \le t \le b\}$; that is, $d(x,y)$ is the least upper bound of the numbers $|x(t) - y(t)|$, as t varies over the interval $[a,b]$. Then, $\mathfrak{X}$ is a metric space. [Note: a continuous function on a closed interval *is* bounded.] ∎

Certain standard notions from the calculus of real numbers have natural generalizations to metric spaces:

1. A sequence of points x_n in a metric space is said to *converge* to the point x in case $d(x_n,x) \to 0$ as $n \to \infty$. This means: given any number $\epsilon > 0$, there is an index N such that $d(x_n,x) \le \epsilon$ whenever $n \ge N$. The point x is then unique; for, if also $d(x_n,y) \to 0$, then $x = y$ results from $0 \le d(x,y) \le d(x,x_n) + d(x_n,y) \to 0 + 0$. The point x is called the *limit* of the sequence x_n. Notations: $x_n \to x$, or $x_n \to x$ as $n \to \infty$, or $x = \lim x_n$, etc. . . .

2. A sequence x_n is said to be *convergent* if there exists a point x such that $x_n \to x$. Otherwise, the sequence is said to be *divergent*.

3. A sequence x_n is said to be *Cauchy* in case $d(x_m,x_n) \to 0$ as $m,n \to \infty$. This means: given any number $\epsilon > 0$, there is an index N such that $d(x_m,x_n) \le \epsilon$ whenever $m,n \ge N$. Every convergent sequence is Cauchy; for, if $x_n \to x$, then $d(x_m,x_n) \le d(x_m,x) + d(x,x_n) \to 0 + 0$ as $m,n \to \infty$. Not every Cauchy sequence is convergent, as is shown in the following example (more sophisticated examples are given in *Examples 7* and *8*):

Example 6. Let $\mathfrak{X}$ be the open interval $(0,1)$ with $d(\alpha,\beta) = |\alpha - \beta|$. Let $\alpha_n = 1/n$ $(n = 1,2,3,\cdots)$. Then, α_n is Cauchy (since it is convergent in the metric space of all real numbers), but the only possible limit (namely 0) lies outside of $\mathfrak{X}$. ∎

In the metric space of all real numbers, with $d(\alpha,\beta) = |\alpha - \beta|$, every Cauchy sequence is convergent (this is the well-known *Cauchy criterion* for convergence). This is an example of an important type of metric space:

Definition 2. *A metric space $\mathfrak{X}$ is said to be* **complete** *in case every Cauchy sequence is convergent. Otherwise, $\mathfrak{X}$ is said to be* **incomplete**.

Examples of complete metric spaces are given in the exercises, and elsewhere in the sequel. The property of completeness owes its importance, to a certain extent, to the existence of prominent metric spaces which do not possess it; two examples of such spaces, both pre-Hilbert spaces, will now be given.

Example 7. Let $\mathcal{P}$ be the pre-Hilbert space of finitely non-zero sequences (*Example 1.3*), with $d(x,y) = \| x - y \|$. It will be shown that $\mathcal{P}$ is an incomplete metric space, by exhibiting a Cauchy sequence that has no limit in $\mathcal{P}$. The proposed sequence x_n is

$$x_1 = (1,0,0,\cdots)$$
$$x_2 = (1,1/2,0,\cdots)$$
$$x_3 = (1,1/2,1/3,0,\cdots)$$
$$\cdot\ \ \cdot\ \ \cdot$$
$$x_n = (1,1/2,1/3,\cdots,1/n,0,\cdots).$$

For all $n,p = 1,2,3,\cdots$,

$$\| x_{n+p} - x_n \|^2 = \left\|\left(0,\cdots,0,\frac{1}{n+1},\frac{1}{n+2},\cdots,\frac{1}{n+p},0,\cdots\right)\right\|^2$$

$$= \sum_{n+1}^{n+p}\frac{1}{k^2}\,;$$

since the series $\sum_1^\infty 1/k^2$ is convergent, $d(x_{n+p},x_n) = \| x_{n+p} - x_n \| \to 0$ as $n \to \infty$. It follows that x_n is a Cauchy sequence of vectors.

Suppose (to the contrary) that $\mathcal{P}$ contained a vector $x = (\lambda_1,\lambda_2,\lambda_3,\cdots,\lambda_N,0,0,\cdots)$ such that $x_n \to x$. If $n \geq N$,

$$\| x_n - x \|^2 = \sum_1^n \left|\frac{1}{k} - \lambda_k\right|^2 + \sum_{n+1}^\infty |\lambda_k|^2$$

$$= \sum_1^n \left|\frac{1}{k} - \lambda_k\right|^2 + 0;$$

letting $n \to \infty$, $\sum_1^\infty \left|\frac{1}{k} - \lambda_k\right|^2 = 0$, hence $\lambda_k = 1/k$ for all k. This contradicts the assumption that x is finitely non-zero. ∎

Example 8. Let $\mathcal{P}$ be the pre-Hilbert space of continuous functions on a closed interval, say $[-1,1]$ for simplicity. Distances are defined as in *Example 1*:

$$d(x,y) = \| x - y \| = \left(\int_{-1}^1 |x(t) - y(t)|^2\, dt\right)^{\frac{1}{2}}.$$

It will be shown that $\mathcal{P}$ is an incomplete metric space. The proposed Cauchy sequence without a limit is the sequence whose n'th term x_n has the following graph:

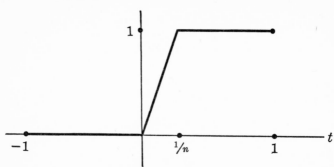

That is,

$$x_n(t) = \begin{cases} 0 & \text{for} \quad -1 \leq t \leq 0 \\ nt & \text{for} \quad\ \ 0 < t < 1/n \\ 1 & \text{for} \quad 1/n \leq t \leq 1. \end{cases}$$

By elementary calculus, $\| x_m - x_n \| \to 0$ as $m,n \to \infty$; specifically, if $m > n$,

$$\int_{-1}^{1} |x_m(t) - x_n(t)|^2 \, dt = \frac{(m-n)^2}{3m^2 n}.$$

Assume to the contrary that $\mathcal{P}$ contains a (continuous) function x such that $x_n \to x$, that is,

$$\int_{-1}^{1} |x_n(t) - x(t)|^2 \, dt \to 0.$$

Since the integrands are ≥ 0,

$$\int_{a}^{b} |x_n(t) - x(t)|^2 \, dt \leq \int_{-1}^{1} |x_n(t) - x(t)|^2 \, dt$$

for any sub-interval $[a,b]$ of $[-1,1]$, hence

$$\int_{a}^{b} |x_n(t) - x(t)|^2 \, dt \to 0.$$

In particular,

$$\int_{-1}^{0} |x_n(t) - x(t)|^2 \, dt \to 0;$$

since $x_n(t) = 0$ on $[-1,0]$, this reduces to

$$\int_{-1}^{0} |x(t)|^2 \, dt \to 0,$$

in other words,

$$\int_{-1}^{0} |x(t)|^2 \, dt = 0.$$

Since x is continuous, it follows that $x(t) = 0$ on $[-1,0]$.

Suppose $0 < \epsilon < 1$. One has

$$\int_{\epsilon}^{1} |x_n(t) - x(t)|^2 \, dt \to 0.$$

But, $x_n(t) = 1$ on $[\epsilon,1]$, provided $n > 1/\epsilon$, hence

$$\int_{\epsilon}^{1} |x_n(t) - x(t)|^2 \, dt = \int_{\epsilon}^{1} |1 - x(t)|^2 \, dt$$

for $n > 1/\epsilon$; letting $n \to \infty$, it follows that

$$\int_{\epsilon}^{1} |1 - x(t)|^2 \, dt = 0,$$

hence $x(t) = 1$ on $[\epsilon,1]$. Since $\epsilon > 0$ is arbitrary, $x(t) = 1$ on the semi-open interval $(0,1]$. Thus,

$$x(t) = \begin{cases} 0 & \text{for} \quad -1 \le t \le 0 \\ 1 & \text{for} \quad\;\; 0 < t \le 1. \end{cases}$$

This contradicts the assumption that x is continuous.   ∎

Returning to general metric spaces,

Theorem 1. *In any metric space:*

(1) $|d(x,z) - d(y,z)| \le d(x,y)$

(2)   *If* $x_n \to x$ *and* $y_n \to y$, *then* $d(x_n,y_n) \to d(x,y)$.

(3)   *If* x_n *and* y_n *are Cauchy sequences, then* $d(x_n,y_n)$ *is a convergent sequence of real numbers.*

Proof.

(1): By the triangle inequality, $d(x,z) \le d(x,y) + d(y,z)$; transposing, $d(x,z) - d(y,z) \le d(x,y)$. Interchanging the role of x and y, $d(y,z) - d(x,z) \le d(y,x)$, that is, $-d(x,y) \le d(x,z) - d(y,z)$.

(2): Using part (1), and the triangle inequality for real numbers, $|d(x,y) - d(x_n,y_n)| \le |d(x,y) - d(x_n,y)| + |d(x_n,y) - d(x_n,y_n)| \le d(x,x_n) + d(y,y_n) \to 0 + 0$ as $n \to \infty$.

(3): Similarly, $|d(x_m,y_m) - d(x_n,y_n)| \le d(x_m,x_n) + d(y_m,y_n) \to 0 + 0$ as $m,n \to \infty$. Since the real numbers are complete, the Cauchy sequence $d(x_n,y_n)$ converges. ∎

The concept of a bounded set of real numbers can be generalized as follows: a set S of points in a metric space is said to be *bounded* in case the distances $d(x,y)$ remain bounded as x and y vary over S; that is, there is a constant $M \ge 0$ such that $d(x,y) \le M$ whenever x and y are points of S.

Examples

9. Let x_0 be a fixed point of the metric space $\mathfrak{X}$, and let ϵ be a fixed real number >0. The set S, of all points x in $\mathfrak{X}$ such that $d(x,x_0) < \epsilon$, is bounded; for, if x and y are two such points, $d(x,y) \le d(x,x_0) + d(x_0,y) < 2\epsilon$. S is called the *open ball* with *center* x_0 and *radius* ϵ. In particular, when $\mathfrak{X}$ is the metric space of real numbers, S is the open interval $(x_0 - \epsilon, x_0 + \epsilon)$.

10. Similarly, the set $\mathfrak{I}$ of all points x such that $d(x,x_0) \le \epsilon$ is bounded; it is called the *closed ball* with center x_0 and radius ϵ. In particular, when $\mathfrak{X}$ is the metric space of real numbers, $\mathfrak{I}$ is the closed interval $[x_0 - \epsilon, x_0 + \epsilon]$.

11. Suppose x_0 is a fixed point of the metric space $\mathfrak{X}$, and S is a set of points of $\mathfrak{X}$. Then, S is bounded if and only if the numbers $d(x,x_0)$ are bounded as x varies over S. For, suppose $d(x,x_0) \le K$ for all x in S; if x and y are points of S, $d(x,y) \le d(x,x_0) + d(x_0,y) \le 2K$, thus S is bounded. Conversely, suppose S is bounded, say $d(x,y) \le M$ for all x and y in S; fix any point y_0 of S; then $d(x,x_0) \le d(x,y_0) + d(y_0,x_0) \le M + d(y_0,x_0)$ for all x in S.

Exercises

1. In a discrete metric space (*Example 3*), $x_n \to x$ if and only if there is an index N such that $x_n = x$ for all $n \ge N$.

2. In the metric space $\mathfrak{X}$ of *Example 5*, $x_n \to x$ means that $x_n(t) \to x(t)$ uniformly for t in $[a,b]$.

3. In the metric space $\mathcal{C}^m$ (see *Example 1*), $x_n \to x$ if and only if: for each $k = 1, \cdots, m$, the k'th component of x_n converges to the k'th component of x.

4. In the metric space $\mathcal{C}^m$, a sequence x_n is Cauchy if and only if: for each $k = 1, \cdots, m$, the sequence of k'th components is a Cauchy sequence of complex numbers. Deduce that $\mathcal{C}^m$ is complete.

5. Every discrete metric space is complete.

6. The metric space $\mathcal{X}$ of *Example 5* is complete.

7. If $\mathcal{S}$ is a non-empty set of points in a metric space $\mathcal{X}$, the following conditions on $\mathcal{S}$ are equivalent:

   (a) $\mathcal{S}$ is bounded;

   (b) given any point x of $\mathcal{X}$, there is a ball centered at x (i.e. there exists a suitable radius $\epsilon > 0$) which includes all the points of $\mathcal{S}$;

   (c) there exists a ball containing all the points of $\mathcal{S}$.

8. In a metric space, the following statements are equivalent:

   (a) $x_n \to x$;

   (b) each ball centered at x contains all but finitely many of the terms x_n;

   (c) each open ball containing x contains all but finitely many of the terms x_n.

   In part (c), can one replace "open ball" by "closed ball"?

§ 5. METRIC NOTIONS IN PRE-HILBERT SPACE; HILBERT SPACES

Let us translate the general metric space concepts of the preceding section into pre-Hilbert space terms; the dictionary is *Example 4.1*:

1. A sequence of vectors x_n *converges* to the *limit* vector x in case $\| x_n - x \| \to 0$ as $n \to \infty$; that is, given any $\epsilon > 0$, there is an index N such that $\| x_n - x \| \leq \epsilon$ whenever $n \geq N$. The vector x is then uniquely determined by the sequence x_n. Notations: $x_n \to x$, or $x_n \to x$ as $n \to \infty$, or $x = \lim x_n$, etc. . . . .

2. A sequence of vectors x_n is *convergent* if there exists a vector x such that $x_n \to x$. Otherwise, the sequence is *divergent*.

3. A sequence of vectors x_n is *Cauchy* in case $\| x_m - x_n \| \to 0$ as $m,n \to \infty$; that is, given any $\epsilon > 0$, there is an index N such that $\| x_m - x_n \| \leq \epsilon$ whenever $m,n \geq N$. Every convergent sequence is Cauchy; the converse fails (see *Examples 4.7* and *4.8*).

4. A set S of vectors is *bounded* if there is a constant $M \geq 0$ such that $\| x \| \leq M$ for all x in S (see *Example 4.11*). In particular, a sequence of vectors x_n is bounded if there is a constant $M \geq 0$ such that $\| x_n \| \leq M$ for all n. If x_0 is a fixed vector, and $\epsilon > 0$, the set of all vectors x such that $\| x - x_0 \| < \epsilon$ is the *open ball* with *center* x_0 and *radius* ϵ; the *closed ball*, with center x_0 and radius ϵ, is the set of all vectors x such that $\| x - x_0 \| \leq \epsilon$; the set of all vectors x such that $\| x - x_0 \| = \epsilon$ is called the *sphere* with center x_0 and radius ϵ. In particular, the *open unit ball, closed unit ball,* and *unit sphere* are defined, respectively, by the conditions $\| x \| < 1$, $\| x \| \leq 1$, and $\| x \| = 1$.

5. A pre-Hilbert space is *complete* in case every Cauchy sequence converges. That is, if $\| x_m - x_n \| \to 0$, there exists a vector x such that $\| x_n - x \| \to 0$.

Definition 1. *A complete pre-Hilbert space is called a* **Hilbert space.**

In the sequel, the letters $\mathcal{3C}$ and $\mathcal{K}$ will invariably denote Hilbert spaces. The most important example is the following:

Example 1. *The Hilbert space l^2.* Denote by $\mathcal{3C}$ the set of all sequences $x = (\lambda_k)$ of complex numbers which are absolutely square-summable, that is, $\sum_1^\infty |\lambda_k|^2 < \infty$ (equivalently, the finite sums $\sum_1^n |\lambda_k|^2$ have a bound independent of n). For such an x, define $N(x) = \left(\sum_1^\infty |\lambda_k|^2 \right)^{\frac{1}{2}}$. If $x = (\lambda_k)$ and $y = (\mu_k)$, write $x = y$ in case $\lambda_k = \mu_k$ for all k.

Lemma 1. If $x = (\lambda_k)$ and $y = (\mu_k)$ are sequences belonging to $\mathcal{3C}$, then so is the sequence $(\lambda_k + \mu_k)$, which is denoted $x + y$.

Proof:

By the parallelogram law for complex numbers, $|\lambda_k + \mu_k|^2 + |\lambda_k - \mu_k|^2 = 2|\lambda_k|^2 + 2|\mu_k|^2$, hence

$$\sum_1^n |\lambda_k + \mu_k|^2 \leq 2 \sum_1^n |\lambda_k|^2 + 2 \sum_1^n |\mu_k|^2$$

for all n. Clearly $\sum_1^\infty |\lambda_k + \mu_k|^2 < \infty$, by the "comparison test." ∎

If $x = (\lambda_k)$ belongs to $\mathcal{3C}$, and λ is a complex number, $\sum_1^n |\lambda \lambda_k|^2 = |\lambda|^2 \sum_1^n |\lambda_k|^2$ shows that the sequence $(\lambda \lambda_k)$ is absolutely square-summable; it is denoted λx.

It is easy to see that $\mathcal{K}$ is a vector space, with respect to the operations $x + y$ and λx. Incidentally, $N(\lambda x) = |\lambda| N(x)$, and the proof of Lemma 1 shows that $N(x + y)^2 + N(x - y)^2 = 2N(x)^2 + 2N(y)^2$.

Lemma 2. If $x = (\lambda_k)$ and $y = (\mu_k)$ belong to $\mathcal{K}$, the series $\sum_1^\infty \lambda_k \mu_k^*$ converges absolutely.

Proof:

If a and b are real numbers, $(a - b)^2 \geq 0$ leads to $ab \leq \frac{1}{2}(a^2 + b^2)$; in particular, $|\lambda_k \mu_k^*| = |\lambda_k| |\mu_k| \leq \frac{1}{2}(|\lambda_k|^2 + |\mu_k|^2)$, thus $\sum_1^\infty |\lambda_k \mu_k^*|$ converges by the comparison test. ∎

Lemma 2 justifies the definition

$$(x|y) = \sum_1^\infty \lambda_k \mu_k^*.$$

The axioms for a pre-Hilbert space are easily verified. Incidentally, $\| x \| = N(x)$.

To show that $\mathcal{K}$ is a Hilbert space, it remains only to prove completeness. Suppose $x^1, x^2, x^3, \cdots$ is a Cauchy sequence in $\mathcal{K}$, that is, $\| x^m - x^n \| \to 0$ as $m, n \to \infty$. Say $x^n = (\lambda_k^n)$. For each k, $|\lambda_k^m - \lambda_k^n|^2$ $\leq \sum_{j=1}^\infty |\lambda_j^m - \lambda_j^n|^2 = \| x^m - x^n \|^2$ shows that the sequence $\lambda_k^1, \lambda_k^2, \lambda_k^3, \cdots$ of k'th components is Cauchy. Since the complex numbers are complete, $\lambda_k^n \to \lambda_k$ as $n \to \infty$, for suitable λ_k. It will be shown that $\sum_1^\infty |\lambda_k|^2 < \infty$, and that x^n converges to $x = (\lambda_k)$.

Given $\epsilon > 0$. Let p be an index such that $\| x^m - x^n \|^2 \leq \epsilon$ whenever $m, n \geq p$. Fix any positive integer r; one has

$$\sum_1^r |\lambda_k^m - \lambda_k^n|^2 \leq \| x^m - x^n \|^2 \leq \epsilon,$$

provided $m, n \geq p$; letting $m \to \infty$,

$$\sum_1^r |\lambda_k - \lambda_k^n|^2 \leq \epsilon$$

provided $n \geq p$; since r is arbitrary,

(*) $$\sum_1^\infty |\lambda_k - \lambda_k^n|^2 \leq \epsilon, \quad \text{whenever} \quad n \geq p.$$

In particular, $\sum_1^\infty |\lambda_k - \lambda_k^p|^2 \leq \epsilon$, hence the sequence $(\lambda_k - \lambda_k^p)$ belongs to $\mathcal{K}$; adding to it the sequence (λ_k^p) of $\mathcal{K}$, one obtains (λ_k), thus $x = (\lambda_k)$ belongs to $\mathcal{K}$. It follows from (*) that $\| x - x^n \|^2 \leq \epsilon$ whenever $n \geq p$. Thus, $x^n \to x$.

The Hilbert space $\mathfrak{IC}$ of absolutely square-summable sequences is denoted l^2. ∎

We resume the discussion of general pre-Hilbert spaces by noting some properties of Cauchy and convergent sequences of vectors:

Lemma. *Every Cauchy sequence is bounded.*

Proof.

Given a Cauchy sequence x_n, let N be an index such that $\| x_n - x_m \| \leq 1$ whenever $m,n \geq N$. If $n \geq N$, $\| x_n \| = \| (x_n - x_N) + x_N \| \leq \| x_n - x_N \| + \| x_N \| \leq 1 + \| x_N \|$. Thus, if M is the largest of the numbers $1 + \| x_N \|, \| x_1 \|, \| x_2 \|, \cdots, \| x_{N-1} \|$, one has $\| x_n \| \leq M$ for *all* n. ∎

Theorem 1. *In any pre-Hilbert space:*

   (1)   *If $x_n \to x$ and $y_n \to y$, then $(x_n | y_n) \to (x | y)$.*

   (2)   *If x_n and y_n are Cauchy sequences of vectors, then $(x_n | y_n)$ is a Cauchy (hence convergent) sequence of scalars.*

Proof.

   (1): For all n, $(x_n | y_n) - (x | y) = (x_n - x | y_n - y) + (x | y_n - y) + (x_n - x | y)$. Using the triangle inequality for complex numbers, and the Cauchy-Schwarz inequality, one has $| (x_n | y_n) - (x | y) | \leq \| x_n - x \| \, \| y_n - y \| + \| x \| \, \| y_n - y \| + \| x_n - x \| \, \| y \|$; clearly the right hand side $\to 0$ as $n \to \infty$.

   (2): Similarly, $| (x_n | y_n) - (x_m | y_m) | \leq \| x_n - x_m \| \, \| y_n - y_m \| + \| x_m \| \, \| y_n - y_m \| + \| x_n - x_m \| \, \| y_m \|$ for all m and n; since $\| x_m \|$ and $\| y_m \|$ are bounded by the *Lemma*, the right side $\to 0$ as $m,n \to \infty$. ∎

Corollary. *In any pre-Hilbert space:*

   (1)   *If $x_n \to x$, then $\| x_n \| \to \| x \|$.*

   (2)   *If x_n is Cauchy, then $\| x_n \|$ converges.*

Exercises

1. Fill in the details in *Example 1*.

2. If $\mathfrak{N}$ is a linear subspace of a pre-Hilbert space $\mathcal{P}$, and $\mathfrak{N}$ contains a ball or a sphere, then $\mathfrak{N}$ contains every vector of $\mathcal{P}$.

3. In a metric space, every Cauchy sequence is bounded.

4. If $x_n \to \theta$ and y_n is bounded, then $(x_n | y_n) \to 0$.

5. Another proof of the Corollary to *Theorem 1* results from the inequality $| \, \| x \| - \| y \| \, | \leq \| x - y \|$.

6. If $\| x_n \| \to \| x \|$, and $(x_n | x) \to (x | x)$, then $x_n \to x$.

7. The argument in *Example 4.7* can be concluded as follows. Assume to the contrary that there is a vector $x = (\lambda_k)$ such that $x_n \to x$. Let $e_1 = (1,0,0,\cdots)$, $e_2 = (0,1,0,\cdots)$, $e_3 = (0,0,1,0,\cdots)$, $\cdots$. For each k, $(x_n | e_k) \to (x | e_k) = \lambda_k$. But $(x_n | e_k) = 1/k$ for $n \geq k$.

§6. ORTHOGONAL VECTORS, ORTHONORMAL VECTORS

Definition 1. *If x and y are vectors in a pre-Hilbert space, one says that x is* **orthogonal** *(or "perpendicular") to y in case $(x | y) = 0$. Notation: $x \perp y$.*

Suggested verbalization of $x \perp y$: "x perp y." The relation of orthogonality is symmetric: if $x \perp y$, then $y \perp x$; this results from $(y | x) = (x | y)^*$. If $x \perp x$, necessarily $x = \theta$. Every vector x is orthogonal to θ.

Theorem 1. *If x is orthogonal to each of $y_1, \cdots, y_n$, then x is orthogonal to every linear combination of the y_k.*

Proof.
    If $x \perp y_k$ for all k, and $y = \sum_1^n \lambda_k y_k$, then $(x | y) = \sum_1^n \lambda_k^* (x | y_k) = \sum_1^n \lambda_k^* 0 = 0$. ∎

Definition 2. *A set S of vectors is said to be* **orthogonal** *in case $x \perp y$ whenever x and y are distinct vectors in S. A sequence (finite or infinite) of vectors x_n is called an* **orthogonal sequence** *if $x_j \perp x_k$ whenever $j \neq k$.*

Examples

1. Let $\lambda_1, \lambda_2, \lambda_3, \cdots$ be any sequence of scalars. In the pre-Hilbert space of finitely non-zero sequences, define $x_1 = (\lambda_1, 0, 0, \cdots)$, $x_2 = (0, \lambda_2, 0, \cdots)$, $x_3 = (0, 0, \lambda_3, 0, \cdots)$, $\cdots$. Then, x_n is an orthogonal sequence of vectors.

2. In the unitary space $\mathbb{C}^3$, the vectors $x_1 = (1,2,2)$, $x_2 = (2,1,-2)$, $x_3 = (2,-2,1)$ are orthogonal. Incidentally, $\| x_k \| = 3$ for all k.

3. In the pre-Hilbert space of continuous functions on $[-\pi,\pi]$, let the sequence of functions x_n be defined by the formulas $x_n(t) = \sin{(nt)}$ $(n = 1,2,3,\cdots)$. The sequence x_n is orthogonal, that is,

$$\int_{-\pi}^{\pi} \sin{(mt)} \sin{(nt)}\, dt = 0, \quad \text{when} \quad m \neq n.$$

Similarly the sequence $y_n(t) = \cos{(nt)}$ $(n = 0,1,2,3,\cdots)$ is orthogonal. Moreover, $x_m \perp y_n$ for all m and n.

Theorem 2. (Pythagorean relation) *If $x \perp y$, then*

$$\| x + y \|^2 = \| x \|^2 + \| y \|^2.$$

More generally, if $x_1,\cdots,x_n$ are orthogonal,

$$\| \textstyle\sum_1^n x_k \|^2 = \sum_1^n \| x_k \|^2.$$

Proof.

If $x \perp y$, $\| x + y \|^2 = (x\,|\,x) + (x\,|\,y) + (y\,|\,x) + (y\,|\,y) = \| x \|^2 + 0 + 0 + \| y \|^2$. This is the case $n = 2$. Assume inductively that $\| \sum_1^{n-1} x_k \|^2 = \sum_1^{n-1} \| x_k \|^2$. Setting $x = \sum_1^{n-1} x_k$ and $y = x_n$, one has $x \perp y$ by *Theorem 1*; then, $\| \sum_1^n x_k \|^2 = \| x + y \|^2 = \| x \|^2 + \| y \|^2 = \sum_1^{n-1} \| x_k \|^2 + \| x_n \|^2$. ∎

Corollary. *If $x_1,x_2,x_3,\cdots$ is an orthogonal sequence (finite or infinite) of non-zero vectors, the x_k are linearly independent.*

Proof.

Suppose $\sum_1^n \lambda_k x_k = \theta$. The vectors $\lambda_1 x_1,\cdots, \lambda_n x_n$ are clearly orthogonal. By *Theorem 2*, $0 = \| \theta \|^2 = \sum_1^n \| \lambda_k x_k \|^2 = \sum_1^n |\lambda_k|^2 \| x_k \|^2$; since $\| x_k \| > 0$ for all k, necessarily $\lambda_k = 0$ for all k. ∎

Definition 3. *A set S of vectors in a pre-Hilbert space is said to be **orthonormal** in case* (i) *S is orthogonal in the sense of Definition 2, and* (ii) *$\| x \| = 1$ for every vector x in S. A sequence (finite or infinite) of vectors x_n is called an **orthonormal sequence** if* (i) *$x_j \perp x_k$ whenever $j \neq k$, and* (ii) *$\| x_k \| = 1$ for all k.*

The condition for the orthonormality of a sequence can be expressed as follows: $(x_j\,|\,x_k) = \delta_{jk}$. In general, the "Kronecker delta" symbol δ_{st} can be defined for s and t varying over a set $\mathfrak{J}$; it has the value 0 when $s \neq t$, and 1 when $s = t$. For example, in the notation of *Exercise I.7.4*, $x_s(t) = \delta_{st}$. A set S of vectors is orthonormal if and only if $(x|y) = \delta_{xy}$ for all x and y in S.

Examples

4. If y_n is any orthogonal sequence of non-zero vectors, the sequence $x_n = \| y_n \|^{-1} y_n$ is orthonormal. For example:

5. In the unitary space $\mathbb{C}^3$, the vectors $(1/3,2/3,2/3)$, $(2/3,1/3,-2/3)$, $(2/3,-2/3,1/3)$ are orthonormal (see *Example 2*).

6. Notation as in *Example 3*. One has $\| y_o \|^2 = 2\pi$, and $\| x_n \|^2 = \| y_n \|^2 = \pi$ for $n = 1,2,3,\cdots$. Define

$$u_n(t) = \frac{1}{\sqrt{\pi}} \sin (nt) \qquad (n = 1,2,3,\cdots)$$

$$v_o(t) = \frac{1}{\sqrt{2\pi}}$$

$$v_n(t) = \frac{1}{\sqrt{\pi}} \cos (nt) \qquad (n = 1,2,3,\cdots).$$

Then, the vectors u_m, v_n are orthonormal.

7. In the pre-Hilbert space of finitely non-zero sequences, let $e_1 = (1,0,0,\cdots)$, $e_2 = (0,1,0,\cdots)$, $e_3 = (0,0,1,0,\cdots),\cdots$. The sequence of vectors e_n is orthonormal.

8. In the Hilbert space l^2 (*Example 5.1*), let e_n be the orthonormal sequence described in *Example 7*. If $x = (\lambda_k)$, evidently $(x|e_k) = \lambda_k$. In particular, for every vector x, $\sum_1^\infty |(x|e_k)|^2 < \infty$; this result holds for any orthonormal sequence, as a consequence of "Bessel's inequality":

Theorem 3. (Bessel's equality and inequality) *Let $x_1,\cdots,x_n$ be orthonormal vectors in a pre-Hilbert space. For every vector x,*

(1) $\| x - \sum_1^n (x|x_k)x_k \|^2 = \| x \|^2 - \sum_1^n |(x|x_k)|^2$,

hence

(2) $\sum_1^n |(x|x_k)|^2 \le \| x \|^2$.

Proof.

If $\lambda_1,\cdots,\lambda_n$ are arbitrary complex numbers, $\|\sum_1^n \lambda_k x_k\|^2 = \sum_1^n \|\lambda_k x_k\|^2 = \sum_1^n |\lambda_k|^2$ by *Theorem 2;* calculating as in the proof of *Theorem 3.4,*

$$\| x - \sum_1^n \lambda_k x_k \|^2 = \| x \|^2 - (\sum_1^n \lambda_k x_k \mid x)$$
$$- (x \mid \sum_1^n \lambda_k x_k) + \sum_1^n |\lambda_k|^2$$
$$= \| x \|^2 - \sum_1^n \lambda_k (x \mid x_k)^*$$
$$- \sum_1^n (x \mid x_k)\lambda_k^* + \sum_1^n \lambda_k \lambda_k^*$$
$$= \| x \|^2 - \sum_1^n |(x \mid x_k)|^2 + \sum_1^n |(x \mid x_k) - \lambda_k|^2.$$

In particular, setting $\lambda_k = (x \mid x_k)$, this reduces to the relation (1); the inequality (2) follows at once. ∎

Corollary. *If $x_1,x_2,x_3,\cdots$ is an orthonormal sequence, then for any vector x,*

$$\sum_1^\infty |(x \mid x_k)|^2 \le \| x \|^2.$$

In particular, $(x \mid x_k) \to 0$ as $k \to \infty$.

Proof.

Bessel's inequality holds for each n. ∎

Remarks

1. From the proof of *Theorem 3*, it is clear that the choice $\lambda_k = (x \mid x_k)$ *minimizes* $\| x - \sum_1^n \lambda_k x_k \|$, and thus provides a "best approximation" of x by a linear combination of $x_1,\cdots,x_n$. Moreover, only one set of coefficients gives best approximation, namely $\lambda_k = (x \mid x_k)$. Note that if $n > m$, then in the best approximation by $x_1,\cdots,x_n$, the first m coefficients are precisely those required for best approximation by $x_1,\cdots,x_m$.

2. Notation as in *Theorem 3*. Let $y = \sum_1^n (x \mid x_k)x_k$ and $z = x - y$. Clearly $(z \mid x_k) = 0$ for all k, hence $(z \mid y) = 0$. Thus, one has a decomposition $x = y + z$, where y is a linear combination of $x_1,\cdots,x_n$, and $z \perp x_k$ for all k. Such a decomposition is easily seen to be unique.

3. Bessel's inequality for $n = 1$ is essentially the Cauchy-Schwarz inequality; see the proof of *Theorem 3.4*.

4. If $y_k \to \theta$, then $(x|y_k) \to (x|\theta) = 0$ for each vector x, by *Theorem 5.1*. The converse of this proposition fails; for, with notation as in the above *Corollary*, $(x|x_k) \to 0$ for each x, although $\| x_k \| = 1$ precludes $x_k \to \theta$.

Example 9. Notation as in *Example 6*. The scalars $\lambda_k = (x|u_k)$ $(k = 1,2,3,\cdots)$ and $\mu_k = (x|v_k)$ $(k = 0,1,2,3,\cdots)$ are called the *Fourier coefficients* of the function x. By the above *Corollary*,

$$\sum_1^\infty |\lambda_k|^2 + \sum_0^\infty |\mu_k|^2 \leq \int_{-\pi}^{\pi} |x(t)|^2 \, dt.$$

[It can be shown that the sum is actually *equal* to the integral.] $\blacksquare$

Every orthonormal sequence of vectors is linearly independent, by the Corollary of *Theorem 2*. On the other hand, there is a systematic procedure for "orthonormalizing" any linearly independent sequence:

Theorem 4. (Gram-Schmidt orthonormalization procedure) *If $y_1, y_2, y_3, \cdots$ is a sequence of linearly independent vectors in a pre-Hilbert space, there exists an orthonormal sequence $x_1, x_2, x_3, \cdots$ such that $[x_1, \cdots, x_n] = [y_1, \cdots, y_n]$ for all n (that is, $x_1, \cdots, x_n$ generate the same linear subspace as $y_1, \cdots, y_n$).*

Proof.
The vectors x_n will be defined inductively. Let $x_1 = \| y_1 \|^{-1} y_1$. Assume inductively that orthonormal vectors $x_1, \cdots, x_{n-1}$ are already defined, in such a way that $[x_1, \cdots, x_k] = [y_1, \cdots, y_k]$ for $k = 1, \cdots, n - 1$. The desired vector x_n must be a linear combination of $y_1, \cdots, y_n$, or equivalently of $x_1, \cdots, x_{n-1}, y_n$; moreover, it must be orthogonal to each of $x_1, \cdots, x_{n-1}$. Guided by *Remark 2* following *Theorem 3*, set $z = y_n - \sum_1^{n-1} (y_n|x_k)x_k$; then, z is orthogonal to $x_1, \cdots, x_{n-1}$. Define $x_n = \| z \|^{-1} z$; this is permissible, since $z = \theta$ would imply that y_n is a linear combination of $x_1, \cdots, x_{n-1}$, hence of $y_1, \cdots, y_{n-1}$, contrary to the independence of the y's. The reader can easily verify that every linear combination of $x_1, \cdots, x_n$ is also a linear combination of $y_1, \cdots, y_n$, and vice versa. $\blacksquare$

The Gram-Schmidt procedure applies equally well to a finite sequence $y_1, \cdots, y_n$ of independent vectors, and leads to orthonormal vectors $x_1, \cdots, x_n$ such that $[x_1, \cdots, x_k] = [y_1, \cdots, y_k]$ for $k = 1, \cdots, n$. In particular:

Corollary. *If $\mathcal{P}$ is a pre-Hilbert space of finite dimension n, $\mathcal{P}$ has a basis $x_1, \cdots, x_n$ of orthonormal vectors.*

Theorem 5. *Every finite-dimensional pre-Hilbert space is complete, hence is a Hilbert space.*

Proof.

By the above *Corollary*, there is a basis $x_1, \cdots, x_n$ of orthonormal vectors. If $x = \sum_1^n \lambda_k x_k$, then $\| x \|^2 = \sum_1^n |\lambda_k|^2$ by *Theorem 2;* completeness can now be proved using a simplification of the argument given for l^2 (see *Example 5.1*). ∎

Exercises

1. The relation $\| x + y \|^2 = \| x \|^2 + \| y \|^2$ is equivalent to $(x|y) + (y|x) = 0$; denote this relation by $x \, \mathrm{P} \, y$. Then $x \perp y$ if and only if $x \, \mathrm{P} \, \lambda y$ for all complex λ.

2. Let $\mathcal{P}$ be the pre-Hilbert space of finitely non-zero functions on a set $\mathfrak{I}$ (*Exercise 1.3*). For each point s of $\mathfrak{I}$, let x_s be defined as in *Exercise I.7.4*. Then, the x_s are an orthonormal set of vectors. That is, $(x_s|x_t) = \delta_{st}$ for all s and t in $\mathfrak{I}$.

3. In the pre-Hilbert space of continuous functions on a symmetric interval $[-a,a]$, every odd function x is orthogonal to every even function y (see *Exercise I.5.6*).

4. Starting with the vector $x_1 = (1,2,2,4)$ in the unitary space $\mathbb{C}^4$, construct an orthogonal set of vectors x_1, x_2, x_3, x_4 such that $\| x_k \| = 5$ for all k (integer components, preferably).

5. In the pre-Hilbert space of finitely non-zero sequences, orthonormalize the sequence of vectors $y_1 = (1,0,0,\cdots)$, $y_2 = (1,1,0,\cdots)$, $y_3 = (1,1,1,0,\cdots), \cdots$.

6. In the pre-Hilbert space of continuous functions on $[0,1]$, orthonormalize the first three terms of the sequence $y_n(t) = t^{n-1}$ $(n = 1,2,3,\cdots)$.

§ 7. INFINITE SUMS IN HILBERT SPACE

In the Hilbert space l^2, consider the orthonormal sequence e_n described in *Example 6.8*. If $x = (\lambda_1, \cdots, \lambda_m, 0, \cdots)$ is a finitely non-zero sequence, clearly $x = \sum_1^m \lambda_k e_k$; one could formally write $x = \sum_1^\infty \lambda_k e_k$, with the understanding that $\lambda_k = 0$ for all $k > m$.

Consider now an arbitrary vector $x = (\lambda_k)$ in l^2. What sense can be made of the expression $x = \sum_1^\infty \lambda_k e_k$? It is natural to define $\sum_1^\infty \lambda_k e_k$ to be the limit of the sequence of "partial sums" $y_n = \sum_1^n \lambda_k e_k$; this limit exists, in fact $y_n \to x$, since $\| x - y_n \|^2 = \| (0, \cdots, 0, \lambda_{n+1}, \lambda_{n+2}, \cdots) \|^2 = \sum_{n+1}^\infty |\lambda_k|^2 \to 0$ as $n \to \infty$.

These considerations will now be generalized for arbitrary orthonormal sequences in Hilbert space.

Lemma. *Let $x_1, x_2, x_3, \cdots$ be an orthonormal sequence of vectors in a pre-Hilbert space, and $\lambda_1, \lambda_2, \lambda_3, \cdots$ a sequence of scalars such that $\sum_1^\infty |\lambda_k|^2 < \infty$. Define $y_n = \sum_1^n \lambda_k x_k$. Then, the sequence y_n is Cauchy.*

Proof.

$$\| y_{n+p} - y_n \|^2 = \| \sum_{n+1}^{n+p} \lambda_k x_k \|^2 = \sum_{n+1}^{n+p} \| \lambda_k x_k \|^2$$

$$= \sum_{n+1}^{n+p} |\lambda_k|^2 \to 0 \quad \text{as} \quad n \to \infty. \quad \blacksquare$$

Throwing in completeness, we have

Theorem 1. *If x_n is an orthonormal sequence of vectors in a Hilbert space, and λ_n is a sequence of scalars such that $\sum_1^\infty |\lambda_k|^2 < \infty$, then the sequence $y_n = \sum_1^n \lambda_k x_k$ converges to a limit x, denoted $x = \sum_1^\infty \lambda_k x_k$.*

More generally:

Definition 1. *If $x_1, x_2, x_3, \cdots$ is a sequence of vectors in a pre-Hilbert space, such that the sequence $y_n = \sum_1^n x_k$ converges to a limit x, one writes $x = \sum_1^\infty x_k$.*

Thus, $\| \sum_1^\infty x_k - \sum_1^n x_k \| \to 0$, by definition. The basic properties of the infinite sums described in *Theorem 1* are as follows:

Theorem 2. *Let x_n be an orthonormal sequence of vectors in a Hilbert space. Suppose $x = \sum_1^\infty \lambda_k x_k$ and $y = \sum_1^\infty \mu_k x_k$, in the sense of Theorem 1. Then:*

(1) $(x|y) = \sum_1^\infty \lambda_k \mu_k{}^*$, *the series converging absolutely.*

(2) $(x|x_k) = \lambda_k$

(3) $\| x \|^2 = \sum_1^\infty |\lambda_k|^2 = \sum_1^\infty |(x|x_k)|^2.$

Proof.

(1): Let $s_n = \sum_1^n \lambda_k x_k$ and $t_n = \sum_1^n \mu_k x_k$. By definition, $s_n \to x$ and $t_n \to y$, hence $(s_n|t_n) \to (x|y)$ by *Theorem 5.1*. Since $(s_n|t_n) = \sum_{j,k=1}^n \lambda_j \mu_k{}^*(x_j|x_k) = \sum_1^n \lambda_k \mu_k{}^*$, one has $(x|y) = \sum_1^\infty \lambda_k \mu_k{}^*$. Replacing (λ_k) by $(|\lambda_k|)$, and (μ_k) by $(|\mu_k|)$, it is clear that the convergence is absolute (see also *Example 5.1*).

(2): This is a special case of (1), with $\mu_k = 1$ and $\mu_j = 0$ for all $j \neq k$.

(3): Take $y = x$ in (1).   ∎

Exercises

1. If x_n is an orthogonal sequence of vectors in a pre-Hilbert space, such that $\sum_1^\infty \| x_k \|^2 < \infty$, then the sequence $y_n = \sum_1^n x_k$ is Cauchy. What if $\sum_1^\infty \| x_k \| < \infty$?

2. Let x_n be a sequence of (not necessarily orthogonal) vectors in a pre-Hilbert space, such that $\sum_1^\infty \| x_k \| < \infty$. Then the sequence $y_n = \sum_1^n x_k$ is Cauchy. Hence, in Hilbert space, $\sum_1^\infty x_k$ exists.

3. If x_n is an orthonormal sequence, and $\sum_1^\infty \lambda_k x_k$ exists in the sense of *Definition 1*, necessarily $\sum_1^\infty |\lambda_k|^2 < \infty$.

4. Give an example of a sequence x_n such that $\sum_1^\infty \| x_k \|^2 < \infty$, but for which the sequence $y_n = \sum_1^n x_k$ is not Cauchy.

5. If $y = \sum_1^\infty y_k$, and $x \perp y_k$ for all k, then $x \perp y$.

6. (*Generalized Pythagorean relation*) Let x_n be an orthogonal sequence in Hilbert space, such that $\sum_1^\infty \| x_k \|^2 < \infty$, and form the vector $x = \sum_1^\infty x_k$ according to *Exercise 1*. Then $\| x \|^2 = \sum_1^\infty \| x_k \|^2$.

7. Suppose x_n is an orthonormal sequence in a pre-Hilbert space, and x is a vector such that $\| x \|^2 = \sum_1^\infty |(x|x_k)|^2$. Then $x = \sum_1^\infty (x|x_k)x_k$.

8. If $y_1, y_2, y_3, \cdots$ is a sequence of vectors in a Hilbert space $\mathcal{JC}$, such that every vector x is a linear combination of finitely many y_k, then $\mathcal{JC}$ is necessarily finite-dimensional.

§ 8. TOTAL SETS, SEPARABLE HILBERT SPACES, ORTHONORMAL BASES

Suppose x_n is an orthonormal sequence of vectors in a Hilbert space. Given any vector x, the scalars $\lambda_k = (x|x_k)$ satisfy $\sum_1^\infty |\lambda_k|^2 < \infty$, by the Corollary of *Theorem 6.3*. According to *Theorem 7.1*, one can form the vector $y = \sum_1^\infty \lambda_k x_k$, and by *Theorem 7.2*, $(y|x_k) = \lambda_k = (x|x_k)$ for all k. When can one conclude that $y = x$? In any case, $(y - x|x_k) = (y|x_k) - (x|x_k) = 0$ for all k. Thus, one could conclude $y = x$ if the vectors x_k had the following property: the only vector z which is orthogonal to every x_k is the vector $z = \theta$. This leads to the following definitions:

Definition 1. *A set* S *of vectors in a pre-Hilbert space* $\mathcal{P}$ *is said to be* **total** *in case the only vector* z *of* $\mathcal{P}$ *which is orthogonal to every vector of* S *is the vector* $z = \theta$. *A sequence (finite or infinite) of vectors* x_n *is called a* **total sequence** *in case: if* $z \perp x_k$ *for all* k, *necessarily* $z = \theta$.

Examples

1. In any pre-Hilbert space $\mathcal{P}$, $\mathcal{P}$ is itself a total set of vectors. For, if $z \perp x$ for every vector x, in particular $z \perp z$.

2. If S is any system of generators (*Definition I.5.4*) for the pre-Hilbert space $\mathcal{P}$, S is total. For, if z is orthogonal to every vector in S, it is orthogonal to every linear combination of vectors in S; in particular, $z \perp z$.

3. In the Hilbert space l^2 (or in the pre-Hilbert space of finitely non-zero sequences), the sequence of vectors $e_1 = (1,0,0,\cdots)$, $e_2 = (0,1,0,\cdots)$, $e_3 = (0,0,1,0,\cdots)$, $\cdots$ is total. So is the sequence $x_1 = (1,0,0,\cdots)$, $x_2 = (1,1,0,\cdots)$, $x_3 = (1,1,1,0,\cdots)$, $\cdots$.

*4. In the pre-Hilbert space of continuous functions on $[-\pi,\pi]$, it can be shown that the functions $1, t, t^2, \cdots$ form a total sequence. So do the functions $u_1, u_2, u_3, \cdots, v_0, v_1, v_2, v_3, \cdots$ described in *Example 6.6*.

Definition 2. *A sequence (finite or infinite) of vectors x_n is called an* **orthonormal basis** *for a Hilbert space* $\mathfrak{IC}$, *if it is* (i) *orthonormal, and* (ii) *total.*

Not every Hilbert space possesses such a sequence; those which do are characterized in *Theorem 3* below.

Example 5. The sequence e_n described in *Example 3* is an orthonormal basis for the Hilbert space l^2. This will be referred to as the *canonical orthonormal basis* of l^2.   ∎

If a Hilbert space $\mathfrak{IC}$ has an orthonormal basis x_n consisting of infinitely many vectors, $\mathfrak{IC}$ is an infinite-dimensional vector space, by the Corollary of *Theorem 6.2*. It follows that the x_n cannot form a *basis*, in the sense of *Definition I.7.2*, for the vector space $\mathfrak{IC}$; that is, not every vector x can be expressed as a linear combination of the x_k (see *Exercise 7.8*).

On the other hand, suppose $\mathcal{P}$ is a pre-Hilbert space possessing a finite sequence $x_1, \cdots, x_n$ which is orthonormal and total. If x is any vector in $\mathcal{P}$, the vector $x - \sum_1^n (x \mid x_k) x_k$ is orthogonal to every x_k, hence is θ. Thus, $x = \sum_1^n (x \mid x_k) x_k$, $\mathcal{P}$ is finite-dimensional, and $x_1, \cdots, x_n$ is a basis for $\mathcal{P}$ in the sense of *Definition I.7.2*. Clearly, in a finite-dimensional space, the concepts "orthonormal basis" and "basis consisting of orthonormal vectors" coincide.

By the remarks at the beginning of the section,

Theorem 1. *If x_n is an orthonormal basis for the infinite-dimensional Hilbert space* $\mathfrak{IC}$, *then for each vector x one has* $x = \sum_1^\infty (x \mid x_k) x_k$.

Alternative descriptions of an orthonormal basis are contained in the following:

Theorem 2. *If x_n is an orthonormal infinite sequence in a Hilbert space* $\mathfrak{IC}$, *the following conditions are equivalent:*

(a)   *The x_n are an orthonormal basis.*

(b) $\sum_1^\infty \mid (x \mid x_k) \mid^2 = \parallel x \parallel^2$, *for each vector x.*

(c) $\sum_1^\infty (x \mid x_k) x_k = x$, *for each vector x.*

Proof.

(a) *implies* (c) by *Theorem 1*.

(c) *implies* (b) by *Theorem 7.2*.

(b) *implies* (a): For, if $(x \mid x_k) = 0$ for all k, clearly $x = \theta$ by (b). ∎

The obvious finite-dimensional analogs of *Theorems 1* and *2* are true; the proofs are elementary.

Which Hilbert spaces possess an orthonormal basis? Such a space necessarily contains a total *sequence;* it will be shown in *Theorem 3* that this condition is also sufficient for the existence of an orthonormal basis.

Definition 3. *A Hilbert space is said to be* **separable** *if it possesses a total sequence (finite or infinite).*

Examples

6. If $\mathcal{K}$ is a finite-dimensional Hilbert space, every basis $y_1, \cdots, y_n$ is total, hence $\mathcal{K}$ is separable.

7. The Hilbert space l^2 is separable (see *Example 5*).

Theorem 3. *The following conditions on a Hilbert space $\mathcal{K}$ are equivalent:*

(a) $\mathcal{K}$ *is separable;*

(b) $\mathcal{K}$ *has an orthonormal basis* x_n.

Proof.

(b) *implies* (a): This is clear from *Definitions 2* and *3*.

(a) *implies* (b): Suppose $z_1, z_2, z_3, \cdots$ is a total sequence in $\mathcal{K}$. By *Theorem I.6.2*, there is a linearly independent subsequence $y_1, y_2, y_3, \cdots$ of the z_k, generating the same linear subspace as the z_k. The y_k are also total; for, if a vector z is orthogonal to every y_k, it is orthogonal to every linear combination of the y_k, hence to every z_k (hence $z = \theta$). By *Theorem 6.4*, there is an orthonormal sequence $x_1, x_2, x_3, \cdots$ generating the same linear subspace as the y_k. The x_k are total, by the above reasoning; thus, the x_k are an orthonormal basis.

Incidentally, if $\mathcal{K}$ is finite-dimensional, the independent sequence y_k must be finite, say $y_1, \cdots, y_n$; then $x_1, \cdots, x_n$ is an orthonormal basis. Both the y_k and the x_k are bases in the sense of Chapter I (see the remarks preceding *Theorem 1*). ∎

There is another frequently used definition of "separable" Hilbert space, equivalent to the one given in *Definition 3;* this material is sketched in *Exercises 3–5.*

Exercises

1. In the pre-Hilbert space of finitely non-zero sequences $x = (\lambda_k)$, let S be the set of all vectors x such that $\sum_1^\infty (1/k)\lambda_k = 0$. Then S is a total set (actually a linear subspace).

2. If a pre-Hilbert space $\mathcal{P}$ possesses a finite total set $x_1, \cdots, x_m$, then $\mathcal{P}$ is finite-dimensional (hence is a Hilbert space). An independent set $y_1, \cdots, y_n$ is a basis if and only if it is total.

3. A metric space is said to be *separable* if it contains a sequence x_n with the following property: given any point x in the space, there is a subsequence x_{n_k} converging to x. Such a sequence x_n is called a *dense* sequence. Show that if x_n is a dense sequence in a Hilbert space $\mathcal{H}$, then x_n is a total sequence, hence $\mathcal{H}$ is a separable Hilbert space in the sense of *Definition 3.*

*4. If $\mathcal{H}$ is a Hilbert space of finite dimension n, and $x_1, \cdots, x_n$ is an orthonormal basis, then the vectors of the form $x = \sum_1^n \gamma_k x_k$, where the γ_k are Gaussian-rational (see Chapter I, § 8), can be enumerated in a sequence, and this sequence is dense. Thus, $\mathcal{H}$ is a separable metric space in the sense of *Exercise 3.* [The sophisticated point is the enumeration.]

*5. Suppose $\mathcal{H}$ is an infinite-dimensional Hilbert space, separable in the sense of *Definition 3.* Then $\mathcal{H}$ is a separable metric space in the sense of *Exercise 3.*

*6. Verify *Example 4.*

*7. It can be shown that every Hilbert space contains a total orthonormal set $\mathcal{I}$; such a set is called an *orthonormal basis* for the space. [However, it may not be possible to enumerate $\mathcal{I}$ in a sequence.]

§9. ISOMORPHIC HILBERT SPACES; CLASSICAL HILBERT SPACE

Definition 1. *A Hilbert space $\mathfrak{IC}$ is said to be* **isomorphic** *with a Hilbert space $\mathfrak{K}$ if there exists a function T which assigns, to each vector x in $\mathfrak{IC}$, one and only one vector Tx in $\mathfrak{K}$, in such a way that the following conditions hold:*

(i)   *If x and y are vectors of $\mathfrak{IC}$ such that $x \neq y$, then $Tx \neq Ty$.*

(ii) *If z is any vector in $\mathfrak{K}$, there is a vector x in $\mathfrak{IC}$ such that $Tx = z$.*

(iii) *$T(x + y) = Tx + Ty$, for all x and y in $\mathfrak{IC}$.*

(iv) *$T(\lambda x) = \lambda(Tx)$, for all x in $\mathfrak{IC}$, and all scalars λ.*

(v)   *$(Tx \mid Ty) = (x \mid y)$, for all x and y in $\mathfrak{IC}$.*

Such a function T is called a **Hilbert space isomorphism** *of $\mathfrak{IC}$ onto $\mathfrak{K}$.*

Isomorphic Hilbert spaces are in a sense "equal," for an isomorphism T distinguishes between distinct points, and "preserves" sums, scalar multiples, and scalar products. One can think of $\mathfrak{K}$ as being essentially the space $\mathfrak{IC}$ with a "tag" T attached to each vector x.

Two types of separable Hilbert spaces were noted in *Examples 8.6* and *8.7:* (1) for each n, the unitary space $\mathfrak{C}^n$ is a separable Hilbert space, and (2) the Hilbert space l^2 is separable. Up to isomorphism, these are the *only* separable Hilbert spaces:

Theorem 1. *Let $\mathfrak{IC}$ be a separable Hilbert space:*

(1)   *If $\mathfrak{IC}$ has finite dimension n, it is isomorphic with $\mathfrak{C}^n$.*

(2)   *If $\mathfrak{IC}$ is infinite-dimensional, it is isomorphic with l^2.*

Proof.

Let us show (2); the proof of (1) is much simpler, and is left to the reader.

Suppose $\mathfrak{IC}$ is infinite-dimensional and separable. An isomorphism T of $\mathfrak{IC}$ onto l^2 will be constructed. By *Theorem 8.3*, $\mathfrak{IC}$ has an orthonormal basis x_n.

Given any vector x in $\mathfrak{IC}$; the problem is to define Tx in l^2. By the Corollary of *Theorem 6.3*, $\sum_1^\infty |(x \mid x_k)|^2 < \infty$, hence we may define $Tx = ((x \mid x_k))$; that is, Tx is the sequence whose k'th term is $(x \mid x_k)$.

Incidentally, $x = \sum_1^\infty (x|x_k)x_k$, by *Theorem 8.1*. Let us verify the properties (i)–(v) of *Definition 1*:

(i): If $x \neq y$, then $x - y \neq \theta$; since the x_k are total, $(x - y|x_j) \neq 0$ for some index j, thus $(x|x_j) \neq (y|x_j)$. It follows that $Tx \neq Ty$, by the definition of equality in l^2 (see *Example 5.1*).

(ii): Given any vector (λ_k) in l^2. Define $x = \sum_1^\infty \lambda_k x_k$ as in *Theorem 7.1*. Since $(x|x_k) = \lambda_k$ by *Theorem 7.2*, one has $Tx = (\lambda_k)$.

(iii): If x and y are vectors in $\mathcal{H}$, $(x + y|x_k) = (x|x_k) + (y|x_k)$ for all k; this shows that $T(x + y) = Tx + Ty$.

(iv): Similarly, $T(\lambda x) = \lambda(Tx)$ results from $(\lambda x|x_k) = \lambda(x|x_k)$.

(v): If x and y are vectors in $\mathcal{H}$, then $x = \sum_1^\infty (x|x_k)x_k$ and $y = \sum_1^\infty (y|x_k)x_k$, hence $(x|y) = \sum_1^\infty (x|x_k)(y|x_k)^*$ by *Theorem 7.2*. In other words, $(x|y) = (Tx|Ty)$. ∎

Thus, up to isomorphism, there is just one infinite-dimensional separable Hilbert space:

Definition 2. *Any infinite-dimensional separable Hilbert space will be referred to as* **classical Hilbert space.**

Exercises

1. If $\mathcal{H}$ and $\mathcal{K}$ are classical Hilbert spaces, there exists an isomorphism of $\mathcal{H}$ onto $\mathcal{K}$.

2. If T is an isomorphism of a classical Hilbert space $\mathcal{H}$ onto a Hilbert space $\mathcal{K}$, then $\mathcal{K}$ is also classical.

3. If $\mathcal{H}$ is isomorphic with $\mathcal{K}$, then $\mathcal{K}$ is isomorphic with $\mathcal{H}$.

Closed Linear Subspaces

§ 1. SOME NOTATIONS FROM SET THEORY

A *set* $\mathfrak{X}$ is composed of objects $x, y, \cdots$ called the *elements* or *members* of the set $\mathfrak{X}$. As in the first two chapters, I assume that these terms are meaningful to the reader, without further elaboration.

The statement "x is a member of the set $\mathfrak{X}$" is symbolized "$x \in \mathfrak{X}$," which may be read "x belongs to $\mathfrak{X}$." For example: if $\mathfrak{V}$ is a vector space, the symbol $x \in \mathfrak{V}$ means that x is a vector in the space $\mathfrak{V}$; if $\mathfrak{X}$ is a metric space, $x \in \mathfrak{X}$ means that x is a point of the space $\mathfrak{X}$; $\lambda \in \mathcal{C}$ means that λ is a complex number.

If $x \in \mathfrak{X}$ and $y \in \mathfrak{X}$, the statement "$x = y$" means that x and y are symbols representing the *same* element of $\mathfrak{X}$. One assumes the following properties of equality: (1) $x = x$ for every $x \in \mathfrak{X}$; (2) if $x = y$, then $y = x$; and (3) if $x = y$ and $y = z$, then $x = z$. These are known as the *reflexive*, *symmetric*, and *transitive* properties of equality.

In addition, the following set-theoretic concepts and notations will be employed in the sequel:

1. Let $\mathfrak{X}$ and $\mathfrak{Y}$ be sets. If every element of $\mathfrak{X}$ is also an element of $\mathfrak{Y}$ (that is, if $x \in \mathfrak{X}$ implies $x \in \mathfrak{Y}$), one says that $\mathfrak{X}$ is a *subset* of $\mathfrak{Y}$. Other terms for this: $\mathfrak{X}$ is *contained* in $\mathfrak{Y}$, $\mathfrak{X}$ is *included* in $\mathfrak{Y}$, $\mathfrak{Y}$ *includes*

$\mathfrak{X}$, $\mathfrak{Y}$ *contains* $\mathfrak{X}$, $\mathfrak{Y}$ is a *superset* of $\mathfrak{X}$. Notations: $\mathfrak{X} \subset \mathfrak{Y}$, or $\mathfrak{Y} \supset \mathfrak{X}$. For example, if $\mathfrak{R}$ is the set of all real numbers, and $\mathcal{S}$ is the set of real numbers in the interval $[a,b]$, then $\mathcal{S} \subset \mathfrak{R}$.

2. If both $\mathfrak{X} \subset \mathfrak{Y}$ and $\mathfrak{Y} \subset \mathfrak{X}$, the sets $\mathfrak{X}$ and $\mathfrak{Y}$ are said to be *equal*. This means: $x \in \mathfrak{X}$ if and only if $x \in \mathfrak{Y}$. Notation: $\mathfrak{X} = \mathfrak{Y}$. For example, if $\mathfrak{X}$ is the set of all real numbers ≥ 0, and $\mathfrak{Y}$ is the set of all real numbers which can be expressed as the square of a real number, then $\mathfrak{X} = \mathfrak{Y}$.

3. Let $\mathfrak{X}$ be a set, and suppose that for each $x \in \mathfrak{X}$ there is given a statement involving x (denoted, say, by $s(x)$), which may or may not be true. The symbol

$$\{x \in \mathfrak{X} : s(x)\}$$

stands for the set of all $x \in \mathfrak{X}$ for which $s(x)$ is true. For example, if $\mathfrak{R}$ is the set of all real numbers, and $\mathcal{S}$ is the interval $[a,b]$, then

$$\mathcal{S} = \{x \in \mathfrak{R} : a \leq x \leq b\}.$$

4. A set $\mathfrak{X}$ is *empty* if it has no members (that is, the relation $x \in \mathfrak{X}$ does not hold for any x). Otherwise, $\mathfrak{X}$ is said to be *non-empty*. The symbol $\varnothing$ denotes an empty set. For example,

$$\{x \in \mathfrak{R} : x > 2 \text{ and } x \leq 1\} = \varnothing,$$

$$\{x \in \mathfrak{R} : x^2 < 0\} = \varnothing.$$

5. The set whose only element is x is denoted $\{x\}$. The set whose only elements are $x_1, \cdots, x_n$ (not necessarily distinct) is denoted $\{x_1, \cdots, x_n\}$. Thus, $x \in \{x_1, \cdots, x_n\}$ if and only if $x = x_k$ for some k.

Exercises

1. If $\mathfrak{X}$, $\mathfrak{Y}$, $\mathfrak{Z}$ are sets,

   (i) $\mathfrak{X} \subset \mathfrak{X}$;

   (ii)   if $\mathfrak{X} \subset \mathfrak{Y}$ and $\mathfrak{Y} \subset \mathfrak{Z}$, then $\mathfrak{X} \subset \mathfrak{Z}$;

   (iii) $\mathfrak{X} = \mathfrak{Y}$ if and only if both $\mathfrak{X} \subset \mathfrak{Y}$ and $\mathfrak{Y} \subset \mathfrak{X}$.

2. If $\mathfrak{X}$, $\mathfrak{Y}$, $\mathfrak{Z}$ are sets,

   (i) $\mathfrak{X} = \mathfrak{X}$;

   (ii)   if $\mathfrak{X} = \mathfrak{Y}$, then $\mathfrak{Y} = \mathfrak{X}$;

   (iii)   if $\mathfrak{X} = \mathfrak{Y}$ and $\mathfrak{Y} = \mathfrak{Z}$, then $\mathfrak{X} = \mathfrak{Z}$.

3. If $\mathfrak{X}$ and $\mathfrak{Y}$ are both empty sets, then $\mathfrak{X} = \mathfrak{Y}$. Thus one can speak of *the* empty set.

§ 2. ANNIHILATORS

Definition 1. *Let* $\mathcal{S}$ *be a subset of a pre-Hilbert space* $\mathcal{P}$. *A vector* $x \in \mathcal{P}$ *is said to be* **orthogonal** *to* $\mathcal{S}$ *in case* $x \perp s$ *for all* $s \in \mathcal{S}$; *notation:* $x \perp \mathcal{S}$. *The set of all such vectors* x *is called the* **annihilator** *of* $\mathcal{S}$, *and is denoted* $\mathcal{S}^\perp$. *Thus:*

$$\mathcal{S}^\perp = \{x \in \mathcal{P} : (x|s) = 0 \quad \text{for all} \quad s \in \mathcal{S}\}.$$

Examples

1. Recall that $\{\theta\}$ is the set whose only element is the vector θ. Then, $\mathcal{P}^\perp = \{\theta\}$. In fact, a subset $\mathcal{S}$ is total if and only if $\mathcal{S}^\perp = \{\theta\}$.

2. Clearly $\{\theta\}^\perp = \mathcal{P}$.

3. The convention is that $\varnothing^\perp = \mathcal{P}$, where $\varnothing$ is the empty subset of $\mathcal{P}$. The rationalization for this is as follows: given any vector $x \in \mathcal{P}$, one has $(x|s) = 0$ whenever $s \in \varnothing$ (which is never).

Theorem 1. *If* $\mathcal{S}$ *is any subset of a pre-Hilbert space* $\mathcal{P}$, *then* $\mathcal{S}^\perp$ *is a linear subspace of* $\mathcal{P}$. *Moreover, if* $x_n \in \mathcal{S}^\perp$ *for all* n, $x \in \mathcal{P}$, *and* $x_n \to x$, *then* $x \in \mathcal{S}^\perp$.

Proof.
   Clearly $\theta \in \mathcal{S}^\perp$, and $\mathcal{S}^\perp$ is a linear subspace by *Theorem II.6.1.* Suppose $x_n \perp \mathcal{S}$ for all n, and $x_n \to x$. For any $s \in \mathcal{S}$, $(x|s) = \lim (x_n|s)$ by *Theorem II.5.1;* since $(x_n|s) = 0$ for all n, $(x|s) = 0$.   ∎

Definition 2. *Let* $\mathcal{S}$ *be a subset of a metric space* $\mathfrak{X}$. *A point* $x \in \mathfrak{X}$ *is said to be* **adherent** *to* $\mathcal{S}$ *in case there exists a sequence* $s_n \in \mathcal{S}$ *such that* $s_n \to x$.

In particular, if $\mathcal{S}$ is a subset of a pre-Hilbert space $\mathcal{P}$, a vector $x \in \mathcal{P}$ is adherent to $\mathcal{S}$ if and only if there is a sequence $s_n \in \mathcal{S}$ such that $\| s_n - x \| \to 0$ as $n \to \infty$.

Definition 3. *Let* $\mathfrak{X}$ *be a metric space,* $\mathcal{S} \subset \mathfrak{X}$. $\mathcal{S}$ *is said to be a* **closed subset** *of* $\mathfrak{X}$ *if it contains every point adherent to it. That is, the relations* $s_n \in \mathcal{S}$, $x \in \mathfrak{X}$, $s_n \to x$, *imply* $x \in \mathcal{S}$.

Examples

4. According to *Theorem 1*, if S is any subset of a pre-Hilbert space $\mathcal{P}$, $S^\perp$ is a closed linear subspace of $\mathcal{P}$.

5. Let $\mathcal{R}$ be the metric space of all real numbers (*Example II.4.2*), S the "closed interval" $[a,b]$, where $a \le b$. Then S is a closed subset of $\mathcal{R}$. For, suppose $a \le s_n \le b$, and $s_n \to x$, that is, $|s_n - x| \to 0$. The assertion is that $a \le x \le b$. Assume to the contrary, say, that $x > b$. Then $\epsilon = x - b > 0$, hence for sufficiently large n, $x - s_n \le |x - s_n| < \epsilon = x - b$, $-s_n < -b$, $s_n > b$, a contradiction. A contradiction is reached similarly if $x < a$.

6. Let $\mathcal{X}$ be a metric space, $y \in \mathcal{X}$, $\epsilon > 0$, and $S = \{x \in \mathcal{X} : d(x,y) \le \epsilon\}$. Then, S is a closed set. For, suppose $x_n \in S$ and $x_n \to x$. By *Theorem II.4.1*, $d(x_n,y) \to d(x,y)$; since $0 \le d(x_n,y) \le \epsilon$ for all n, one has $0 \le d(x,y) \le \epsilon$ by *Example 5*.

7. The convention is that the empty subset of any metric space is closed. For, if x is adherent to $\varnothing$ (which is never, since a sequence cannot be extracted from $\varnothing$), then $x \in \varnothing$.

8. Every sphere $\{x : d(x,y) = \epsilon\}$ is a closed subset.

9. In a pre-Hilbert space, every closed ball $\{x : \| x - y \| \le \epsilon\}$, and every sphere $\{x : \| x - y \| = \epsilon\}$, is a closed subset. In particular, the closed unit ball $\{x : \| x \| \le 1\}$, and the unit sphere $\{x : \| x \| = 1\}$, are closed subsets.

10. In a metric space $\mathcal{X}$, $\mathcal{X}$ itself is a closed subset.

11. Every finite subset $S = \{y_1, \cdots, y_m\}$ of a metric space $\mathcal{X}$ is closed. For, suppose $x_n \in S$ and $x_n \to x$; for some $y_j \in S$, $x_n = y_j$ for infinitely many n, hence $x = y_j \in S$. In particular, every one-point subset $\{y\}$ is closed. ∎

If S is a subset of the pre-Hilbert space $\mathcal{P}$, one writes $S^{\perp\perp}$ for the annihilator of $S^\perp$; thus, $S^{\perp\perp} = (S^\perp)^\perp$. It is not necessary to define further "higher order perps," in view of part (3) of the following

Theorem 2. *If S and $\mathfrak{I}$ are subsets of a pre-Hilbert space $\mathcal{P}$,*

(1) $S \subset S^{\perp\perp}$;

(2) $S \subset \mathfrak{I}$ *implies* $\mathfrak{I}^\perp \subset S^\perp$;

(3) $(S^{\perp\perp})^\perp = S^\perp$.

Proof.

(1): Let $x \in S$. For any $y \in S^{\perp}$, one has $y \perp x$, hence $x \perp S^{\perp}$, that is, $x \in (S^{\perp})^{\perp}$. Thus, $x \in S$ implies $x \in S^{\perp\perp}$.

(2): Suppose $S \subset \mathfrak{J}$. If $x \perp \mathfrak{J}$, then all the more $x \perp S$; thus, $x \in \mathfrak{J}^{\perp}$ implies $x \in S^{\perp}$.

(3): Clearly $(S^{\perp})^{\perp\perp} = (S^{\perp\perp})^{\perp}$, since in each case one starts with S and perps three times. Applying part (2) to the relation $S \subset S^{\perp\perp}$, one has $S^{\perp} \supset (S^{\perp\perp})^{\perp}$. Also, $S^{\perp} \subset (S^{\perp})^{\perp\perp}$ by part (1). The last two inclusions combine to give the desired equality (3).   ∎

Definition 4. *If S and $\mathfrak{J}$ are subsets of a pre-Hilbert space $\mathcal{P}$, one says that S is* **orthogonal to** *$\mathfrak{J}$ in case $x \perp y$ whenever $x \in S$ and $y \in \mathfrak{J}$. Notation: $S \perp \mathfrak{J}$.*

Evidently $S \perp S^{\perp}$, and $\{\theta\} \perp S$, for every subset S. The convention is that $\varnothing \perp S$, for every subset S.

Theorem 3. *If $\mathfrak{M}$ and $\mathfrak{N}$ are linear subspaces of a pre-Hilbert space $\mathcal{P}$, such that $\mathfrak{M} \perp \mathfrak{N}$, then every vector $x \in \mathfrak{M} + \mathfrak{N}$ has a* **unique** *representation $x = y + z$ with $y \in \mathfrak{M}$ and $z \in \mathfrak{N}$.*

Proof.

See *Definition I.5.2* for the notation. Suppose $x = y_1 + z_1 = y_2 + z_2$, where $y_k \in \mathfrak{M}$ and $z_k \in \mathfrak{N}$. The problem is to show that $y_1 = y_2$ and $z_1 = z_2$. Define $w = y_1 - y_2 = z_2 - z_1$. Clearly $w \in \mathfrak{M}$ and $w \in \mathfrak{N}$; since $\mathfrak{M} \perp \mathfrak{N}$, one has $w \perp w$, hence $w = \theta$.   ∎

Definition 5. *Notation as in Theorem 3. One writes $\mathfrak{M} \oplus \mathfrak{N}$ for the linear subspace $\mathfrak{M} + \mathfrak{N}$. Thus, the use of the symbol $\oplus$ entails orthogonality of the summands.*

Exercises

1. Let S be a non-empty subset of a metric space $\mathfrak{X}$, and $x \in \mathfrak{X}$. Then, x is adherent to S if and only if: given any $\epsilon > 0$, there is at least one point $s \in S$ such that $d(s,x) \leq \epsilon$.

2. If $\mathcal{C}$ is the metric space of all complex numbers (*Example II.4.2*), and $\mathcal{R}$ is the set of all real numbers, then $\mathcal{R}$ is a closed subset of $\mathcal{C}$. Also, the set S of all complex numbers λ such that $|\lambda| \geq \epsilon$ is a closed subset of $\mathcal{C}$.

3. Let $\mathcal{K}$ be classical Hilbert space (*Definition II.9.2*), and x_n an orthonormal basis for $\mathcal{K}$. Let $\mathfrak{N}$ be the linear subspace generated by the x_k, that is, the set of all finite linear combinations of the x_k. Then:

   (i)   Every vector $x \in \mathcal{K}$ is adherent to $\mathfrak{N}$.

   (ii) $\mathfrak{N}$ is *not* a closed subset of $\mathcal{K}$.

4. If $\mathcal{S}$ and $\mathcal{J}$ are subsets of a pre-Hilbert space $\mathcal{P}$, the following statements are equivalent:

   (a) $\mathcal{S} \perp \mathcal{J}$

   (b) $\mathcal{S} \subset \mathcal{J}^\perp$

   (c) $\mathcal{J} \subset \mathcal{S}^\perp$.

5. If $\mathcal{S}$ is an orthogonal set (*Definition II.6.2*) of non-zero vectors, and $\mathcal{S}_1$, $\mathcal{S}_2$ are subsets of $\mathcal{S}$, then $\mathcal{S}_1 \perp \mathcal{S}_2$ if and only if $\mathcal{S}_1$ and $\mathcal{S}_2$ have no vectors in common.

6. If $\mathfrak{M}$ and $\mathfrak{N}$ are linear subspaces of a pre-Hilbert space $\mathcal{P}$, then $\mathfrak{M} \perp \mathfrak{N}$ if and only if $\| x + y \|^2 = \| x \|^2 + \| y \|^2$ whenever $x \in \mathfrak{M}$ and $y \in \mathfrak{N}$.

7. If $\mathfrak{M}$ and $\mathfrak{N}$ are linear subspaces of a pre-Hilbert space $\mathcal{P}$, such that $\mathfrak{M} \oplus \mathfrak{N} = \mathcal{P}$, then $\mathfrak{M}^\perp = \mathfrak{N}$, $\mathfrak{N}^\perp = \mathfrak{M}$, hence $\mathfrak{M}^{\perp\perp} = \mathfrak{M}$ and $\mathfrak{N}^{\perp\perp} = \mathfrak{N}$. In particular, $\mathfrak{M}$ and $\mathfrak{N}$ are closed linear subspaces.

8. In the pre-Hilbert space $\mathcal{P}$ of continuous functions on $[-a,a]$, let $\mathfrak{M}$ be the subspace of even functions, and $\mathfrak{N}$ the subspace of odd functions (see *Exercise I.5.6*). Then, $\mathcal{P} = \mathfrak{M} \oplus \mathfrak{N}$.

§ 3. CLOSED LINEAR SUBSPACES

A linear subspace $\mathfrak{N}$ of a pre-Hilbert space $\mathcal{P}$ can be enlarged to a *closed* linear subspace by forming $\mathfrak{N}^{\perp\perp}$ (see *Theorems 2.1, 2.2*). Another procedure for enlarging a linear subspace to a closed linear subspace is given in *Theorem 2* below. It will be shown in § 6 that these two procedures yield the same closed linear subspace when $\mathcal{P}$ is a Hilbert space.

Definition 1. *If $\mathcal{S}$ is a subset of a metric space $\mathcal{X}$, the* **closure** *(or "adherence") of $\mathcal{S}$ in $\mathcal{X}$ is defined to be the set of all points $x \in \mathcal{X}$ which are* adherent to S *in the sense of Definition 2.2; it is denoted* $\overline{S}$. *Thus,*

$$\overline{S} = \{x \in \mathfrak{X} : x \text{ is adherent to } S\}.$$

If $\overline{S} = \mathfrak{X}$, S *is called a* **dense subset** *of* $\mathfrak{X}$.

Remarks

1. $x \in \overline{S}$ if and only if there exists a sequence $s_n \in S$ such that $s_n \to x$.

2. The convention is that $\overline{\varnothing} = \varnothing$. For, there are no points x adherent to $\varnothing$.

3. S is a closed subset of $\mathfrak{X}$ if and only if $\overline{S} \subset S$ (see *Definition 2.3*).

4. $S \subset \overline{S}$, for every subset S. That is, every point $s \in S$ is adherent to S (take $s_n = s$ for all n).

5. $S = \overline{S}$ if and only if S is closed.

6. If $S \subset \mathfrak{I}$, then $\overline{S} \subset \overline{\mathfrak{I}}$. For, suppose $x \in \overline{S}$. Say $s_n \to x$, where $s_n \in S$. Since also $s_n \in \mathfrak{I}$, x is adherent to $\mathfrak{I}$.

7. $\mathfrak{X}$ is a dense subset of $\mathfrak{X}$. If S is a dense subset of $\mathfrak{X}$, and $\mathfrak{I} \supset S$, then $\mathfrak{I}$ is also a dense subset of $\mathfrak{X}$.

Theorem 1. *Let* S *be a subset of a metric space* $\mathfrak{X}$. *Then:*

(1) $\overline{S}$ *is a closed subset of* $\mathfrak{X}$.

(2) $S \subset \overline{S}$.

(3)   *If* $\mathfrak{I}$ *is a closed subset of* $\mathfrak{X}$ *such that* $\mathfrak{I} \supset S$, *necessarily* $\mathfrak{I} \supset \overline{S}$.

In other words, $\overline{S}$ *is the smallest closed subset of* $\mathfrak{X}$ *which contains* S.

Proof.

(1): Suppose y is adherent to $\overline{S}$. It must be shown that $y \in \overline{S}$. Choose any sequence $x_n \in \overline{S}$ such that $x_n \to y$. For each n, choose a point $s_n \in S$ such that $d(s_n, x_n) \leq 1/n$. Then, $d(s_n, y) \leq d(s_n, x_n) + d(x_n, y) \leq 1/n + d(x_n, y) \to 0 + 0$. Thus, $s_n \to y$, $y \in \overline{S}$.

(2): See Remark 4 above.

(3): If $S \subset \mathfrak{I}$, and $\mathfrak{I}$ is closed, then $\overline{S} \subset \overline{\mathfrak{I}} = \mathfrak{I}$ results from Remarks 6 and 5. ∎

Lemma. *In a pre-Hilbert space:*

(1)   *If $x_n \to x$ and $y_n \to y$, then $x_n + y_n \to x + y$.*

(2)   *If $x_n \to x$ and $\lambda_n \to \lambda$, then $\lambda_n x_n \to \lambda x$.*

Proof.

(1): $\| (x_n + y_n) - (x + y) \| = \| (x_n - x) + (y_n - y) \| \leq$
$\| x_n - x \| + \| y_n - y \| \to 0 + 0$.

(2): $\| \lambda_n x_n - \lambda x \| = \| (\lambda_n - \lambda)(x_n - x) + \lambda(x_n - x) + (\lambda_n - \lambda)x \|$
$\leq |\lambda_n - \lambda| \cdot \| x_n - x \| + |\lambda| \| x_n - x \| + |\lambda_n - \lambda| \cdot \| x \| \to 0 \cdot 0 +$
$|\lambda| \cdot 0 + 0 \cdot \| x \| = 0$. ∎

Theorem 2. *If $\mathfrak{N}$ is a linear subspace of a pre-Hilbert space $\mathcal{P}$, then $\overline{\mathfrak{N}}$ is a closed linear subspace of $\mathcal{P}$. Moreover, $\overline{\mathfrak{N}}$ is the smallest closed linear subspace which contains $\mathfrak{N}$.*

Proof.

Suppose $x,y \in \overline{\mathfrak{N}}$, and λ is a scalar. Choose sequences $x_n \in \mathfrak{N}$, $y_n \in \mathfrak{N}$ such that $x_n \to x$ and $y_n \to y$. Then, $x_n + y_n \to x + y$ and $\lambda x_n \to \lambda x$, by the *Lemma*. Since $x_n + y_n \in \mathfrak{N}$ and $\lambda x_n \in \mathfrak{N}$, $x + y$ and λx are adherent to $\mathfrak{N}$, that is, they belong to $\overline{\mathfrak{N}}$. This proves that $\overline{\mathfrak{N}}$ is a linear subspace; it is closed by *Theorem 1*. ∎

Corollary. *If $\mathfrak{N}$ is a linear subspace of a pre-Hilbert space $\mathcal{P}$, then $\overline{\mathfrak{N}} \subset \mathfrak{N}^{\perp\perp}$.*

Proof.

$\mathfrak{N}^{\perp\perp}$ is a closed linear subspace containing $\mathfrak{N}$, by *Theorems 2.1* and *2.2*. ∎

Exercises

1. In a pre-Hilbert space: if x_n and y_n are Cauchy sequences of vectors, and λ_n is a Cauchy sequence of scalars, then $x_n + y_n$ and $\lambda_n x_n$ are Cauchy sequences of vectors.

2. If $\mathcal{S}$ is a subset of a pre-Hilbert space, then $\mathcal{S}$ and $\overline{\mathcal{S}}$ have the same annihilator, that is, $\mathcal{S}^\perp = (\overline{\mathcal{S}})^\perp$.

3. If x_n is an orthonormal basis for the classical Hilbert space $\mathcal{H}$, and $\mathfrak{N}$ is the linear subspace generated by the x_k, then $\mathfrak{N}$ is dense in $\mathcal{H}$.

4. Notation as in *Exercise 3*. Let $\mathcal{S}$ be the set of all vectors x which can be expressed as a linear combination of the x_k with Gaussian-

rational coefficients. Then, $\mathcal{S}$ is not a linear subspace, but it is a dense subset of $\mathcal{3C}$.

5. Let $\mathcal{S}$ and $\mathcal{3}$ be subsets of a metric space $\mathcal{X}$. If every $x \in \mathcal{X}$ is adherent to $\mathcal{3}$, and every $t \in \mathcal{3}$ is adherent to $\mathcal{S}$, then $\mathcal{S}$ is a dense subset of $\mathcal{X}$.

6. In a pre-Hilbert space $\mathcal{P}$, the closure of $\{x : \|x - y\| < \epsilon\}$ is $\{x : \|x - y\| \leq \epsilon\}$. In a metric space, the closure of $\{x : d(x,y) < \epsilon\}$ is contained in $\{x : d(x,y) \leq \epsilon\}$.

7. If $\mathcal{S}$ is any subset of a pre-Hilbert space $\mathcal{P}$, then $\bar{\mathcal{S}} \subset \mathcal{S}^{\perp\perp}$.

§ 4. COMPLETE LINEAR SUBSPACES

The principal result of this chapter is the following theorem: if $\mathfrak{N}$ is a closed linear subspace of a Hilbert space $\mathcal{3C}$, every vector $x \in \mathcal{3C}$ can be written in the form $x = y + z$ with $y \in \mathfrak{N}$ and $z \in \mathfrak{N}^{\perp}$. This result is proved in § 6, with the decisive lemma coming in § 5. The purpose of the present section is to introduce and illustrate a concept which plays an important role in these results: the concept of a "complete subset."

If $\mathcal{S}$ is a non-empty subset of a metric space $\mathcal{X}$, $\mathcal{S}$ is itself a metric space (*Example II.4.4*), it being understood that distances in $\mathcal{S}$ are measured as they already are in $\mathcal{X}$.

Definition 1. *Let $\mathcal{X}$ be a metric space, $\mathcal{S} \subset \mathcal{X}$. If $\mathcal{S}$ is a complete metric space, $\mathcal{S}$ is called a* **complete subset** *of $\mathcal{X}$. This means: if $s_n \in \mathcal{S}$ and $d(s_m, s_n) \to 0$, there is a point s in $\mathcal{S}$ such that $d(s_n, s) \to 0$.*

Remarks

1. The convention is that $\varnothing$ is a complete subset of $\mathcal{X}$.

2. Every closed subset $\mathcal{S}$ of a complete metric space $\mathcal{X}$ is a complete subset. For, suppose $s_n \in \mathcal{S}$, $d(s_m, s_n) \to 0$. Since $\mathcal{X}$ is complete, there is a point $x \in \mathcal{X}$ such that $s_n \to x$. Since $\mathcal{S}$ is closed, $x \in \mathcal{S}$.

3. Every complete subset $\mathcal{S}$ of a metric space $\mathcal{X}$ is a closed subset of $\mathcal{X}$. For, suppose $s_n \in \mathcal{S}$, $x \in \mathcal{X}$, and $s_n \to x$. Since $d(s_m, s_n) \to 0$, and $\mathcal{S}$ is complete, there is a point $s \in \mathcal{S}$ such that $s_n \to s$. By the uniqueness of limits, $x = s \in \mathcal{S}$. Thus, $\mathcal{S}$ contains every point x which is adherent to $\mathcal{S}$.

Combining Remarks 2 and 3,

Theorem 1. *In a complete metric space (in particular, in a Hilbert space), a subset is closed if and only if it is complete.*

Corollary. *If $\mathfrak{N}$ is a closed linear subspace of a Hilbert space, $\mathfrak{N}$ is itself a Hilbert space.*

The role of completeness is emphasized by the existence of theorems concerning closed subsets of Hilbert space which are valid for complete subsets of pre-Hilbert space. Important examples of this will be given in the next two sections; another is the following:

Theorem 2. *If $\mathfrak{M}$ and $\mathfrak{N}$ are complete linear subspaces of a pre-Hilbert space $\mathcal{P}$, and $\mathfrak{M} \perp \mathfrak{N}$, then $\mathfrak{M} \oplus \mathfrak{N}$ is also a complete linear subspace of $\mathcal{P}$.*

Proof.

See *Definitions 2.4* and *2.5* for the notations. Let x_n be a Cauchy sequence in $\mathfrak{M} + \mathfrak{N}$; say $x_n = y_n + z_n$, with $y_n \in \mathfrak{M}$ and $z_n \in \mathfrak{N}$. By the Pythagorean relation, $\| y_m - y_n \|^2 + \| z_m - z_n \|^2 = \| (y_m - y_n) + (z_m - z_n) \|^2 = \| (y_m + z_m) - (y_n + z_n) \|^2 = \| x_m - x_n \|^2 \to 0$, hence y_n is a Cauchy sequence in $\mathfrak{M}$, and z_n is a Cauchy sequence in $\mathfrak{N}$. Since $\mathfrak{M}$ and $\mathfrak{N}$ are complete, $y_n \to y$ and $z_n \to z$ for suitable $y \in \mathfrak{M}$ and $z \in \mathfrak{N}$. Then, $x_n = y_n + z_n \to y + z$, by the Lemma to *Theorem 3.2.* ∎

Corollary. *If $\mathfrak{M}$ and $\mathfrak{N}$ are closed linear subspaces of a Hilbert space $\mathcal{K}$, and $\mathfrak{M} \perp \mathfrak{N}$, then $\mathfrak{M} \oplus \mathfrak{N}$ is a closed linear subspace of $\mathcal{K}$.*

It will be shown in § 6 that if $\mathfrak{N}$ is a closed linear subspace of a Hilbert space $\mathcal{K}$, then $\mathcal{K} = \mathfrak{N} \oplus \mathfrak{N}^{\perp}$. For finite-dimensional $\mathfrak{N}$, this is easy:

Theorem 3. *Let $\mathfrak{N}$ be a finite-dimensional linear subspace of a pre-Hilbert space $\mathcal{P}$. Then:*

(1) $\mathfrak{N}$ *is complete (hence closed).*

(2) $\mathcal{P} = \mathfrak{N} \oplus \mathfrak{N}^{\perp}$.

(3) $\mathfrak{N} = \mathfrak{N}^{\perp\perp}$.

Proof.

(1): $\mathfrak{N}$ is complete by *Theorem II.6.5.*

(2): Let $y_1, \cdots, y_n$ be an orthonormal basis for $\mathfrak{N}$. Given any vector $x \in \mathcal{P}$, define $y = \sum_1^n (x \,|\, y_k) y_k$ and $z = x - y$. Clearly $z \perp y_k$ for all

k, hence $z \perp \mathfrak{N}$. Thus, $x = y + z$, with $y \in \mathfrak{N}$ and $z \in \mathfrak{N}^{\perp}$. See *Definition 2.5*.

(3): By *Theorem 2.2*, $\mathfrak{N} \subset \mathfrak{N}^{\perp\perp}$. Conversely, assuming $x \in \mathfrak{N}^{\perp\perp}$, let us show that $x \in \mathfrak{N}$. By (2), we may write $x = y + z$, with $y \in \mathfrak{N}$ and $z \in \mathfrak{N}^{\perp}$. Since both $x \in \mathfrak{N}^{\perp\perp}$ and $y \in \mathfrak{N}^{\perp\perp}$, one has $z = x - y \in \mathfrak{N}^{\perp\perp}$; that is, $z \perp \mathfrak{N}^{\perp}$, and in particular $z \perp z$. Thus, $z = \theta$, and $x = y \in \mathfrak{N}$. ∎

Exercises

1. Let $\mathfrak{N}$ be a complete linear subspace of the pre-Hilbert space $\mathcal{P}$, and suppose $\mathfrak{N}$ is separable (*Definition II.8.3*). Generalize *Theorem 3*. [One can even get along without separability; see *Theorem 6.1*].

2. If $\mathcal{P}$ is any pre-Hilbert space, $\mathcal{P}^{\perp\perp} = \mathcal{P}$ even if $\mathcal{P}$ is incomplete. In the pre-Hilbert space of finitely non-zero sequences $x = (\lambda_k)$, let $\mathfrak{N}$ be the set of all vectors x such that $\lambda_1 = 0$. Then $\mathfrak{N} = \mathfrak{N}^{\perp\perp}$, but $\mathfrak{N}$ is not complete.

§5. CONVEX SETS, MINIMIZING VECTOR

If x,y,z are any three points in a metric space, $d(x,y) \leq d(x,z) + d(z,y)$. If $d(x,y) = d(x,z) + d(z,y)$ for three particular points x,y,z, it is natural to say that "z lies on the segment joining x and y" (see, however, *Exercise 9*). In pre-Hilbert space, this condition reads $\| x - y \| = \| x - z \| + \| z - y \|$; one can show that this condition is in turn equivalent to the existence of a real number α, $0 \leq \alpha \leq 1$, such that $z = \alpha x + (1 - \alpha)y$ (see *Exercise II.3.5*). The latter condition makes sense in any vector space:

Definition 1. *Let $\mathcal{V}$ be any vector space. If x and y are any two vectors, the **segment** joining x and y is the set of all vectors z of the form $z = \alpha x + (1 - \alpha)y$, where $0 \leq \alpha \leq 1$. A non-empty subset S of $\mathcal{V}$ is said to be **convex** if S contains the segment joining any two of its vectors; that is, the relations $x \in S, y \in S, 0 \leq \alpha \leq 1$ imply $\alpha x + (1 - \alpha)y \in S$.*

Examples

1. Every linear subspace of $\mathcal{V}$ is convex.

2. In a pre-Hilbert space, the closed unit ball $S = \{x : \| x \| \leq 1\}$ is convex. For, if $x \in S$, $y \in S$, and $0 \leq \alpha \leq 1$, then $\| \alpha x + (1 - \alpha)y \| \leq$

$\| \alpha x \| + \| (1 - \alpha)y \| = \alpha \| x \| + (1 - \alpha) \| y \| \leq \alpha + (1 - \alpha) = 1$ shows that $\alpha x + (1 - \alpha)y \in S$.

Theorem 1. (Minimizing vector) *Let* S *be a complete and convex subset of a pre-Hilbert space* $\mathcal{P}$. *Given any vector* $x \in \mathcal{P}$; *there exists one and only one vector* $y_o \in S$ *such that* $\| x - y_o \| \leq \| x - y \|$ *for all* $y \in S$.

Proof.

Let $\delta = \text{GLB} \{ \| x - y \| : y \in S \}$, and choose any sequence $y_n \in S$ such that $\| x - y_n \| \rightarrow \delta$. It will be shown that (1) y_n is a Cauchy sequence, hence converges to a vector $y_o \in S$ such that $\| x - y_o \| = \delta$, and (2) this equality determines $y_o \in S$ uniquely.

By the parallelogram law, $\| (y_m - x) + (x - y_n) \|^2 + \| (y_m - x) - (x - y_n) \|^2 = 2 \| y_m - x \|^2 + 2 \| x - y_n \|^2$, hence

$$\| y_m - y_n \|^2 = 2 \| y_m - x \|^2 + 2 \| x - y_n \|^2 - \| (y_m + y_n) - 2x \|^2$$
$$= 2 \| y_m - x \|^2 + 2 \| x - y_n \|^2 - 4 \| \tfrac{1}{2}(y_m + y_n) - x \|^2.$$

Since S is convex, it contains the vector $\tfrac{1}{2}(y_m + y_n) = \tfrac{1}{2}y_m + \tfrac{1}{2}y_n$, hence $\| \tfrac{1}{2}(y_m + y_n) - x \| \geq \delta$ by the definition of δ. It follows that

$$\| y_m - y_n \|^2 \leq 2 \| y_m - x \|^2 + 2 \| x - y_n \|^2 - 4\delta^2;$$

as $m, n \rightarrow \infty$, the right member of the inequality $\rightarrow 2\delta^2 + 2\delta^2 - 4\delta^2 = 0$, thus y_n is a Cauchy sequence in S. Since S is complete, $y_n \rightarrow y_o$ for suitable $y_o \in S$. Since $y_n - x \rightarrow y_o - x$ by the Lemma of *Theorem 3.2*, one has $\| y_n - x \| \rightarrow \| y_o - x \|$. Thus, $\| y_o - x \| = \delta$.

Suppose also $z_o \in S$ satisfies $\| z_o - x \| = \delta$. Since S contains the vector $\tfrac{1}{2}(y_o + z_o)$, $y_o = z_o$ results from the calculation

$$\| y_o - z_o \|^2 = 2 \| y_o - x \|^2 + 2 \| x - z_o \|^2 - \| (y_o + z_o) - 2x \|^2$$
$$= 2\delta^2 + 2\delta^2 - 4 \| \tfrac{1}{2}(y_o + z_o) - x \|^2$$
$$\leq 2\delta^2 + 2\delta^2 - 4\delta^2 = 0. \quad \blacksquare$$

Quoting *Theorem 4.1*,

Corollary 1. *Let* S *be a closed and convex subset of a Hilbert space* $\mathcal{H}$. *Given any* $x \in \mathcal{H}$; *there exists a unique vector* $y_o \in S$ *such that* $\| x - y_o \| \leq \| x - y \|$ *for all* $y \in S$.

Corollary 2. *If* S *is a complete and convex subset of a pre-Hilbert space* $\mathcal{P}$, S *contains a unique vector* y_o *of minimum norm.*

Proof.

Take $x = \theta$ in *Theorem 1*. ∎

Exercises

1. In a pre-Hilbert space:

(i) The balls $\{x: \| x \| \leq \epsilon\}$ and $\{x: \| x \| < \epsilon\}$ are convex.

(ii) If S is convex, so is $y + S$ ($=$ the set of all vectors $y + x$ with $x \in S$).

(iii) The open and closed balls with center y and radius ϵ are convex.

2. If S and $\mathfrak{I}$ are convex subsets of a vector space, and λ, μ are scalars, then $S + \mathfrak{I}, \lambda S$, and hence $\lambda S + \mu \mathfrak{I}$ are convex.

3. In the pre-Hilbert space of finitely non-zero sequences, the set S of all vectors $x = (\lambda_k)$ such that λ_k is real and ≥ 0 is convex. Similarly in the Hilbert space l^2.

4. If S is a non-empty subset of a metric space $\mathfrak{X}$, and x is a point of $\mathfrak{X}$, the *distance* from x to S is defined to be the non-negative real number GLB $\{d(x,y): y \in S\}$; it is denoted $d(x,S)$. Prove: x is adherent to S if and only if $d(x,S) = 0$; that is,

$$\bar{S} = \{x \in \mathfrak{X}: d(x,S) = 0\}.$$

5. The conclusion of *Theorem 1* may hold for certain non-complete convex sets. For example, let $\mathcal{P}$ be any pre-Hilbert space, and $S = \{x: \| x \| \leq 1\}$.

(i) In the notation of *Theorem 1*, $y_o = x$ when $\| x \| \leq 1$, and $y_o = \| x \|^{-1}x$ when $\| x \| > 1$.

(ii) $\mathcal{P}$ is complete if and only if S is a complete subset.

(iii) Incidentally, $\mathcal{P}$ is complete if and only if $\{x: \| x \| = 1\}$ is a complete subset.

6. Here is an example of *Corollary 2*. In the unitary space $\mathbb{C}^n$, let S be the set of all $y = (\lambda_1, \cdots, \lambda_n)$ such that $\sum_1^n \lambda_k = 1$. It is easy to see that S is a closed (hence complete) convex subset of $\mathbb{C}^n$. The vector $y_o \in S$ of smallest norm is $y_o = (1/n, \cdots, 1/n)$.

7. If S is not complete, the conclusion of *Theorem 1* may not hold. For example, let $\mathcal{P}$ be the pre-Hilbert space of finitely non-zero sequences $x = (\lambda_k)$, and S the set of all x such that $\sum_1^\infty \lambda_k = 1$. It

is easy to see that $\mathcal{S}$ is convex. However, $\mathcal{S}$ does not contain a vector y_o of minimum norm. Incidentally, $\mathcal{S}$ is not closed. An example with $\mathcal{S}$ closed is given in *Exercise 4* of the next section.

8. If $\mathcal{S}$ is a convex subset of a pre-Hilbert space, then $\bar{\mathcal{S}}$ is also convex.

9. Let $\mathcal{U}$ be the vector space of continuous functions on $[0,1]$ (*Example I.1.3*), regarded as a metric space via $d(x,y) = $ LUB $\{|x(t) - y(t)| : 0 \le t \le 1\}$ (see *Example II.4.5*). Let x,y,z be the functions defined by the formulas $x(t) = t$, $y(t) = -1$, and $z(t) = 0$. Then, (i) $d(x,y) = d(x,z) + d(z,y)$, but (ii) there does not exist a real number α such that $z = \alpha x + (1 - \alpha)y$.

§ 6. ORTHOGONAL COMPLEMENT

Theorem 1. *If $\mathfrak{N}$ is a complete linear subspace of a pre-Hilbert space $\mathcal{P}$, then $\mathcal{P} = \mathfrak{N} \oplus \mathfrak{N}^{\perp}$, and $\mathfrak{N}^{\perp\perp} = \mathfrak{N}$.*

Proof.

Given any vector $x \in \mathcal{P}$, let us show that there is a decomposition $x = y_o + z$ with $y_o \in \mathfrak{N}$ and $z \in \mathfrak{N}^{\perp}$.

Since $\mathfrak{N}$ is complete and convex, there exists, by *Theorem 5.1*, a vector $y_o \in \mathfrak{N}$ such that $\| x - y_o \| \le \| x - y \|$ for all $y \in \mathfrak{N}$. Define $z = x - y_o$; it will suffice to prove that $z \perp \mathfrak{N}$.

Given any $y \in \mathfrak{N}$, let us show that $(y|z) = 0$; there is no loss of generality in assuming $\| y \| = 1$. By the calculation made in the proof of *Theorem II.3.4*,

$$\| z - \lambda y \|^2 = \| z \|^2 - |(z|y)|^2 + |(z|y) - \lambda|^2,$$

for every scalar λ. In particular, for $\lambda_o = (z|y)$,

$$(*) \qquad\qquad \| z - \lambda_o y \|^2 = \| z \|^2 - |(z|y)|^2.$$

Now, $z - \lambda_o y = (x - y_o) - \lambda_o y = x - (y_o + \lambda_o y)$; since $y_o + \lambda_o y \in \mathfrak{N}$, one has $\| x - y_o \| \le \| x - (y_o + \lambda_o y) \|$, by the choice of y_o. That is, $\| z \| \le \| z - \lambda_o y \|$; combining this with $(*)$,

$$\| z \|^2 \le \| z - \lambda_o y \|^2 = \| z \|^2 - |(z|y)|^2 \le \| z \|^2.$$

Clearly $(z|y) = 0$.

The proof of $\mathfrak{N}^{\perp\perp} = \mathfrak{N}$ is the same as in *Theorem 4.3*.   ∎

Quoting *Theorem 4.1*,

Theorem 2. *If $\mathfrak{N}$ is a closed linear subspace of a Hilbert space $\mathfrak{K}$, then $\mathfrak{K} = \mathfrak{N} \oplus \mathfrak{N}^{\perp}$, and $\mathfrak{N}^{\perp\perp} = \mathfrak{N}$.*

Definition 1. *If $\mathfrak{N}$ is a closed linear subspace of a Hilbert space $\mathfrak{K}$, $\mathfrak{N}^{\perp}$ is called the* **orthogonal complement** *of $\mathfrak{N}$.*

Remarks

1. If $\mathfrak{N}$ is a closed linear subspace of a Hilbert space $\mathfrak{K}$, the relation $(\mathfrak{N}^{\perp})^{\perp} = \mathfrak{N}$ shows that the orthogonal complement of $\mathfrak{N}^{\perp}$ is $\mathfrak{N}$.

2. If $\mathcal{P}$ is a pre-Hilbert space such that every closed linear subspace $\mathfrak{N}$ of $\mathcal{P}$ satisfies the condition $\mathfrak{N}^{\perp\perp} = \mathfrak{N}$, then $\mathcal{P}$ is necessarily complete (hence is a Hilbert space). See *Exercise V.1.3.* This remark will not be used in the sequel.

Theorem 3. *If $\mathcal{S}$ is any subset of a Hilbert space $\mathfrak{K}$, then $\mathcal{S}^{\perp\perp}$ is the smallest closed linear subspace of $\mathfrak{K}$ which contains $\mathcal{S}$. That is,*

(1) $\mathcal{S}^{\perp\perp}$ *is a closed linear subspace of $\mathfrak{K}$;*

(2) $\mathcal{S} \subset \mathcal{S}^{\perp\perp}$;

(3) *if $\mathfrak{M}$ is a closed linear subspace of $\mathfrak{K}$ such that $\mathcal{S} \subset \mathfrak{M}$, necessarily $\mathcal{S}^{\perp\perp} \subset \mathfrak{M}$.*

Proof.

(1): see *Theorem 2.1.*

(2): see *Theorem 2.2.*

(3): Suppose $\mathcal{S} \subset \mathfrak{M}$, where $\mathfrak{M}$ is a closed linear subspace of $\mathfrak{K}$. Then, $\mathcal{S}^{\perp} \supset \mathfrak{M}^{\perp}$, $\mathcal{S}^{\perp\perp} \subset \mathfrak{M}^{\perp\perp}$; quote *Theorem 2.* ∎

Corollary 1. *If $\mathfrak{N}$ is any linear subspace of a Hilbert space $\mathfrak{K}$, $\overline{\mathfrak{N}} = \mathfrak{N}^{\perp\perp}$.*

Proof.
Compare *Theorem 3* with *Theorem 3.2.* ∎

Corollary 2. *Let $\mathfrak{N}_k$ be a sequence of closed linear subspaces of a Hilbert space $\mathfrak{K}$. There exists a smallest closed linear subspace $\mathfrak{N}$ such that $\mathfrak{N}_k \subset \mathfrak{N}$ for all k. One has $x \perp \mathfrak{N}$ if and only if $x \perp \mathfrak{N}_k$ for all k.*

Proof.
Let $\mathcal{S}$ be the set of all vectors $x \in \mathfrak{K}$ such that $x \in \mathfrak{N}_k$ for some k. Clearly $\mathfrak{N}_k \subset \mathcal{S}$ for all k, and $\mathcal{S}$ is the smallest subset of $\mathfrak{K}$ with this property. Set $\mathfrak{N} = \mathcal{S}^{\perp\perp}$. Evidently $\mathfrak{N}_k \subset \mathcal{S} \subset \mathfrak{N}$ for all k. If $\mathfrak{M}$ is a

closed linear subspace such that $\mathfrak{N}_k \subset \mathfrak{M}$ for all k, then $\mathbb{S} \subset \mathfrak{M}$, hence $\mathfrak{N} \subset \mathfrak{M}$ by *Theorem 3*. The last assertion follows from $\mathfrak{N}^\perp = \mathbb{S}^{\perp\perp\perp} = \mathbb{S}^\perp$ (see *Theorem 2.2*). ▌

Exercises

1. If $\mathfrak{N}$ is a finite-dimensional linear subspace of a pre-Hilbert space $\mathcal{P}$, another proof of $\mathcal{P} = \mathfrak{N} \oplus \mathfrak{N}^\perp$ (this is *Theorem 4.3*) can be deduced from *Theorem 1* and *Theorem II.6.5*. Both proofs, at some point, make use of an orthonormal basis of $\mathfrak{N}$.

2. Let $\mathfrak{N}$ be a linear subspace of a Hilbert space $\mathcal{K}$. Then $\mathfrak{N}$ is a dense subset of $\mathcal{K}$ if and only if it is a total subset of $\mathcal{K}$.

3. In the pre-Hilbert space of finitely non-zero sequences $x = (\lambda_k)$, let $\mathfrak{N}$ be the set of all x such that $\sum_1^\infty (1/k)\lambda_k = 0$ Then $\mathfrak{N}$ is a closed linear subspace, but $\mathfrak{N} \neq \mathfrak{N}^{\perp\perp}$.

4. Completeness is essential for *Theorem 5.1* (theorem on minimizing vector). For example, let $\mathbb{S}$ be a linear subspace of a pre-Hilbert space, such that $\mathbb{S} \neq \mathbb{S}^{\perp\perp}$ (for instance, $\mathbb{S}$ may be the closed linear subspace described in *Exercise 3*). Then, *Theorem 5.1* fails for the convex set $\mathbb{S}$. Indeed, if x is any vector which belongs to $\mathbb{S}^{\perp\perp}$ but not to $\mathbb{S}$, no minimizing vector y_o exists.

5. Let $\mathcal{P}$ be a pre-Hilbert space possessing a total sequence x_n (*Definition II.8.1*). If $\mathfrak{N}$ is a complete linear subspace of $\mathcal{P}$, then $\mathfrak{N}$ also possesses a total sequence y_n, hence is a separable Hilbert space.

*6. (i) If $\mathfrak{X}$ is a separable metric space (*Exercise II.8.3*), and $\mathbb{S}$ is a non-empty subset of $\mathfrak{X}$, then $\mathbb{S}$ is a separable metric space.

(ii) In particular, if $\mathcal{K}$ is a separable Hilbert space, and $\mathfrak{N}$ is a closed linear subspace of $\mathcal{K}$, then $\mathfrak{N}$ is a separable Hilbert space (see *Exercises II.8.3,4*, and *5*). Using an orthonormal basis for $\mathfrak{N}$, deduce another proof of $\mathcal{K} = \mathfrak{N} \oplus \mathfrak{N}^\perp$.

*7. In *Exercise II.8.5*, it is proved that a classical Hilbert space $\mathcal{K}$ is a separable metric space; in the proof sketched there, use is made of an orthonormal basis, and hence of the Gram-Schmidt procedure. Another proof runs as follows. Let x_n be any total sequence in $\mathcal{K}$, and let $\mathbb{S}$ be the set of all finite linear combinations of the x_n with Gaussian-rational coefficients. Then, $\overline{\mathbb{S}}$ is a closed *linear* subspace, having orthogonal complement $\{\theta\}$, so $\overline{\mathbb{S}} = \mathcal{K}$ results from *Theorem 2*. Since $\mathbb{S}$ can be enumerated in a sequence, $\mathbb{S}$ is a dense sequence in $\mathcal{K}$.

§7. MAPPINGS

Suppose $\mathfrak{N}$ is a closed linear subspace of a Hilbert space $\mathfrak{IC}$. Given any vector $x \in \mathfrak{IC}$, there is a decomposition $x = y + z$ with $y \in \mathfrak{N}$ and $z \in \mathfrak{N}^\perp$ (*Theorem 6.2*); moreover, the vectors y and z are uniquely determined by x (see *Theorem 2.3*). Thus, one passes from the vector $x \in \mathfrak{IC}$ to the vector $y \in \mathfrak{N}$ in a perfectly definite way. One may say: "y depends on x," "given any x there is determined a corresponding y," and so on. This is the familiar language of functional dependence. The terminology and notation of functions, to be used in the sequel, will now be described.

1. Let $\mathfrak{X}$ and $\mathfrak{Y}$ be sets, both non-empty. One says that "T is a *mapping* of $\mathfrak{X}$ into $\mathfrak{Y}$" in case: for each $x \in \mathfrak{X}$, there is determined one and only one element $y \in \mathfrak{Y}$, denoted $y = Tx$ [or $y = T(x)$], called the *value* of T at x. The symbol $T: \mathfrak{X} \to \mathfrak{Y}$ means that T is a mapping of $\mathfrak{X}$ into $\mathfrak{Y}$. One also speaks of "the mapping $x \to Tx$ $(x \in \mathfrak{X})$." Synonyms for "mapping": *function, transformation*.

2. If $T: \mathfrak{X} \to \mathfrak{Y}$ is a mapping, $\mathfrak{X}$ is called the *initial set*, or *domain of definition* of T; $\mathfrak{Y}$ is called the *final set* of T.

3. Mappings $S: \mathfrak{X} \to \mathfrak{Y}$ and $T: \mathfrak{X} \to \mathfrak{Y}$ are said to be *equal* in case $Sx = Tx$ for all $x \in \mathfrak{X}$; that is, S and T are "pointwise equal." Notation: $S = T$.

4. If $T: \mathfrak{X} \to \mathfrak{Y}$, and $\mathcal{S}$ is a subset of $\mathfrak{X}$, $T(\mathcal{S})$ denotes the set of all $Tx \in \mathfrak{Y}$ as x varies over $\mathcal{S}$. Thus,

$$T(\mathcal{S}) = \{y \in \mathfrak{Y}: y = Tx \text{ for some } x \in \mathcal{S}\}$$

$$= \{Tx: x \in \mathcal{S}\}.$$

In particular, $T(\mathfrak{X})$ is called the *range* of T.

5. A mapping $T: \mathfrak{X} \to \mathfrak{Y}$ is said to be *injective* if it takes distinct values at distinct elements of $\mathfrak{X}$. That is, the relations $x_1 \in \mathfrak{X}$, $x_2 \in \mathfrak{X}$, $x_1 \neq x_2$ imply $Tx_1 \neq Tx_2$. Equivalently: $Tx_1 = Tx_2$ implies $x_1 = x_2$. An injective mapping is said to be *one-to-one*.

6. A mapping $T: \mathfrak{X} \to \mathfrak{Y}$ is said to be *surjective* if $T(\mathfrak{X}) = \mathfrak{Y}$. That is, given any $y \in \mathfrak{Y}$, there exists at least one $x \in \mathcal{S}$ such that $Tx = y$. A surjective mapping $T: \mathfrak{X} \to \mathfrak{Y}$ is said to be a mapping of $\mathfrak{X}$ *onto* $\mathfrak{Y}$.

7. A mapping $T: \mathfrak{X} \to \mathcal{Y}$ is said to be *bijective* if it is both injective and surjective. This means: given any $y \in \mathcal{Y}$, there is *exactly one* $x \in \mathfrak{X}$ such that $Tx = y$. Thus, a bijective mapping is a one-to-one mapping of $\mathfrak{X}$ onto $\mathcal{Y}$; such a mapping is also called a *one-to-one correspondence*.

Examples

1. Let $\mathfrak{R}$ be the set of all real numbers, $\mathfrak{X} = \{x \in \mathfrak{R}: x \geq -1\}$, and $\mathcal{Y} = \{x \in \mathfrak{R}: x \geq 0\}$. The mapping $T: \mathfrak{X} \to \mathcal{Y}$ defined by $Tx = x + 2$ is injective, but not surjective.

2. $\mathfrak{X}$ and $\mathcal{Y}$ as in *Example 1*. The mapping $S: \mathfrak{X} \to \mathcal{Y}$ defined by $Sx = x^2$ is surjective, but not injective.

3. $\mathfrak{X}$ and $\mathcal{Y}$ as in *Example 1*. The mapping $U: \mathfrak{X} \to \mathcal{Y}$ defined by $Ux = x + 1$ is bijective.

§ 8. PROJECTION

Definition 1. *Let $\mathfrak{N}$ be a closed linear subspace of a Hilbert space $\mathcal{K}$. Given a vector $x \in \mathcal{K}$, suppose $x = y + z$ is the unique decomposition with $y \in \mathfrak{N}$ and $z \in \mathfrak{N}^{\perp}$ (see Theorem 6.2); the vector y is called the* **orthogonal projection** *of x on $\mathfrak{N}$.*

Theorem 1. *Let $\mathfrak{N}$ be a closed linear subspace of a Hilbert space $\mathcal{K}$. For each $x \in \mathcal{K}$, denote by Px the orthogonal projection of x on $\mathfrak{N}$. Then, the mapping $P: \mathcal{K} \to \mathcal{K}$ has the following properties:*

(1) $(Px_1 \,|\, x_2) = (x_1 \,|\, Px_2)$ *for all $x_1, x_2 \in \mathcal{K}$.*

(2) $Py = y$ *for all $y \in \mathfrak{N}$.*

(3) $Pz = \theta$ *for all $z \in \mathfrak{N}^{\perp}$.*

Moreover:

(4) $P(x_1 + x_2) = Px_1 + Px_2$

(5) $P(\lambda x) = \lambda(Px)$

(6) $P(Px) = Px$

(7) $(Px \,|\, x) = \| Px \|^2 \leq \| x \|^2$

(8) $\mathfrak{N}$ *is the range of P.*

(9) $\quad \mathfrak{N} = \{x \in \mathcal{H}: Px = x\}$

(10) $\quad \mathfrak{N}^{\perp} = \{x \in \mathcal{H}: Px = \theta\}.$

Proof.

(1): Let $x_1 = y_1 + z_1$ and $x_2 = y_2 + z_2$ be the orthogonal decompositions of x_1 and x_2 relative to $\mathfrak{N}$; that is, $y_k \in \mathfrak{N}$ and $z_k \in \mathfrak{N}^{\perp}$. Then, $Px_1 = y_1$, $Px_2 = y_2$, and $(Px_1 | x_2) = (y_1 | y_2 + z_2) = (y_1 | y_2) + (y_1 | z_2) = (y_1 | y_2)$, while $(x_1 | Px_2) = (y_1 + z_1 | y_2) = (y_1 | y_2) + (z_1 | y_2) = (y_1 | y_2)$.

(2): If $y \in \mathfrak{N}$, the unique orthogonal decomposition of y is $y = y + \theta$.

(3): If $z \in \mathfrak{N}^{\perp}$, its orthogonal decomposition is $z = \theta + z$.

(4): With notation as in (1), $x_1 + x_2 = (y_1 + y_2) + (z_1 + z_2)$; since $y_1 + y_2 \in \mathfrak{N}$ and $z_1 + z_2 \in \mathfrak{N}^{\perp}$, $P(x_1 + x_2) = y_1 + y_2 = Px_1 + Px_2$.

(5): If $x = y + z$ is the orthogonal decomposition of x, then $\lambda x = \lambda y + \lambda z$ is the orthogonal decomposition of λx, hence $P(\lambda x) = \lambda y = \lambda(Px)$.

(6): For any $x \in \mathcal{H}$, $Px \in \mathfrak{N}$ by *Definition 1*, hence $P(Px) = Px$ by (2).

(7): With notation as in (5), $\| x \|^2 = \| y \|^2 + \| z \|^2 \geq \| y \|^2 = \| Px \|^2$; also, $(Px | x) = (y | y + z) = (y | y) + (y | z) = \| y \|^2 = \| Px \|^2$.

(8): If $x \in P(\mathcal{H})$, then $x \in \mathfrak{N}$ by the definition of P. Conversely if $x \in \mathfrak{N}$, then $x = Px \in P(\mathcal{H})$ by (2).

(9), (10): obvious from the definition of P. $\blacksquare$

Definition 2. *The mapping P described in Theorem 1 is called the* **projection** *of $\mathcal{H}$ on $\mathfrak{N}$. The notation $P_{\mathfrak{N}}$ is used to indicate the relationship of P to the closed linear subspace $\mathfrak{N}$.*

Exercises

1. Let $\mathfrak{N}$ be a closed linear subspace of a Hilbert space $\mathcal{H}$, and suppose $T: \mathcal{H} \to \mathcal{H}$ is a mapping satisfying the following conditions:

(1') $(Tx_1 | x_2) = (x_1 | Tx_2)$ for all $x_1, x_2 \in \mathcal{K}$; (2') $Ty = y$ when $y \in \mathfrak{N}$; and (3') $Tz = \theta$ when $z \in \mathfrak{N}^\perp$. Then $T = P_{\mathfrak{N}}$.

2. Notation as in *Theorem 1*. Show:
(i) $P(x - y) = Px - Py$;
(ii) if $x_n \to x$, then $Px_n \to Px$.

3. Notation as in *Theorem 1*. If $x = y + z$ is the orthogonal decomposition of x with respect to $\mathfrak{N}$, define $Qx = z$. Then:
   (i) $Px + Qx = x$ for all $x \in \mathcal{K}$;
   (ii) $P(Qx) = Q(Px) = \theta$ for all $x \in \mathcal{K}$;
   (iii) Q is the projection of $\mathcal{K}$ on $\mathfrak{N}^\perp$.

4. If $\mathfrak{M}$ and $\mathfrak{N}$ are closed linear subspaces of a Hilbert space $\mathcal{K}$, $P = P_{\mathfrak{M}}$, $Q = P_{\mathfrak{N}}$, and $\mathfrak{M} \perp \mathfrak{N}$, then $P(Qx) = Q(Px) = \theta$ for all $x \in \mathcal{K}$.

5. If $\mathfrak{M}$ and $\mathfrak{N}$ are closed linear subspaces of a Hilbert space $\mathcal{K}$, $P = P_{\mathfrak{M}}$, and $Q = P_{\mathfrak{N}}$, then $\mathfrak{M} \subset \mathfrak{N}$ if and only if $Q(Px) = Px$ for all $x \in \mathcal{K}$. In this case, $Pw = \theta$ for all $w \in \mathfrak{N}^\perp$, and $P(Qx) = Px$ for all $x \in \mathcal{K}$.

Continuous Linear Mappings **IV**

§ 1. LINEAR MAPPINGS

If $\mathcal{N}$ is a closed linear subspace of a Hilbert space $\mathcal{K}$, and P is the projection of $\mathcal{K}$ on $\mathcal{N}$ (described in *Theorem III.8.1*), the mapping $P: \mathcal{K} \to \mathcal{K}$ satisfies the conditions $P(x + y) = Px + Py$ and $P(\lambda x) = \lambda(Px)$. So to speak, P respects vector addition and multiplication by scalars. These conditions make sense for a mapping between any two vector spaces, and the mappings which satisfy them are of the greatest importance:

Definition 1. *If* $\mathcal{V}$ *and* $\mathcal{W}$ *are vector spaces, a mapping* $T: \mathcal{V} \to \mathcal{W}$ *is said to be* **linear** *in case*

(i) T *is* **additive**: $T(x + y) = Tx + Ty$, *for all* $x,y \in \mathcal{V}$;

(ii) T *is* **homogeneous**: $T(\lambda x) = \lambda(Tx)$ *for all* $x \in \mathcal{V}$ *and scalar* λ.

Examples

1. $\mathcal{V}$ and $\mathcal{W}$ any two vector spaces, $T: \mathcal{V} \to \mathcal{W}$ defined by $Tx = \theta$ for all $x \in \mathcal{V}$. T is called the *zero mapping* (or *null mapping*), and is denoted $T = 0$.

2. $\mathcal{V}$ any vector space, $T: \mathcal{V} \to \mathcal{V}$ defined by $Tx = x$ for all $x \in \mathcal{V}$. T is called the *identity mapping* of $\mathcal{V}$, and is denoted $T = I$.

3. $\mathcal{V}$ any vector space, μ a fixed scalar, $T: \mathcal{V} \to \mathcal{V}$ defined by $Tx = \mu x$ for all $x \in \mathcal{V}$. The additivity and homogeneity of T come out of the axioms for a vector space: $\mu(x + y) = \mu x + \mu y$, and $\mu(\lambda x) = (\mu\lambda)x = (\lambda\mu)x = \lambda(\mu x)$. Such a linear mapping is called a *scalar mapping* in $\mathcal{V}$. Clearly 0 and I are scalar mappings.

4. $\mathcal{V}$ the vector space of n-ples (*Example I.1.1*), $T: \mathcal{V} \to \mathcal{V}$ defined by $T(\lambda_1, \cdots, \lambda_n) = (0, \lambda_2, \cdots, \lambda_n)$.

5. $\mathcal{V}$ the space of n-ples, $\mathcal{W}$ the space of m-ples, $n > m$, and $T: \mathcal{V} \to \mathcal{W}$ defined by $T(\lambda_1, \cdots, \lambda_n) = (\lambda_1, \cdots, \lambda_m)$.

6. $\mathcal{V}$ and $\mathcal{W}$ as in *Example 5*, and $S: \mathcal{W} \to \mathcal{V}$ defined by $S(\lambda_1, \cdots, \lambda_m) = (\lambda_1, \cdots, \lambda_m, 0, \cdots, 0)$.

7. $\mathcal{V}$ the vector space of polynomial functions on $[a,b]$ (*Example I.1.4*), with $a < b$, and $T: \mathcal{V} \to \mathcal{V}$ defined by $Tx = x'$ ($=$ derivative of x).

8. $\mathcal{V}$ as in *Example 7*. Define $S: \mathcal{V} \to \mathcal{V}$ as follows. If $x \in \mathcal{V}$, let Sx be the unique polynomial y such that $y' = x$ on $[a,b]$ and $y(a) = 0$. Thus,

$$(Sx)(t) = \int_a x(u)\, du \qquad (a \le t \le b).$$

9. $\mathcal{V}$ the vector space of finitely non-zero sequences (*Example I.1.6*), $T: \mathcal{V} \to \mathcal{V}$ defined by $T(\lambda_1, \lambda_2, \lambda_3, \cdots) = (\lambda_2, \lambda_3, \cdots)$.

10. $\mathcal{V}$ as in *Example 9*, $S: \mathcal{V} \to \mathcal{V}$ defined by $S(\lambda_1, \lambda_2, \lambda_3, \cdots) = (0, \lambda_1, \lambda_2, \lambda_3, \cdots)$.

11. Let $\mathcal{V}$ be the vector space of n-ples, and suppose $1', \cdots, n'$ is any rearrangement of $1, \cdots, n$. Let $T: \mathcal{V} \to \mathcal{V}$ be defined by $T(\lambda_1, \cdots, \lambda_n) = (\lambda_{1'}, \cdots, \lambda_{n'})$.

12. Let $\mathcal{V}$ be the vector space of n-ples, $\mathcal{W}$ the vector space of m-ples, and suppose α_{jk} are fixed scalars ($j = 1, \cdots, m; k = 1, \cdots, n$). Define

$$T(\lambda_1, \cdots, \lambda_n) = \left(\sum_{k=1}^{n} \alpha_{1k}\lambda_k, \cdots, \sum_{k=1}^{n} \alpha_{mk}\lambda_k \right). \quad \blacksquare$$

By definition, a linear mapping "preserves" sums and scalar multiples; it also preserves θ, negatives, differences, and linear combinations:

Theorem 1. *If* $T: \mathcal{V} \to \mathcal{W}$ *is any linear mapping,*

(1) $T\theta = \theta$

(2) $T(-x) = -(Tx)$

(3) $T(x - y) = Tx - Ty$

(4) $T\left(\sum_1^n \lambda_k x_k \right) = \sum_1^n \lambda_k (Tx_k).$

Proof.

(4): The proof is by induction on n. The case $n = 1$ is simply the assertion that T is homogeneous. Assuming $T\left(\sum_1^{n-1} \lambda_k x_k \right) = \sum_1^{n-1} \lambda_k (Tx_k)$, one has $T\left(\sum_1^n \lambda_k x_k \right) = T\left(\sum_1^{n-1} \lambda_k x_k + \lambda_n x_n \right) = T\left(\sum_1^{n-1} \lambda_k x_k \right) + T(\lambda_n x_n) = \sum_1^{n-1} \lambda_k (Tx_k) + \lambda_n (Tx_n) = \sum_1^n \lambda_k (Tx_k).$

(1), (2), and (3) are special cases of (4), since $\theta = 0x$, $-x = (-1)x$, and $x - y = 1x + (-1)y$. ∎

A linear mapping is uniquely determined by its effect on any system of generators:

Theorem 2. *Suppose* $S: \mathcal{V} \to \mathcal{W}$ *and* $T: \mathcal{V} \to \mathcal{W}$ *are linear mappings, and* $\mathcal{S}$ *is a system of generators for* $\mathcal{V}$. *If* $Sx = Tx$ *for all* $x \in \mathcal{S}$, *then* $S = T$.

Proof.

Let $\mathfrak{N} = \{x \in \mathcal{V}: Sx = Tx\}$; by assumption, $\mathcal{S} \subset \mathfrak{N}$. Clearly $\theta \in \mathfrak{N}$; if $x \in \mathfrak{N}$, $y \in \mathfrak{N}$, and λ is scalar, $S(x + y) = Sx + Sy = Tx + Ty = T(x + y)$ and $S(\lambda x) = \lambda(Sx) = \lambda(Tx) = T(\lambda x)$, hence $\mathfrak{N}$ is a linear subspace. Since $\mathcal{V}$ is the smallest linear subspace containing $\mathcal{S}$ (see *Theorem I.5.2*), $\mathcal{V} = \mathfrak{N}$. That is, $Sx = Tx$ for all $x \in \mathcal{V}$. ∎

A useful source of linear mappings is the following:

Theorem 3. *Let $\mathcal{V}$ be a vector space of finite dimension n, and $\mathcal{W}$ any vector space. If $x_1, \cdots, x_n$ is a basis for $\mathcal{V}$, and $y_1, \cdots, y_n$ are arbitrary given vectors in $\mathcal{W}$, there exists one and only one linear mapping $T: \mathcal{V} \to \mathcal{W}$ such that $Tx_k = y_k$ for all k.*

Proof.

Given any vector $x \in \mathcal{V}$, the problem is to define $Tx \in \mathcal{W}$. Suppose $x = \sum_1^n \lambda_k x_k$; since the coefficients λ_k are uniquely determined by x (*Theorem I.6.1*), one can unambiguously define $Tx = \sum_1^n \lambda_k y_k$. The linearity of T is immediate from *Theorem I.4.1*, and clearly $Tx_k = y_k$.

If $S: \mathcal{V} \to \mathcal{W}$ is another linear mapping such that $Sx_k = y_k$ for all k, $S = T$ by *Theorem 2*. ∎

If $T: \mathcal{X} \to \mathcal{Y}$ is any mapping, and $\mathfrak{I}$ is a subset of $\mathcal{Y}$, the set of all $x \in \mathcal{X}$ such that $Tx \in \mathfrak{I}$ is called the *inverse image* of $\mathfrak{I}$ under T, and is denoted $T^{-1}(\mathfrak{I})$. Similarly, if $\mathcal{S} \subset \mathcal{X}$, the set $T(\mathcal{S})$ described in § 7 of Chapter III is called the *direct image* of $\mathcal{S}$ under T.

Definition 2. *If $T: \mathcal{V} \to \mathcal{W}$ is a linear mapping, the set $\mathfrak{N}$ of all vectors $x \in \mathcal{V}$ such that $Tx = \theta$ is called the* **null space** *of T. Thus,*

$$\mathfrak{N} = \{x \in \mathcal{V}: Tx = \theta\} = T^{-1}(\{\theta\}).$$

Under a linear mapping, the direct and inverse images of linear subspaces are themselves linear subspaces:

Theorem 4. *Let $T: \mathcal{V} \to \mathcal{W}$ be a linear mapping:*

(1) *If $\mathcal{V}_o$ is a linear subspace of $\mathcal{V}$, $T(\mathcal{V}_o)$ is a linear subspace of $\mathcal{W}$. In particular, the range $T(\mathcal{V})$ of T is a linear subspace of $\mathcal{W}$.*

(2) *If $\mathcal{W}_o$ is a linear subspace of $\mathcal{W}$, $T^{-1}(\mathcal{W}_o)$ is a linear subspace of $\mathcal{V}$. In particular, the null space $\mathfrak{N} = T^{-1}(\{\theta\})$ of T is a linear subspace of $\mathcal{V}$.*

(3) *$Tx_1 = Tx_2$ if and only if $x_1 - x_2 \in \mathfrak{N}$.*

(4) *T is injective if and only if $\mathfrak{N} = \{\theta\}$.*

Proof.

(1): Since $\theta \in \mathcal{V}_o$, $\theta = T\theta \in T(\mathcal{V}_o)$. Suppose $y_1, y_2 \in T(\mathcal{V}_o)$, and λ is scalar. Say $y_k = Tx_k$, where $x_k \in \mathcal{V}_o$. Since $x_1 + x_2 \in \mathcal{V}_o$ and $\lambda x_1 \in \mathcal{V}_o$, one has $y_1 + y_2 = Tx_1 + Tx_2 = T(x_1 + x_2) \in T(\mathcal{V}_o)$ and $\lambda y_1 = \lambda(Tx_1) = T(\lambda x_1) \in T(\mathcal{V}_o)$.

(2): Since $T\theta = \theta \in \mathcal{W}_o$, $\theta \in T^{-1}(\mathcal{W}_o)$. Suppose $x_1, x_2 \in T^{-1}(\mathcal{W}_o)$, and λ is scalar. Since $\mathcal{W}_o$ contains Tx_1 and Tx_2, it contains $Tx_1 + Tx_2 = T(x_1 + x_2)$ and $\lambda(Tx_1) = T(\lambda x_1)$, hence $x_1 + x_2$ and λx_1 belong to $T^{-1}(\mathcal{W}_o)$.

(3): The following relations imply one another: $Tx_1 = Tx_2$, $Tx_1 - Tx_2 = \theta$, $T(x_1 - x_2) = \theta$, $x_1 - x_2 \in \mathfrak{N}$.

(4): Suppose T is injective; if $x \in \mathfrak{N}$, then $Tx = \theta = T\theta$, hence $x = \theta$. Suppose, conversely, that $\mathfrak{N} = \{\theta\}$; if $Tx_1 = Tx_2$, then $x_1 - x_2 \in \mathfrak{N}$, hence $x_1 - x_2 = \theta$. ∎

Suppose $\mathcal{P}$ is any pre-Hilbert space, and y is a fixed vector in $\mathcal{P}$. Defining $Tx = (x|y)$, one obtains a linear mapping $T: \mathcal{P} \to \mathcal{C}$. On the other hand, the mapping $S: \mathcal{P} \to \mathcal{C}$ defined by $Sx = (y|x)$ satisfies the conditions $S(x_1 + x_2) = Sx_1 + Sx_2$ and $S(\lambda x) = \lambda^*(Sx)$. This is an example of another important type of mapping between vector spaces:

Definition 3. *If $\mathcal{V}$ and $\mathcal{W}$ are vector spaces, a mapping $S: \mathcal{V} \to \mathcal{W}$ is said to be **conjugate-linear** (or "semilinear") in case*

(i) *S is **additive**: $S(x + y) = Sx + Sy$*
(ii) *S is **conjugate-homogeneous**: $S(\lambda x) = \lambda^*(Sx)$.*

Several important examples of conjugate-linear mappings will occur in the sequel, notably in § 10.

Exercises

1. If $T: \mathcal{V} \to \mathcal{W}$ is merely additive (and not necessarily homogeneous), formulas (1), (2), (3) of *Theorem 1* still hold.

2. If $T: \mathcal{C}^n \to \mathcal{C}^m$ is any linear mapping, there exist scalars α_{jk} in terms of which T can be expressed as in *Example 12*.

3. In *Examples 1* through *12*, discuss null space and range. Which of these mappings is injective (resp. surjective, resp. bijective)?

4. Let $T: \mathcal{V} \to \mathcal{W}$ be a linear mapping, $\mathcal{S}$ a system of generators for $\mathcal{V}$, and $\mathcal{I}$ an independent subset of $\mathcal{V}$. Then:
(i) If T is surjective, $T(\mathcal{S})$ is a system of generators for $\mathcal{W}$.
(ii) If T is injective, $T(\mathcal{I})$ is an independent subset of $\mathcal{W}$.
If $\mathcal{S}$ is an arbitrary subset of $\mathcal{V}$, $[T(\mathcal{S})] = T([\mathcal{S}])$ (see *Definition I.5.3*).

5. Let $T: \mathcal{V} \to \mathcal{W}$ be a linear mapping.

(i) If T is surjective, and $\mathcal{V}$ is finite-dimensional, then $\mathcal{W}$ is finite-dimensional.

(ii) If T is injective, and $\mathcal{V}$ is infinite-dimensional, then $\mathcal{W}$ is infinite-dimensional.

(i') If T is surjective, and $\mathcal{W}$ is infinite-dimensional, then $\mathcal{V}$ is infinite-dimensional.

(ii') If T is injective, and $\mathcal{W}$ is finite-dimensional, then $\mathcal{V}$ is finite-dimensional.

6. Suppose $\mathcal{V}$ has dimension n, $\mathcal{W}$ has dimension m, and $T: \mathcal{V} \to \mathcal{W}$ is a linear mapping. Given a basis $x_1, \cdots, x_n$ for $\mathcal{V}$, and a basis $y_1, \cdots, y_m$ for $\mathcal{W}$, one has $Tx_k = \sum_{j=1}^{m} \alpha_{jk} y_j$ for suitable scalars $\alpha_{jk}(j = 1, \cdots, m; k = 1, \cdots, n)$. The coefficients (α_{jk}) can be arranged in a rectangular array, of m rows and n columns, with α_{jk} occurring as the intersection of the j'th row and k'th column. This array is called the *matrix* of T with respect to the given bases. If $S: \mathcal{V} \to \mathcal{W}$ is another linear mapping, with matrix (β_{jk}) relative to the same given bases, then $S = T$ if and only if $\beta_{jk} = \alpha_{jk}$ for all j and k.

*7. It can be shown that every vector space $\mathcal{V}$ has a basis $\mathfrak{I}$, in the sense of *Definition I.7.2*. Granted this result, if $\mathcal{W}$ is another vector space and $T: \mathfrak{I} \to \mathcal{W}$ is any mapping, show that there exists one and only one linear mapping $S: \mathcal{V} \to \mathcal{W}$ such that $Sx = Tx$ for all $x \in \mathfrak{I}$.

8. The obvious analogs of *Theorems 1* through *4* hold for conjugate-linear mappings.

§ 2. ISOMORPHIC VECTOR SPACES

Definition 1. *A vector space $\mathcal{V}$ is said to be* **isomorphic** *with a vector space $\mathcal{W}$ in case there exists a bijective linear mapping $T: \mathcal{V} \to \mathcal{W}$. Such a mapping T is called a* **vector space isomorphism** *of $\mathcal{V}$ onto $\mathcal{W}$. The symbol $\mathcal{V} \cong \mathcal{W}$ denotes that $\mathcal{V}$ is isomorphic with $\mathcal{W}$.*

Examples

1. If $\mathcal{V}$ and $\mathcal{W}$ have the same finite dimension n, then $\mathcal{V}$ is isomorphic with $\mathcal{W}$. For, suppose $x_1, \cdots, x_n$ is a basis for $\mathcal{V}$, and $y_1, \cdots, y_n$ is a basis for $\mathcal{W}$. By *Theorem 1.3* there exists a linear mapping $T: \mathcal{V} \to \mathcal{W}$ such that $Tx_k = y_k$ for all k. It is easy to see that T is bijective (see also *Exercise 1.4*).

2. If $\mu \neq 0$, the scalar mapping $Tx = \mu x$ is a vector space isomorphism of $\mathcal{V}$ onto $\mathcal{V}$. For, $T(\mu^{-1}y) = y$ shows that T is surjective, and T is injective by *Theorem I.2.1*.

3. The mapping $T(\lambda_1,\cdots,\lambda_n) = (\lambda_{1'},\cdots,\lambda_{n'})$ described in *Example 1.11* is a vector space isomorphism. ∎

If $T: \mathcal{X} \to \mathcal{Y}$ is any bijective mapping, one can produce, in a natural way, a mapping $S: \mathcal{Y} \to \mathcal{X}$ in the "reverse direction." The mapping S, called the *inverse* of T, is defined as follows: given $y \in \mathcal{Y}$; since T is bijective, there is exactly one $x \in \mathcal{X}$ such that $Tx = y$, hence one can unambiguously define $Sy = x$. Thus, Sy is the unique element of $\mathcal{X}$ such that $T(Sy) = y$. If $x \in \mathcal{X}$, $S(Tx) = x$; for, setting $y = Tx$, $Tx = y$ shows that $Sy = x$.

Definition 2. *If $T: \mathcal{X} \to \mathcal{Y}$ is a bijective mapping, the* **inverse** *of T, is denoted T^{-1}. Thus:*

(i) $T^{-1}: \mathcal{Y} \to \mathcal{X}$.

(ii) $T^{-1}(Tx) = x$ for all $x \in \mathcal{X}$.

(iii) $T(T^{-1}y) = y$ for all $y \in \mathcal{Y}$.

It is easy to see that if $T: \mathcal{X} \to \mathcal{Y}$ is bijective, then T^{-1} is also bijective, and $(T^{-1})^{-1} = T$.

Theorem 1. *If $T: \mathcal{V} \to \mathcal{W}$ is a vector space isomorphism, then $T^{-1}: \mathcal{W} \to \mathcal{V}$ is also a vector space isomorphism.*

Proof.
Since $S = T^{-1}$ is bijective, the problem is to show that S is additive and homogeneous. Given $y_1, y_2 \in \mathcal{W}$, and λ scalar. One has $T[S(y_1 + y_2)] = y_1 + y_2 = T(Sy_1) + T(Sy_2) = T(Sy_1 + Sy_2)$; since T is injective, $S(y_1 + y_2) = Sy_1 + Sy_2$. Also, $T[S(\lambda y)] = \lambda y = \lambda[T(Sy)] = T[\lambda(Sy)]$, hence $S(\lambda y) = \lambda(Sy)$. ∎

Example 4. Let $\mathcal{V}$ be the vector space of polynomial functions on $[a,b]$, T the linear mapping $Tx = x'$ (*Example 1.7*), and S the linear mapping described in *Example 1.8*. If y is any polynomial, $T(Sy) = y$ shows that T is surjective. However, T is not injective, for its null space $\mathfrak{N}$ is the set of all constant polynomials. The mapping S is injective; for, if $Sy = 0$, then $y = T(Sy) = T0 = 0$. However, S is not surjective, since its range is the set of all polynomials which are divisible by $t - a$ (recall that $(Sy)(a) = 0$).

Exercises

1. Let $T: \mho \to \mathcal{W}$ be a linear mapping, $\mathfrak{I}$ a basis for $\mho$. Then, T is an isomorphism if and only if $T(\mathfrak{I})$ is a basis for $\mathcal{W}$.

2. If $\mho$ has finite dimension n, then $\mho \cong \mathcal{W}$ if and only if $\mathcal{W}$ has finite dimension n.

3. If $\mho$ is the vector space of n-ples, and $\mathcal{W}$ is the vector space of polynomial functions of degree $\leq n - 1$ defined on the interval $[a,b]$, $a < b$, then $\mho \cong \mathcal{W}$.

4. The vector space of finitely non-zero sequences is isomorphic with the vector space of all polynomial functions on $[a,b]$, $a < b$.

5. If $\mho$ is a finite-dimensional vector space, and $T: \mho \to \mho$ is a linear mapping, the following conditions are equivalent:
(a) T is bijective
(b) T is injective
(c) T is surjective.

6. Suppose $T: \mathcal{X} \to \mathcal{Y}$ and $S: \mathcal{Y} \to \mathcal{X}$.
(i) If $S(Tx) = x$ for all $x \in \mathcal{X}$, then T is injective.
(ii) If $T(Sy) = y$ for all $y \in \mathcal{Y}$, then T is surjective.

7. If $T: \mathcal{X} \to \mathcal{Y}$ is bijective, and $\mathcal{S} \subset \mathcal{Y}$, the two possible interpretations of the symbol $T^{-1}(\mathcal{S})$ are consistent; that is, the inverse image of $\mathcal{S}$ under T coincides with the direct image of $\mathcal{S}$ under T^{-1}.

8. Notation as in *Examples 1.9* and *1.10*. Discuss $T(Sx)$, $S(Tx)$ injectivity, surjectivity, bijectivity.

9. Let $T: \mathcal{X} \to \mathcal{Y}$, and suppose there exist mappings $R: \mathcal{Y} \to \mathcal{X}$ and $S: \mathcal{Y} \to \mathcal{X}$ such that $S(Tx) = x$ for all $x \in \mathcal{X}$, and $T(Ry) = y$ for all $y \in \mathcal{Y}$. Then, T is bijective, and $R = S = T^{-1}$.

10. Suppose $T: \mathcal{X} \to \mathcal{Y}$ is bijective.
(i) If $S: \mathcal{Y} \to \mathcal{X}$, and $S(Tx) = x$ for all $x \in \mathcal{X}$, then $S = T^{-1}$.
(ii) If $R: \mathcal{Y} \to \mathcal{X}$, and $T(Ry) = y$ for all $y \in \mathcal{Y}$, then $R = T^{-1}$.

§ 3. THE VECTOR SPACE $\mathcal{L}(\mho,\mathcal{W})$

Definition 1. *If $\mho$ and $\mathcal{W}$ are vector spaces, $\mathcal{L}(\mho,\mathcal{W})$ denotes the set of all linear mappings $T: \mho \to \mathcal{W}$.*

Thus, the statement "$T \in \mathcal{L}(\mathcal{V}, \mathcal{W})$" means that T is a linear mapping of $\mathcal{V}$ into $\mathcal{W}$. If $S, T \in \mathcal{L}(\mathcal{V}, \mathcal{W})$, $S = T$ means that $Sx = Tx$ for all $x \in \mathcal{V}$.

It will be shown in this section that $\mathcal{L}(\mathcal{V}, \mathcal{W})$ is itself a vector space, with appropriate definitions of $S + T$ and λT. The necessary definitions are as follows:

1. The zero mapping belongs to $\mathcal{L}(\mathcal{V}, \mathcal{W})$; that is, $0 \in \mathcal{L}(\mathcal{V}, \mathcal{W})$, where $0x = \theta$ for all $x \in \mathcal{V}$.

2. If $S, T \in \mathcal{L}(\mathcal{V}, \mathcal{W})$, define $S + T: \mathcal{V} \to \mathcal{W}$ by the formula $(S + T)x = Sx + Tx$. If $x, y \in \mathcal{V}$ and λ is scalar, $(S + T)(x + y) = S(x + y) + T(x + y) = Sx + Sy + Tx + Ty = (Sx + Tx) + (Sy + Ty) = (S + T)x + (S + T)y$, and $(S + T)(\lambda x) = S(\lambda x) + T(\lambda x) = \lambda(Sx) + \lambda(Tx) = \lambda(Sx + Tx) = \lambda[(S + T)x]$; thus, $S + T \in \mathcal{L}(\mathcal{V}, \mathcal{W})$.

3. If $T \in \mathcal{L}(\mathcal{V}, \mathcal{W})$, and λ is scalar, define $\lambda T: \mathcal{V} \to \mathcal{W}$ by the formula $(\lambda T)x = \lambda(Tx)$. If $x, y \in \mathcal{V}$ and μ is scalar, $(\lambda T)(x + y) = \lambda[T(x + y)] = \lambda(Tx + Ty) = \lambda(Tx) + \lambda(Ty) = (\lambda T)x + (\lambda T)y$, and $(\lambda T)(\mu x) = \lambda[T(\mu x)] = \lambda[\mu(Tx)] = (\lambda \mu)(Tx) = (\mu \lambda)(Tx) = \mu[\lambda(Tx)] = \mu[(\lambda T)x]$; thus, $\lambda T \in \mathcal{L}(\mathcal{V}, \mathcal{W})$.

4. If $T \in \mathcal{L}(\mathcal{V}, \mathcal{W})$, define $-T: \mathcal{V} \to \mathcal{W}$ by the formula $(-T)x = -(Tx) = (-1)(Tx)$. Thus, $-T = (-1)T \in \mathcal{L}(\mathcal{V}, \mathcal{W})$.

Theorem 1. *If $\mathcal{V}$ and $\mathcal{W}$ are vector spaces, the set $\mathcal{L}(\mathcal{V}, \mathcal{W})$ of all linear mappings $T: \mathcal{V} \to \mathcal{W}$ is a vector space, with respect to the following definitions:*

$$0x = \theta$$

$$(-T)x = -(Tx)$$

$$(S + T)x = Sx + Tx$$

$$(\lambda T)x = \lambda(Tx).$$

Proof.

The problem is to verify the axioms for a vector space, listed in § 1 of Chapter I. For example, the proof of (A1) for $\mathcal{L}(\mathcal{V}, \mathcal{W})$ depends, in a perfectly direct way, on its validity in $\mathcal{W}$. Thus, suppose $S, T \in \mathcal{L}(\mathcal{V}, \mathcal{W})$; given any $x \in \mathcal{V}$, $(S + T)x = Sx + Tx = Tx + Sx = (T + S)x$, hence $S + T = T + S$. The verification of the remaining axioms is left to the reader. ∎

Example 1. If μ is a scalar, and $T: \mathcal{V} \to \mathcal{V}$ is the scalar mapping $Tx = \mu x$, then $T = \mu I$, where I is the identity mapping.

Exercises

1. Let $\mathfrak{I}$ be any non-empty set, $\mathfrak{W}$ any vector space, and let $\mathfrak{X}(\mathfrak{I},\mathfrak{W})$ be the set of all mappings $x \colon \mathfrak{I} \to \mathfrak{W}$. If $x,y \in \mathfrak{X}(\mathfrak{I},\mathfrak{W})$, and λ is scalar, define

$$(x + y)(t) = x(t) + y(t)$$

$$(\lambda x)(t) = \lambda x(t)$$

for all $t \in \mathfrak{I}$. Then, $\mathfrak{X}(\mathfrak{I},\mathfrak{W})$ is a vector space relative to the operations $x + y$, λx (obvious definitions of 0 and $-x$).

2. A linear subspace of the vector space $\mathfrak{X}(\mathfrak{I},\mathfrak{W})$ described in *Exercise 1* is obtained by considering the set of all mappings $x \colon \mathfrak{I} \to \mathfrak{W}$ such that $x(t) = \theta$ for all but finitely many t.

3. Suppose $\mathfrak{V}$ has finite dimension n, and $\mathfrak{W}$ has finite dimension m. Then $\mathcal{L}(\mathfrak{V},\mathfrak{W})$ has finite dimension mn.

4. Notation as in *Exercise 3*. Let $S,T \in \mathcal{L}(\mathfrak{V},\mathfrak{W})$, λ scalar. Given bases for $\mathfrak{V}$ and $\mathfrak{W}$, describe the matrices of $S + T$ and λT in terms of the matrices of S and T (see *Exercise 1.6*).

5. If $\mathfrak{V},\mathfrak{W}$ are finite-dimensional, show that $\mathcal{L}(\mathfrak{V},\mathfrak{W})$ is isomorphic with $\mathcal{L}(\mathfrak{W},\mathfrak{V})$.

6. Notation as in *Exercise 1*, and assume $\mathfrak{W} \neq \{\theta\}$. Suppose $\mathfrak{X}(\mathfrak{I},\mathfrak{W})$ has finite dimension N. Then, $\mathfrak{I}$ has a finite number n of points, $\mathfrak{W}$ has finite dimension m, and $N = mn$.

§ 4. COMPOSITION OF MAPPINGS

Given mappings $T \colon \mathfrak{X} \to \mathfrak{Y}$ and $S \colon \mathfrak{Y} \to \mathfrak{Z}$, there is a natural way of defining a mapping of $\mathfrak{X}$ into $\mathfrak{Z}$: if $x \in \mathfrak{X}$, then $Tx \in \mathfrak{Y}$, hence $S(Tx) \in \mathfrak{Z}$. The mapping $x \to S(Tx)$ is called the *composite* of S and T, and is denoted ST. Thus,

$$ST \colon \mathfrak{X} \to \mathfrak{Z}$$

$$(ST)x = S(Tx) \qquad (x \in \mathfrak{X}).$$

Schematically,

To define the composite ST, it is required that the initial set of S coincide with the final set of T. It follows that if one is given mappings $T\colon \mathfrak{X} \to \mathfrak{Y}$, $S\colon \mathfrak{Y} \to \mathfrak{Z}$, and $R\colon \mathfrak{Z} \to \mathfrak{Z}$, all of the following composites are definable: RS, ST, $(RS)T$, and $R(ST)$. Such composites obey the "associative law":

Theorem 1. *If $T\colon \mathfrak{X} \to \mathfrak{Y}$, $S\colon \mathfrak{Y} \to \mathfrak{Z}$, and $R\colon \mathfrak{Z} \to \mathfrak{Z}$, then $R(ST) = (RS)T$.*

Proof.
   For all $x \in \mathfrak{X}$, $[R(ST)]x = R[(ST)x] = R[S(Tx)]$ and $[(RS)T]x = (RS)(Tx) = R[S(Tx)]$. ∎

Example 1. If $T\colon \mathfrak{X} \to \mathfrak{Y}$ is bijective, and $S = T^{-1}$, the identities $S(Tx) = x$ and $T(Sy) = y$ can be written $ST = I$ and $TS = I$.

Theorem 2. *If $\mathfrak{U},\mathfrak{V},\mathfrak{W}$ are vector spaces, and $T\colon \mathfrak{U} \to \mathfrak{V}$, $S\colon \mathfrak{V} \to \mathfrak{W}$ are linear mappings, the composite $ST\colon \mathfrak{U} \to \mathfrak{W}$ is also linear.*

Proof.
   If $x,y \in \mathfrak{U}$ and λ is scalar, $(ST)(x + y) = S[T(x + y)] = S(Tx + Ty) = S(Tx) + S(Ty) = (ST)x + (ST)y$, and $(ST)(\lambda x) = S[T(\lambda x)] = S[\lambda(Tx)] = \lambda[S(Tx)] = \lambda[(ST)x]$. ∎

Exercises

1. Given $T\colon \mathfrak{X} \to \mathfrak{Y}$, $S\colon \mathfrak{Y} \to \mathfrak{Z}$.
(i)   If S and T are both injective, then ST is injective.
(ii) If ST is injective, then T is injective.
(iii) If ST is injective, and T is surjective, then S is injective.
(iv) Give an example where ST is injective, but S is not injective.

2. Given $T\colon \mathfrak{X} \to \mathfrak{Y}$, $S\colon \mathfrak{Y} \to \mathfrak{Z}$.
(i)   If S and T are both surjective, then ST is surjective.
(ii) If ST is surjective, then S is surjective.
(iii) If ST is surjective, and S is injective, then T is surjective.
(iv) Give an example where ST is surjective, but T is not surjective.

3. Given $T\colon \mathfrak{X} \to \mathfrak{Y}$, $S\colon \mathfrak{Y} \to \mathfrak{Z}$.
(i)   If S and T are both bijective, then ST is bijective.
(ii) If ST is bijective, then S is surjective and T is injective.
(iii) If ST is bijective, and either S is injective, or T is surjective, then both S and T are bijective.

(iv) Give an example where ST is bijective, but one of S,T (hence both) fails to be bijective.

4. Let $T: \mathfrak{X} \rightarrow \mathcal{Y}$. One says that T is *left-invertible* if there exists a mapping $S: \mathcal{Y} \rightarrow \mathfrak{X}$ such that $ST = I$ ($=$ identity mapping of $\mathfrak{X}$); S is then called a *left-inverse* for T. One says that T is *right-invertible* if there exists a mapping $R: \mathcal{Y} \rightarrow \mathfrak{X}$ such that $TR = I$ ($=$ identity mapping of $\mathcal{Y}$); R is then called a *right-inverse* for T. Prove:

(i) T is injective if and only if T has a left-inverse S.

*(ii) T is surjective if and only if T has a right-inverse R.

(iii) T is bijective if and only if T has both a left-inverse S and a right inverse R. In this case, $R = S = T^{-1}$, and in particular all left-inverses and right-inverses for T coincide with the mapping T^{-1}.

5. Given $T: \mathfrak{X} \rightarrow \mathcal{Y}$, $S: \mathcal{Y} \rightarrow \mathcal{Z}$, let $R = ST$. If $\mathcal{J} \subset \mathcal{Z}$, then $R^{-1}(\mathcal{J}) = T^{-1}(S^{-1}(\mathcal{J}))$.

6. Notation as in *Theorem 2*, with $\mathcal{U},\mathcal{V},\mathcal{W}$ finite-dimensional. Choose bases for $\mathcal{U},\mathcal{V},\mathcal{W}$, and describe the matrix of ST in terms of the matrix of S and the matrix of T. [See *Exercise 1.6*.]

7. Let $\mathcal{U},\mathcal{V},\mathcal{W}$ be vector spaces. Prove:

(i) $\mathcal{U} \cong \mathcal{U}$.

(ii)   If $\mathcal{U} \cong \mathcal{V}$, then $\mathcal{V} \cong \mathcal{U}$.

(iii)   If $\mathcal{U} \cong \mathcal{V}$ and $\mathcal{V} \cong \mathcal{W}$, then $\mathcal{U} \cong \mathcal{W}$. [See *Definition 2.1* for the notation.]

§5. THE ALGEBRA $\mathcal{L}(\mathcal{V})$

Definition 1. *If $\mathcal{V}$ is a vector space, $\mathcal{L}(\mathcal{V})$ denotes the set of all linear mappings $T: \mathcal{V} \rightarrow \mathcal{V}$.*

By *Theorem 3.1*, $\mathcal{L}(\mathcal{V}) = \mathcal{L}(\mathcal{V},\mathcal{V})$ is a vector space. Thus, if $S,T \in \mathcal{L}(\mathcal{V})$ and λ is scalar, $\mathcal{L}(\mathcal{V})$ contains the linear mappings $S + T$ and λT; it also contains the composite ST, by *Theorem 4.2*.

Theorem 1. *If $R,S,T \in \mathcal{L}(\mathcal{V})$, and λ is scalar,*

(1) $R(ST) = (RS)T$

(2) $R(S + T) = RS + RT$

(3) $(S + T)R = SR + TR$

(4) $\lambda(ST) = (\lambda S)T = S(\lambda T)$.

Proof.

(1): See *Theorem 4.1.*

(2): $[R(S + T)]x = R[(S + T)x] = R(Sx + Tx) = R(Sx) + R(Tx)$
$= (RS)x + (RT)x = (RS + RT)x.$

(3): $[(S + T)R]x = (S + T)(Rx) = S(Rx) + T(Rx) = (SR)x + (TR)x = (SR + TR)x.$

(4): $[\lambda(ST)]x = \lambda[(ST)x] = \lambda[S(Tx)]$
$[(\lambda S)T]x = (\lambda S)(Tx) = \lambda[S(Tx)]$
$[S(\lambda T)]x = S[(\lambda T)x] = S[\lambda(Tx)] = \lambda[S(Tx)].$ ∎

Thus, $\mathcal{L}(\mathcal{V})$ provides an example of the following type of abstract mathematical system:

Definition 2. *An* **algebra** *is a vector space* $\mathcal{C}$ *such that for each pair of elements* $a,b \in \mathcal{C}$, *there is determined an element of* $\mathcal{C}$ *called the* **product** *of a and b, denoted* ab, *subject to the following axioms:*

(A1) $a(b + c) = ab + ac$

(A2) $(b + c)a = ba + ca$

(A3) $\lambda(ab) = (\lambda a)b = a(\lambda b).$

If moreover

(A4) $a(bc) = (ab)c$

holds for all elements a,b,c, then $\mathcal{C}$ *is called an* **associative algebra.**

Examples

1. If $\mathcal{V}$ is any vector space, $\mathcal{L}(\mathcal{V})$ is an associative algebra (see *Theorem 3.1* and *Theorem 1*).

2. Let $\mathcal{C}$ be the vector space of all scalar-valued functions defined on a non-empty set $\mathfrak{J}$ (*Example I.1.2*). If $x,y \in \mathcal{C}$, define xy by the formula $(xy)(t) = x(t)y(t)$. With this "pointwise" definition of products, it is easy to see that $\mathcal{C}$ is an associative algebra. Also, $xy = yx$ for all $x,y \in \mathcal{C}$ (such algebras are called *commutative*).

3. The vector space $\mathcal{C}$ of continuous functions on $[a,b]$ (*Example I.1.3*), with products defined pointwise as in *Example 2*, is an associative and commutative algebra. [Note: The product of continuous functions *is* continuous.]

4. The vector space $\mathcal{C}$ of polynomial functions on $[a,b]$ (*Example I.1.4*), with products defined pointwise, is an associative and commutative algebra.

5. Notation as in *Example 2*. Suppose moreover that $\mathfrak{I} = \mathcal{C}$, the set of all scalars λ. Then, if $x: \mathcal{C} \to \mathcal{C}$ and $y: \mathcal{C} \to \mathcal{C}$ are any two elements of $\mathcal{C}$, there is also available a "composite product" of x and y, defined as in § 4; let us denote this xoy, as distinguished from the pointwise product xy defined in *Example 2*. Specifically, $(xoy)(t) = x(y(t))$. With respect to the products xoy, the vector space $\mathcal{C}$ does *not* form an algebra, since the identities (A1) and (A3) are not valid for composite products; the identities (A2) and (A4) do hold, and $\lambda(xoy) = (\lambda x)oy$.

Exercises

1. Let $x_1, \cdots, x_n$ be a basis for the vector space $\mathcal{V}$. For each pair of indices j,k $(j = 1, \cdots, n; k = 1, \cdots, n)$, let E_{jk} be the linear mapping such that $E_{jk}x_k = x_j$ and $E_{jk}x_i = \theta$ when $i \neq k$ (see *Theorem 1.3*). Then:
   (i) $E_{ij}E_{jk} = E_{ik}$.
   (ii) $E_{ij}E_{rk} = 0$ when $j \neq r$.
   (iii) $\sum_1^n E_{ii} = I$.

2. Suppose $\mathcal{V}$ is a vector space of finite dimension n. A "set of $n \times n$ matrix units" in $\mathcal{L}(\mathcal{V})$ is a set of linear mappings $E_{jk} \in \mathcal{L}(\mathcal{V})$ $(j = 1, \cdots, n; k = 1, \cdots, n)$, satisfying the relations (i), (ii), (iii) of *Exercise 1*. Given such a set, prove there exists a basis $x_1, \cdots, x_n$ of $\mathcal{V}$ such that $E_{jk}x_k = x_j$ and $E_{jk}x_i = \theta$ when $i \neq k$.

3. If $\mathcal{C}$ is an algebra, and $\mathfrak{I}$ is a non-empty set, the set of all mappings $x: \mathfrak{I} \to \mathcal{C}$ is an algebra (with operations defined pointwise, as in *Example 2*).

4. Let $\mathcal{C}$ be any algebra, with products denoted ab. Introduce a new product $[a,b]$ between elements $a,b \in \mathcal{C}$, via the formula $[a,b] = ab - ba$; together with the vector space operations already given, $\mathcal{C}$ is an algebra (generally non-associative) relative to the products $[a,b]$.

5. Let $\mathcal{C}$ be any algebra, with products denoted ab. Define a new product $\{a,b\}$ via the formula $\{a,b\} = \frac{1}{2}(ab + ba)$. Then $\mathcal{C}$ is an algebra (generally non-associative) relative to the products $\{a,b\}$.

6. Starting with an algebra $\mathfrak{a}$, with products ab, let $\mathfrak{a}_1$ be the algebra constructed in *Exercise 4*. If the construction in *Exercise 5* is applied to the algebra $\mathfrak{a}_1$, describe the resulting algebra. Similarly, start with $\mathfrak{a}$, apply *Exercise 5* to get an algebra $\mathfrak{a}_2$, then apply *Exercise 4* to $\mathfrak{a}_2$.

§ 6. CONTINUOUS MAPPINGS

Suppose $\mathfrak{N}$ is a closed linear subspace of a Hilbert space $\mathfrak{K}$, and $P: \mathfrak{K} \to \mathfrak{K}$ is the projection of $\mathfrak{K}$ on $\mathfrak{N}$ (*Definition III.8.2*). If $x_n \to x$, then $Px_n \to Px$; for, by *Theorem III.8.1*, $\| Px_n - Px \| = \| P(x_n - x) \| \leq \| x_n - x \| \to 0$. So to speak, P "preserves" convergent sequences. This type of condition makes sense for metric spaces:

Definition 1. *Let $\mathfrak{X}$ and $\mathfrak{Y}$ be metric spaces, $T: \mathfrak{X} \to \mathfrak{Y}$. Let $x \in \mathfrak{X}$; the mapping T is said to be* **continuous at** x *in case $x_n \to x$ implies $Tx_n \to Tx$. If T is continuous at every $x \in \mathfrak{X}$, it is called a* **continuous mapping.**

Examples

1. If $\mathfrak{N}$ is a closed linear subspace of a Hilbert space $\mathfrak{K}$, the projection $P: \mathfrak{K} \to \mathfrak{K}$ of $\mathfrak{K}$ on $\mathfrak{N}$ is a continuous mapping.

2. If the metric spaces $\mathfrak{X}$ and $\mathfrak{Y}$ in *Definition 1* are sets of complex numbers, with $d(\lambda, \mu) = |\lambda - \mu|$, the notions of continuity are the classical ones.

3. Let $\mathfrak{X}$ be a metric space, y a fixed point of $\mathfrak{X}$. The mapping $T: \mathfrak{X} \to \mathfrak{R}$ defined by $Tx = d(x,y)$ is continuous by *Theorem II.4.1*. For example, if y is a fixed vector in a pre-Hilbert space $\mathfrak{P}$, then $x \to \| x - y \|$ is a continuous mapping of $\mathfrak{P}$ into the metric space $\mathfrak{R}$ of real numbers; in particular, $x \to \| x \|$ is continuous (see also the Corollary of *Theorem II.5.1*).

4. If y is a fixed vector in a pre-Hilbert space $\mathfrak{P}$, then $x \to (x|y)$ is a continuous mapping of $\mathfrak{P}$ into the metric space $\mathfrak{C}$ of complex numbers (see *Theorem II.5.1*).

Theorem 1. *If $\mathfrak{X}$ and $\mathfrak{Y}$ are metric spaces, the following conditions on a mapping $T: \mathfrak{X} \to \mathfrak{Y}$ are equivalent:*

(a) *T is a continuous mapping.*

(b) *If $\mathfrak{S}$ is any closed subset of $\mathfrak{Y}$, $T^{-1}(\mathfrak{S})$ is a closed subset of $\mathfrak{X}$.*

Proof.

(a) *implies* (b): Let S be a closed subset of $\mathcal{Y}$, and suppose $x \in \mathcal{X}$ is adherent to $T^{-1}(S)$. Choose any sequence $x_n \in T^{-1}(S)$ such that $x_n \to x$. Then $Tx_n \in S$, and since $Tx_n \to Tx$ by the continuity of T, Tx is adherent to S; since S is closed, $Tx \in S$, thus $x \in T^{-1}(S)$.

(b) *implies* (a): Given $x_n \to x$, the problem is to show that $Tx_n \to Tx$. Assume to the contrary that for some $\epsilon > 0, d(Tx_n, Tx) \geq \epsilon$ for infinitely many n. Passing to a subsequence, we may suppose $d(Tx_n, Tx) \geq \epsilon$ for *all* n. Let $S = \{y \in \mathcal{Y}: d(y, Tx) \geq \epsilon\}$. It is easy to see that S is a closed subset of $\mathcal{Y}$ (see *Example III.2.6*). Now, $d(Tx_n, Tx) \geq \epsilon$ shows that $Tx_n \in S$, $x_n \in T^{-1}(S)$, hence x is adherent to $T^{-1}(S)$; since $T^{-1}(S)$ is a closed subset of $\mathcal{X}$ by the assumption (b), $x \in T^{-1}(S)$. Thus, $Tx \in S$, $d(Tx, Tx) \geq \epsilon$, a contradiction. ∎

Corollary. *If $\mathcal{X}$ and $\mathcal{Y}$ are metric spaces, $T: \mathcal{X} \to \mathcal{Y}$ is a continuous mapping, and $y \in \mathcal{Y}$, then $\{x \in \mathcal{X}: Tx = y\}$ is a closed subset of $\mathcal{X}$.*

Proof.

$\{y\}$ is a closed subset of $\mathcal{Y}$. ∎

Exercises

1. Let $\mathcal{X}$ and $\mathcal{Y}$ be metric spaces, $S: \mathcal{X} \to \mathcal{Y}$ and $T: \mathcal{X} \to \mathcal{Y}$ continuous mappings. Prove:

(i) $\{x \in \mathcal{X}: Sx = Tx\}$ is a closed subset of $\mathcal{X}$.

(ii) If S is a dense subset of $\mathcal{X}$, and $Sx = Tx$ for all $x \in S$, then $S = T$.

2. If $\mathcal{X}, \mathcal{Y}, \mathcal{Z}$ are metric spaces, and $T: \mathcal{X} \to \mathcal{Y}$, $S: \mathcal{Y} \to \mathcal{Z}$ are continuous mappings, then $ST: \mathcal{X} \to \mathcal{Z}$ is a continuous mapping.

§7. NORMED SPACES, BANACH SPACES, CONTINUOUS LINEAR MAPPINGS

From Chapter VI onward, we will be concerned primarily with continuous linear mappings $T: \mathcal{H} \to \mathcal{H}$ of a Hilbert space $\mathcal{H}$ into itself. Much of what can be said about such mappings can be expressed directly in terms of the norm, and properties of the norm, without having to refer explicitly to the scalar product from which the norm is derived. A convenient vehicle for discussions of this sort is the concept of a normed space:

Definition 1. *A **normed space** is a vector space $\mathcal{E}$ such that for each vector $x \in \mathcal{E}$, there is defined a non-negative real number called the **norm** of x, denoted $\| x \|$, subject to the following axioms:*

(N1) $\| x \| > 0$ *whenever* $x \neq \theta$; $\| \theta \| = 0$.

(N2) $\| x + y \| \leq \| x \| + \| y \|$.

(N3) $\| \lambda x \| = |\lambda| \cdot \| x \|$.

In words, the real-valued function $x \rightarrow \| x \|$ $(x \in \mathcal{E})$ is *strictly positive, subadditive,* and *absolutely homogeneous.* It is clear from (N3) that $\| -x \| = \| ix \| = \| x \|$.

Examples

1. Every pre-Hilbert space is a normed space, with norms defined by the formula $\| x \| = (x|x)^{\frac{1}{2}}$ (see *Theorems II.3.1* and *II.3.5*).

2. Let $\mathcal{E}$ be the vector space of continuous functions on $[a,b]$ (see *Example II.4.5*), and define the norm of x to be the number LUB $\{ |x(t)| : a \leq t \leq b \}$. This norm is denoted $\| x \|_\infty$, to distinguish it from the pre-Hilbert space norm described in *Example II.3.2.*

3. If $\mathcal{E}$ is a normed space, and $\mathfrak{N}$ is a linear subspace of $\mathcal{E}$, then $\mathfrak{N}$ is itself a normed space. ∎

Every normed space $\mathcal{E}$ is a metric space, with distances defined by the formula $d(x,y) = \| x - y \|$ (see the proof of *Theorem II.3.6*). Thus (see § 5 of Chapter II), a sequence x_n is (i) *convergent* to a vector x in case $\| x_n - x \| \rightarrow 0$, (ii) *Cauchy* in case $\| x_m - x_n \| \rightarrow 0$, (iii) *bounded* if there is a constant M such that $\| x_n \| \leq M$ for all n. If $\epsilon > 0$, the sets $\{x : \| x - y \| < \epsilon\}$, $\{x : \| x - y \| \leq \epsilon\}$, and $\{x : \| x - y \| = \epsilon\}$ are called, respectively, the *open ball, closed ball,* and *sphere,* of *center* y and *radius* ϵ. Spheres and closed balls are closed subsets of $\mathcal{E}$ (see *Example III.2.9*).

Theorem 1. *In any normed space:*

(1) *If* $x_n \rightarrow x$ *and* $y_n \rightarrow y$, *then* $x_n + y_n \rightarrow x + y$.

(2) *If* $x_n \rightarrow x$ *and* $\lambda_n \rightarrow \lambda$, *then* $\lambda_n x_n \rightarrow \lambda x$.

(3) *If* x_n *and* y_n *are Cauchy sequences of vectors, and* λ_n *is a Cauchy sequence of scalars, then* $x_n + y_n$ *and* $\lambda_n x_n$ *are Cauchy sequences.*

(4) $|\,\|\,x\,\| - \|\,y\,\|\,| \le \|\,x - y\,\|.$

(5) *If* $x_n \to x$, *then* $\|\,x_n\,\| \to \|\,x\,\|$. *If* x_n *is Cauchy, then* $\|\,x_n\,\|$ *is Cauchy (hence convergent).*

Proof.

(1), (2), (3): See the proof of the Lemma to *Theorem III.3.2.*

(4): See *Theorem II.4.1.*

(5): Immediate from (4).   ∎

In conformity with *Definition 6.1*, a mapping $T\colon \mathcal{E} \to \mathcal{F}$ between normed spaces is *continuous at* $x \in \mathcal{E}$ in case $\|\,x_n - x\,\| \to 0$ implies $\|\,Tx_n - Tx\,\| \to 0$. It is a *continuous mapping* if it is continuous at every $x \in \mathcal{E}$.

Theorem 2. *If* $\mathcal{E}$ *and* $\mathcal{F}$ *are normed spaces, and* $T\colon \mathcal{E} \to \mathcal{F}$ *is a continuous linear mapping, the null space* $\mathfrak{N}$ *of* T *is a closed linear subspace of* $\mathcal{E}$.

Proof.

$\mathfrak{N}$ is a linear subspace of $\mathcal{E}$ by *Theorem 1.4.* Suppose $x_n \in \mathfrak{N}$ and $x_n \to x$. Since T is continuous, $Tx_n \to Tx$. Thus, $Tx = \lim Tx_n = \lim \theta = \theta$, hence $x \in \mathfrak{N}$. Thus, $\mathfrak{N}$ is a closed subset of $\mathcal{E}$ (one could also quote the Corollary of *Theorem 6.1*).   ∎

For a *linear* mapping between normed spaces, continuity has several useful reformulations:

Theorem 3. *Let* $\mathcal{E}$ *and* $\mathcal{F}$ *be normed spaces,* $T\colon \mathcal{E} \to \mathcal{F}$ *a linear mapping. The following conditions on* T *are equivalent:*

(a) T *is a continuous mapping.*

(b) T *is continuous at some point* $x_o \in \mathcal{E}$.

(c) T *is continuous at* $\theta \in \mathcal{E}$.

(d) $\{\|\,Tx\,\| : \|\,x\,\| \le 1\}$ *is a bounded set of real numbers.*

(e)   *There exists a constant* $M \ge 0$ *such that* $\|\,Tx\,\| \le M \|\,x\,\|$ *for all* $x \in \mathcal{E}$.

Proof.

(a) *implies* (b): trivial.

(b) *implies* (c): Suppose $x_n \to \theta$. By *Theorem 1*, $x_n + x_o \to \theta + x_o = x_o$. By assumption (b), $T(x_n + x_o) \to Tx_o$, thus $Tx_n + Tx_o \to Tx_o$, $Tx_n = (Tx_n + Tx_o) - Tx_o \to \theta$.

(c) *implies* (d): Assume to the contrary that $\{ \| Tx \| : \| x \| \leq 1 \}$ is unbounded. For each $n = 1,2,3,\cdots$, choose a vector $x_n \in \mathcal{E}$ such that $\| x_n \| \leq 1$ and $\| Tx_n \| \geq n$. Define $y_n = (1/n)x_n$. Since $\| y_n \| = (1/n) \| x_n \| \leq 1/n$, $y_n \to \theta$. By assumption (c), $Ty_n \to \theta$. But, $\| Ty_n \| = (1/n) \| Tx_n \| \geq 1$, a contradiction.

(d) *implies* (e): Assume to the contrary that no such constant M exists. In particular, the constants $1,2,3,\cdots$ fail; for each n, choose $x_n \in \mathcal{E}$ so that $\| Tx_n \| > n \| x_n \|$. Clearly $x_n \neq \theta$; defining $y_n = \| x_n \|^{-1} x_n$, one has $\| y_n \| = 1$, but $\| Ty_n \| > n$, contrary to (d).

(e) *implies* (a): If $x_n \to x$, then $\| Tx_n - Tx \| = \| T(x_n - x) \| \leq M \| x_n - x \| \to 0$, hence $Tx_n \to Tx$. $\blacksquare$

In view of condition (d), continuous linear mappings between normed spaces are also called *bounded* linear mappings.

Definition 2. *If $\mathcal{E}$ and $\mathcal{F}$ are normed spaces, and $T: \mathcal{E} \to \mathcal{F}$ is a continuous linear mapping, the non-negative real number*

$$\text{LUB} \{ \| Tx \| : \| x \| \leq 1 \}$$

is called the **norm** *of T, and is denoted $\| T \|$.*

Theorem 4. *Let $\mathcal{E}$ and $\mathcal{F}$ be normed spaces, $T: \mathcal{E} \to \mathcal{F}$ a continuous linear mapping. Then:*

(1) $\| T \| = \text{LUB} \{ \| Tx \| : \| x \| < 1 \}$.

(2)   *If $\mathcal{E} \neq \{\theta\}$, $\| T \| = \text{LUB} \{ \| Tx \| : \| x \| = 1 \}$.*

(3) $\| Tx \| \leq \| T \| \cdot \| x \|$ *for all $x \in \mathcal{E}$.*

(4)   *If $M \geq 0$ and $\| Tx \| \leq M \| x \|$ for all $x \in \mathcal{E}$, necessarily $\| T \| \leq M$.*

Proof.

(1): Let $K = \text{LUB} \{ \| Tx \| : \| x \| < 1 \}$; clearly $K \leq \| T \|$. Suppose $\| x \| \leq 1$; given any $\epsilon > 0$, the vector $y = (\| x \| + \epsilon)^{-1} x$ has norm < 1, hence $\| Ty \| \leq K$; that is, $\| Tx \| \leq K(\| x \| + \epsilon)$. Letting $\epsilon \to 0$, $\| Tx \| \leq K \| x \| \leq K$. Taking LUB over $\| x \| \leq 1$, $\| T \| \leq K$.

(2): Since $\mathcal{E} \neq \{\theta\}$, there exist vectors $x \in \mathcal{E}$ such that $\| x \| = 1$. Define $N = \text{LUB} \{\| Tx \| : \| x \| = 1\}$; clearly $N \leq \| T \|$. Suppose $\| x \| \leq 1$. If $x = \theta$, then $Tx = \theta$, hence $\| Tx \| = 0 \leq N$. If $x \neq \theta$, the vector $y = \| x \|^{-1}x$ has norm 1, hence $\| Ty \| \leq N$; that is, $\| Tx \| \leq N \| x \| = N$. Thus, $\| Tx \| \leq N$ whenever $\| x \| \leq 1$; it follows that $\| T \| \leq N$.

(3): Given any $x \in \mathcal{E}$. If $x = \theta$, clearly $\| Tx \| \leq \| T \| \cdot \| x \|$. If $x \neq \theta$, let $y = \| x \|^{-1}x$; since $\| y \| = 1$, $\| Ty \| \leq \| T \|$, that is, $\| Tx \| \leq \| T \| \cdot \| x \|$.

(4): Suppose $M \geq 0$ and $\| Tx \| \leq M \| x \|$ for all $x \in \mathcal{E}$. If $\| x \| \leq 1$, $\| Tx \| \leq M \| x \| \leq M$; taking LUB over $\| x \| \leq 1$, $\| T \| \leq M$. ∎

Examples

4. Let y be a fixed vector in a pre-Hilbert space $\mathcal{P}$, and define $T: \mathcal{P} \rightarrow \mathcal{C}$ by the formula $Tx = (x|y)$. Then, T is a linear mapping of $\mathcal{P}$ into the one-dimensional Hilbert space $\mathcal{C}$, and $|Tx| = |(x|y)| \leq \| x \| \| y \|$ shows that T is continuous, and $\| T \| \leq \| y \|$. In fact, $\| T \| = \| y \|$. This is clear if $y = \theta$; if $y \neq \theta$, $\| T \| \| y \| \geq |Ty| = |(y|y)| = \| y \|^2$ shows that $\| T \| \geq \| y \|$.

5. If $\mathcal{P}$ and $\mathcal{Q}$ are pre-Hilbert spaces, and $T: \mathcal{P} \rightarrow \mathcal{Q}$ is a continuous linear mapping, then $\| T \| = \text{LUB} \{ |(Tx|y)| : \| x \| \leq 1, \| y \| \leq 1 \}$. For, let K denote the indicated LUB. If $x \in \mathcal{P}$, $y \in \mathcal{Q}$, $\| x \| \leq 1$, $\| y \| \leq 1$, then $|(Tx|y)| \leq \| Tx \| \| y \| \leq \| T \| \| x \| \| y \| \leq \| T \|$; hence K is a finite real number, and $K \leq \| T \|$. If $\| x \| \leq 1$ and $\| y \| \leq 1$, $|(y|Tx)| = |(Tx|y)| \leq K$; fixing x and taking LUB over y, $\| Tx \| \leq K$ by *Example 4*. Taking LUB over x, $\| T \| \leq K$.

6. If $\mathcal{H}$ is a Hilbert space of *finite dimension n*, and $\mathcal{F}$ is any normed space, then *every* linear mapping $T: \mathcal{H} \rightarrow \mathcal{F}$ is continuous. For, let $x_1, \cdots, x_n$ be an orthonormal basis for $\mathcal{H}$. If $x = \sum_1^n \lambda_k x_k$ is any vector in $\mathcal{H}$,

$$\| Tx \| = \left\| \sum_1^n \lambda_k (Tx_k) \right\| \leq \sum_1^n |\lambda_k| \, \| Tx_k \|$$

$$\leq \left(\sum_1^n |\lambda_k|^2 \right)^{1/2} \left(\sum_1^n \| Tx_k \|^2 \right)^{1/2}$$

by the Corollary of *Theorem II.3.4*. Thus, $\| Tx \| \le M \| x \|$, where $M = \left(\sum_1^n \| Tx_k \|^2 \right)^{\frac{1}{2}}$ is independent of x. This shows that T is continuous, and $\| T \| \le M$. ∎

The most obviously continuous mappings are those which preserve distance:

Definition 3. *If $\mathfrak{X}$ and $\mathfrak{Y}$ are metric spaces, a mapping $T: \mathfrak{X} \to \mathfrak{Y}$ is said to be* **isometric** *in case $d(Tx_1, Tx_2) = d(x_1, x_2)$ for all $x_1, x_2 \in \mathfrak{X}$.*

Theorem 5. *If $\mathcal{E}$ and $\mathfrak{F}$ are normed spaces, a linear mapping $T: \mathcal{E} \to \mathfrak{F}$ is isometric if and only if $\| Tx \| = \| x \|$ for all $x \in \mathcal{E}$.*

Proof.
This is immediate from the relations $\| Tx - Ty \| = \| T(x - y) \|$ and $\| Tx \| = \| Tx - T\theta \|$. ∎

Metric spaces in which every Cauchy sequence is convergent are said to be *complete*. Pre-Hilbert spaces with this property are called *Hilbert spaces*. A normed space with this property is called a *Banach space*:

Definition 4. *A* **Banach space** *is a complete normed space.*

Thus, a Banach space is a normed space $\mathfrak{B}$ with the following property: if $x_n \in \mathfrak{B}$ and $\| x_m - x_n \| \to 0$, there exists an $x \in \mathfrak{B}$ such that $\| x_n - x \| \to 0$.

Examples

7. Every Hilbert space is a Banach space. In particular, $\mathcal{C}$ is a one-dimensional Banach space.

8. If $\mathfrak{B}$ is a Banach space, every closed linear subspace $\mathfrak{N}$ of $\mathfrak{B}$ is also a Banach space (see *Theorem III.4.1*). ∎

Further examples of Banach spaces will be found in the exercises. The following theorem is a simple and useful application of completeness:

Theorem 6. *Let $S: \mathfrak{N} \to \mathfrak{B}$ be a continuous linear mapping, where $\mathfrak{B}$ is a Banach space, and $\mathfrak{N}$ is a dense linear subspace of a normed space $\mathcal{E}$. Then, there exists one and only one continuous linear mapping $T: \mathcal{E} \to \mathfrak{B}$ such that $Tx = Sx$ whenever $x \in \mathfrak{N}$. One has $\| T \| = \| S \|$.*

Proof.

Given $x \in \mathcal{E}$, the problem is to define $Tx \in \mathcal{B}$. Choose any sequence $y_n \in \mathfrak{N}$ such that $y_n \to x$. Since $\| Sy_m - Sy_n \| = \| S(y_m - y_n) \| \leq \| S \| \| y_m - y_n \| \to 0$, Sy_n is a Cauchy sequence in $\mathcal{B}$. Since $\mathcal{B}$ is complete, Sy_n is convergent. If also $z_n \in \mathfrak{N}$ and $z_n \to x$, Sz_n is also convergent, and since $\| Sy_n - Sz_n \| = \| S(y_n - z_n) \| \leq \| S \| \| y_n - z_n \| \leq \| S \| (\| y_n - x \| + \| x - z_n \|) \to 0$, one has $\lim Sy_n = \lim Sz_n$. Thus, one can unambiguously define $Tx = \lim Sy_n$. Since $\| Sy_n \| \leq \| S \| \| y_n \|$, letting $n \to \infty$ one has $\| Tx \| \leq \| S \| \| x \|$.

The linearity of $T \colon \mathcal{E} \to \mathcal{B}$ is easily deduced from the linearity of S, using *Theorem 1*. The above calculation then shows that T is continuous, and $\| T \| \leq \| S \|$. Since $Ty = Sy$ when $y \in \mathfrak{N}$, it is clear that $\| T \| \geq \| S \|$.

The proof of uniqueness is left to the reader. See for instance *Exercise 6.1.* ∎

Exercises

1. If $\mathfrak{N}$ is a linear subspace of a normed space $\mathcal{E}$, $\overline{\mathfrak{N}}$ is a closed linear subspace of $\mathcal{E}$.

2. If $\mathcal{E}$ and $\mathfrak{F}$ are normed spaces, $T \colon \mathcal{E} \to \mathfrak{F}$ is a continuous linear mapping, and x_n is a Cauchy sequence in $\mathcal{E}$, then Tx_n is a Cauchy sequence in $\mathfrak{F}$. Does the analogous result hold for a continuous mapping between metric spaces?

3. If $\mathcal{E}$ is a normed space, $\mathcal{B}$ is a Banach space, and $T \colon \mathcal{E} \to \mathcal{B}$ is a vector space isomorphism such that both T and T^{-1} are continuous, then $\mathcal{E}$ is a Banach space.

4. If $\mathcal{E}$ and $\mathfrak{F}$ are normed spaces, $T \colon \mathcal{E} \to \mathfrak{F}$ is linear, $K > 0$, and either $\{ \| Tx \| : \| x \| < K \}$ or $\{ \| Tx \| : \| x \| = K \}$ is bounded, then T is continuous.

5. If $\mathcal{E}$ is a normed space, and $\mathcal{Q}$ is a pre-Hilbert space, a linear mapping $T \colon \mathcal{E} \to \mathcal{Q}$ is continuous if and only if the set

$$\{ |(Tx|y)| : \| x \| \leq 1, \| y \| \leq 1 \}$$

is bounded; the LUB of this set is then $= \| T \|$.

6. Let $\mathcal{E}$ be the vector space of n-ples $x = (\lambda_1, \cdots, \lambda_n)$, and define $\| x \|_1 = \sum_1^n |\lambda_k|$. The result is a Banach space.

7. Let ε be the vector space of continuous functions x on $[a,b]$, where $a < b$, and define

$$\| x \|_1 = \int_a^b |x(t)| \, dt.$$

Then, ε is a normed space, but is not a Banach space.

8. Let $\mathfrak{I}$ be a non-empty set. A scalar-valued function x defined on $\mathfrak{I}$ is said to be *bounded* if there exists a constant K such that $|x(t)| \leq K$ for all $t \in \mathfrak{I}$. Denote by ε the set of all such x, and define

$$(x + y)(t) = x(t) + y(t)$$

$$(\lambda x)(t) = \lambda x(t)$$

$$\| x \|_\infty = \text{LUB} \, \{|x(t)| : t \in \mathfrak{I}\}.$$

Then, ε is a Banach space.

9. Let ε be the vector space of continuous functions on $[a,b]$, normed as in *Example 2*. Then, ε is a Banach space.

10. (i) If ε is any normed space, the identity linear mapping $I: \varepsilon \to \varepsilon$ is continuous. If $\varepsilon \neq \{\theta\}$, $\| I \| = 1$.

(ii) If ε and $\mathfrak{F}$ are normed spaces, and $T: \varepsilon \to \mathfrak{F}$ is a vector space isomorphism such that both T and T^{-1} are continuous, then $\| T^{-1} \| \geq \| T \|^{-1}$.

11. Why does the argument in *Example 6* fail for infinite-dimensional $\mathfrak{IC}$? Why does it fail if $\mathfrak{IC}$ is replaced by a finite-dimensional normed space ε (even though T is nevertheless continuous by *Exercise 9.1* below)?

*12. If $\mathfrak{F}$ is a normed space of finite dimension n, $\mathbb{C}^n$ is the n-dimensional unitary space, and $T: \mathbb{C}^n \to \mathfrak{F}$ is any vector space isomorphism, then both T and T^{-1} are continuous.

*13. Every finite-dimensional normed space $\mathfrak{F}$ is a Banach space.

*14. Every finite-dimensional linear subspace of a normed space is closed.

15. Let ε be the set of all sequences $x = (\lambda_k)$ of scalars which are *absolutely summable*, that is, $\sum_1^\infty |\lambda_k| < \infty$. With equality, sums, and scalar multiples defined as in *Example I.1.6*, and with $\| x \|_1 = \sum_1^\infty |\lambda_k|$, ε is a Banach space.

16. Let $\mathcal{E}_1, \mathcal{E}_2, \mathcal{E}_3, \cdots$ be a sequence of normed spaces, $\mathcal{E}$ the set of all "sequences" $x = (x_k)$, with $x_k \in \mathcal{E}_k$, such that $\sum_1^\infty \|x_k\| < \infty$. With the obvious definitions (see *Exercise 15*), $\mathcal{E}$ is a normed space. $\mathcal{E}$ is a Banach space if and only if every $\mathcal{E}_k$ is a Banach space.

17. Let $\mathcal{E}_1, \mathcal{E}_2, \mathcal{E}_3, \cdots$ be a sequence of normed spaces, $\mathcal{E}$ the set of all "sequences" $x = (x_k)$, with $x_k \in \mathcal{E}_k$, such that $\sum_1^\infty \|x_k\|^2 < \infty$. Define

$$\|x\|_2 = \left(\sum_1^\infty \|x_k\|^2\right)^{\frac{1}{2}},$$

and define $x + y$, λx in the obvious way. Then, $\mathcal{E}$ is a normed space. $\mathcal{E}$ is a Banach space if and only if every $\mathcal{E}_k$ is a Banach space.

*18. Let $\mathcal{E}$ be the vector space of n-ples $x = (\lambda_1, \cdots, \lambda_n)$, p a fixed real number > 1, and define $\|x\|_p = \left(\sum_1^n |\lambda_k|^p\right)^{1/p}$. Then, $\mathcal{E}$ is a Banach space.

*19. Let $\mathcal{E}$ be the vector space of continuous functions x on $[a,b]$, where $a < b$, and let p be a fixed real number > 1. Define

$$\|x\|_p = \left(\int_a^b |x(t)|^p \, dt\right)^{1/p}.$$

Then, $\mathcal{E}$ is a normed space, but is not a Banach space.

20. Let $\mathcal{E}$ be the vector space of n-ples $x = (\lambda_1, \cdots, \lambda_n)$; with $\|x\|_\infty = \max\{|\lambda_1|, \cdots, |\lambda_n|\}$, $\mathcal{E}$ is a Banach space (see *Exercise 8*). If $\|x\|_p$ is defined as in *Exercise 18*,

$$\|x\|_\infty = \lim_{p \to \infty} \|x\|_p.$$

*21. Suppose $\mathcal{E}$ is a normed space such that $\|x + y\|^2 + \|x - y\|^2 = 2\|x\|^2 + 2\|y\|^2$ for all $x, y \in \mathcal{E}$. Then, there exists a scalar product $(x|y)$ on $\mathcal{E}$, satisfying the axioms for a pre-Hilbert space, such that $\|x\| = (x|x)^{\frac{1}{2}}$. Thus, a Hilbert space can be described as a Banach space whose norm satisfies the "parallelogram law."

§ 8. THE NORMED SPACE $\mathcal{L}_c(\mathcal{E}, \mathcal{F})$

Definition 1. *If $\mathcal{E}$ and $\mathcal{F}$ are normed spaces, $\mathcal{L}_c(\mathcal{E}, \mathcal{F})$ denotes the set of all continuous linear mappings $T: \mathcal{E} \to \mathcal{F}$.*

Theorem 1. *If $\mathcal{E}$ and $\mathcal{F}$ are normed spaces, $\mathcal{L}_c(\mathcal{E},\mathcal{F})$ is a linear subspace of $\mathcal{L}(\mathcal{E},\mathcal{F})$, and is a normed space with $\| T \| = \mathrm{LUB}\, \{\| Tx \| : \| x \| \leq 1\}$.*

Proof.

See *Theorem 3.1* for the definition of the vector space $\mathcal{L}(\mathcal{E},\mathcal{F})$.

Clearly $0 \in \mathcal{L}_c(\mathcal{E},\mathcal{F})$, and $\| 0 \| = 0$. If $S,T \in \mathcal{L}_c(\mathcal{E},\mathcal{F})$, and λ is scalar, then for any $\| x \| \leq 1$, $\| (S + T)x \| = \| Sx + Tx \| \leq \| Sx \| + \| Tx \| \leq \| S \| + \| T \|$, and $\| (\lambda T)x \| = \| \lambda(Tx) \| = |\lambda| \cdot \| Tx \| \leq |\lambda| \cdot \| T \|$; thus $S + T$ and λT are continuous, and taking LUB over $\| x \| \leq 1$, one has $\| S + T \| \leq \| S \| + \| T \|$ and $\| \lambda T \| = |\lambda| \cdot \| T \|$. Clearly $\| T \| > 0$ unless $T = 0$. ∎

Theorem 2. *If $\mathcal{E}$ is a normed space and $\mathcal{B}$ is a Banach space, then $\mathcal{L}_c(\mathcal{E},\mathcal{B})$ is a Banach space.*

Proof.

Given a sequence of continuous linear mappings $T_n \colon \mathcal{E} \to \mathcal{B}$ such that $\| T_m - T_n \| \to 0$, the problem is to construct a continuous linear mapping $T \colon \mathcal{E} \to \mathcal{B}$ such that $\| T - T_n \| \to 0$.

For each $x \in \mathcal{E}$, $\| T_m x - T_n x \| = \| (T_m - T_n)x \| \leq \| T_m - T_n \| \| x \| \to 0$ shows that $T_n x$ is a Cauchy sequence in $\mathcal{B}$. Since $\mathcal{B}$ is complete, $T_n x$ converges to a unique limit, which we denote Tx. Thus, the mapping $T \colon \mathcal{E} \to \mathcal{B}$ is defined by the formula $Tx = \lim T_n x$. It will be shown that (i) T is linear, (ii) T is continuous, and (iii) $\| T - T_n \| \to 0$.

By *Theorem 7.1*, $T(x + y) = \lim T_n(x + y) = \lim (T_n x + T_n y) = \lim T_n x + \lim T_n y = Tx + Ty$, and $T(\lambda x) = \lim T_n(\lambda x) = \lim \lambda(T_n x) = \lambda \lim T_n x = \lambda(Tx)$. Thus, T is linear.

Since every Cauchy sequence is bounded (see the Lemma of *Theorem II.5.1*), there is a constant $K \geq 0$ such that $\| T_n \| \leq K$ for all n. Given any $x \in \mathcal{E}$; since $T_n x \to Tx$, $\| T_n x \| \to \| Tx \|$ by *Theorem 7.1*. Passing to the limit in the inequality $\| T_n x \| \leq K \| x \|$, one has $\| Tx \| \leq K \| x \|$. Thus, T is continuous, and $\| T \| \leq K$. It is now meaningful to write $\| T - T_n \|$.

Given $\epsilon > 0$, let N be an index such that $\| T_m - T_n \| \leq \epsilon$ whenever $m,n \geq N$. Given $x \in \mathcal{E}$, $\| x \| \leq 1$. If $m,n \geq N$, $\| T_m x - T_n x \| = \| (T_m - T_n)x \| \leq \| T_m - T_n \| \| x \| \leq \epsilon \| x \| \leq \epsilon$; fixing $n \geq N$ and letting $m \to \infty$, one has $\| Tx - T_n x \| \leq \epsilon$. Thus, $\| Tx - T_n x \| \leq \epsilon$ provided $n \geq N$ and $\| x \| \leq 1$; fixing $n \geq N$ and taking LUB over $\| x \| \leq 1$, $\| T - T_n \| \leq \epsilon$. Summarizing: given any $\epsilon > 0$, there is an index N such that $\| T - T_n \| \leq \epsilon$ whenever $n \geq N$. ∎

Exercises

1. (i) If $\mathcal{E}$ and $\mathcal{F}$ are normed spaces such that $\mathcal{L}_c(\mathcal{E},\mathcal{F})$ is complete, $\mathcal{F}$ is not necessarily complete.

(ii) If $\mathcal{P}$ is a pre-Hilbert space, $\mathcal{P} \neq \{\theta\}$, and $\mathcal{L}_c(\mathcal{P},\mathcal{F})$ is complete, then $\mathcal{F}$ is necessarily complete.

*(iii) If $\mathcal{E} \neq \{\theta\}$ and $\mathcal{L}_c(\mathcal{E},\mathcal{F})$ is complete, it can be shown that $\mathcal{F}$ is necessarily complete.

2. Let $\mathcal{E}$ and $\mathcal{F}$ be normed spaces, and T_n, $T \in \mathcal{L}_c(\mathcal{E},\mathcal{F})$. One says that "$T_n \to T$ *uniformly*" in case $\| T_n - T \| \to 0$, that is, $T_n \to T$ in the normed space $\mathcal{L}_c(\mathcal{E},\mathcal{F})$. One says that "$T_n \to T$ *strongly*" in case $T_n x \to Tx$ for each $x \in \mathcal{E}$, that is, $\| T_n x - Tx \| \to 0$ for each $x \in \mathcal{E}$. Prove:

(i) If $T_n \to T$ uniformly, then $T_n \to T$ strongly.

(ii) $T_n \to T$ uniformly, if and only if: given any $\epsilon > 0$, there is an index N such that $\| T_n x - Tx \| \le \epsilon$ whenever $n \ge N$ and $\| x \| \le 1$ (so to speak, $T_n x \to Tx$ uniformly for x in the closed unit ball of $\mathcal{E}$).

3. Let $\mathcal{E}$ and $\mathcal{F}$ be normed spaces, $T_n: \mathcal{E} \to \mathcal{F}$ a sequence of continuous linear mappings, and assume there is a constant K such that $\| T_n \| \le K$ for all n.

(i) Let $\mathfrak{N} = \{x \in \mathcal{E}: T_n x \text{ is Cauchy}\}$. Then, $\mathfrak{N}$ is a closed linear subspace of $\mathcal{E}$.

(ii) If $\mathcal{F}$ is a Banach space, there is a continuous linear mapping $T: \mathfrak{N} \to \mathcal{F}$ such that $T_n x \to Tx$ for all $x \in \mathfrak{N}$.

(iii) Suppose $\mathcal{F}$ is a Banach space, and $\mathfrak{M}$ is a dense linear subspace of $\mathcal{E}$ such that $T_n x$ is convergent for each $x \in \mathfrak{M}$. Then, there exists one and only one continuous linear mapping $T: \mathcal{E} \to \mathcal{F}$ such that $T_n \to T$ strongly in the sense of *Exercise 2*. This result is known as the "Banach-Steinhaus theorem."

*4. Let $\mathfrak{B}$ be a Banach space, $\mathcal{E}$ a normed space, and $\mathfrak{I}$ a set of continuous linear mappings $T: \mathfrak{B} \to \mathcal{E}$; in other words, $\mathfrak{I} \subset \mathcal{L}_c(\mathfrak{B},\mathcal{E})$. Suppose $\mathfrak{I}$ is "pointwise bounded," in the sense that for each $x \in \mathfrak{B}$ there exists a constant M_x such that $\| Tx \| \le M_x$ for all $T \in \mathfrak{I}$. Then, it can be shown that there exists a constant M such that $\| T \| \le M$ for all $T \in \mathfrak{I}$. This result is known as the "principle of uniform boundedness."

*5. If $\mathfrak{B}$ is a Banach space, $\mathcal{E}$ is a normed space, $T_n, T \in \mathcal{L}_c(\mathfrak{B},\mathcal{E})$, and $T_n \to T$ strongly, in the sense of *Exercise 2*, there exists a constant M such that $\| T_n \| \le M$ for all $n = 1, 2, 3, \cdots$.

*6. Let $\mathcal{E}$ and $\mathcal{F}$ be Banach spaces, $\mathfrak{N}$ a dense linear subspace of $\mathcal{E}$, and $T_n: \mathcal{E} \rightarrow \mathcal{F}$ a sequence of continuous linear mappings. Suppose $T_n x$ is convergent, for each $x \in \mathfrak{N}$. In order that T_n converge strongly, in the sense of *Exercise 2*, to a continuous linear mapping $T: \mathcal{E} \rightarrow \mathcal{F}$, it is necessary and sufficient that there exist a constant M such that $\| T_n \| \leq M$ for all $n = 1,2,3,\cdots$.

§9. THE NORMED ALGEBRA $\mathcal{L}_c(\mathcal{E})$, BANACH ALGEBRAS

Definition 1. *If $\mathcal{E}$ is a normed space, $\mathcal{L}_c(\mathcal{E})$ denotes the set of all continuous linear mappings $T: \mathcal{E} \rightarrow \mathcal{E}$.*

Thus, $\mathcal{L}_c(\mathcal{E})$ is the normed space $\mathcal{L}_c(\mathcal{E},\mathcal{E})$ described in *Theorem 8.1*. In addition, $\mathcal{L}_c(\mathcal{E})$ contains the composite ST of any two of its members:

Theorem 1. *Suppose $T: \mathcal{E} \rightarrow \mathcal{F}$ and $S: \mathcal{F} \rightarrow \mathcal{G}$ are continuous linear mappings, where $\mathcal{E}$, $\mathcal{F}$, and $\mathcal{G}$ are normed spaces. Then $ST: \mathcal{E} \rightarrow \mathcal{G}$ is a continuous linear mapping, and $\| ST \| \leq \| S \| \| T \|$.*

Proof.
ST is linear by *Theorem 4.2*. For any $x \in \mathcal{E}$, $\| (ST)x \| = \| S(Tx) \| \leq \| S \| \| Tx \| \leq \| S \| \| T \| \| x \|$; this shows that ST is continuous, and $\| ST \| \leq \| S \| \| T \|$ by *Theorem 7.4*. See also *Exercise 6.2*. ∎

One already knows that $\mathcal{L}(\mathcal{E})$ is an associative algebra (*Example 5.1*). Since $\mathcal{L}_c(\mathcal{E})$ contains the composite ST of any two of its elements, and since the identities of *Theorem 5.1* hold in particular for the elements of $\mathcal{L}_c(\mathcal{E})$, it is clear that $\mathcal{L}_c(\mathcal{E})$ is itself an associative algebra. Moreover, it is a normed space, and $\| ST \| \leq \| S \| \| T \|$ for every pair of elements. This is an example of the following:

Definition 2. *A **normed algebra** is an associative algebra $\mathcal{A}$ which is also a normed space, such that $\| ab \| \leq \| a \| \| b \|$ for all $a,b \in \mathcal{A}$. If moreover $\mathcal{A}$ is complete (hence is a Banach space), $\mathcal{A}$ is called a **Banach algebra**.*

In the above definition, it is assumed that $a + b$ and λa have the same meaning for the algebra structure and the normed space structure. Summarizing,

Theorem 2. *If $\mathcal{E}$ is a normed space, $\mathcal{L}_c(\mathcal{E})$ is a normed algebra. If $\mathcal{B}$ is a Banach space, $\mathcal{L}_c(\mathcal{B})$ is a Banach algebra.*

Proof.

If $\mathfrak{B}$ is a Banach space, $\mathcal{L}_c(\mathfrak{B})$ is complete by *Theorem 8.2*.   ∎

In particular,

Theorem 3. *If $\mathfrak{IC}$ is a Hilbert space, the set $\mathcal{L}_c(\mathfrak{IC})$ of all continuous linear mappings $T: \mathfrak{IC} \to \mathfrak{IC}$ is a Banach algebra, relative to the definitions*

$$(S + T)x = Sx + Tx$$

$$(\lambda T)x = \lambda(Tx)$$

$$(ST)x = S(Tx)$$

$$\| T \| = \text{LUB} \{\| Tx \| : \| x \| \le 1\}.$$

Exercises

1. If $\mathcal{E}, \mathcal{F}$ are normed spaces, and $\mathcal{E}$ is finite-dimensional, then every linear mapping $T: \mathcal{E} \to \mathcal{F}$ is continuous.

2. Let $\mathfrak{I}$ be a non-empty set, $\mathfrak{A}$ the Banach space of all bounded scalar-valued functions x defined on $\mathfrak{I}$, with

$$\| x \|_\infty = \text{LUB} \{|x(t)| : t \in \mathfrak{I}\}$$

(see *Exercise 7.8*). With products xy defined by $(xy)(t) = x(t)y(t)$, $\mathfrak{A}$ is a commutative Banach algebra.

3. Let $\mathfrak{A}$ be the Banach space of continuous scalar-valued functions x defined on the closed interval $[a,b]$, with

$$\| x \|_\infty = \text{LUB} \{|x(t)| : a \le t \le b\}$$

(see *Exercise 7.9*). With products defined by $(xy)(t) = x(t)y(t)$, $\mathfrak{A}$ is a commutative Banach algebra.

*4. If $\mathcal{E}$ is a normed space such that $\mathcal{L}_c(\mathcal{E})$ is a Banach algebra, $\mathcal{E}$ is necessarily a Banach space.

§ 10. THE DUAL SPACE $\mathcal{E}'$

Definition 1. *A **linear form** on the vector space $\mathcal{V}$ is a linear mapping $f: \mathcal{V} \to \mathcal{C}$; that is, $f \in \mathcal{L}(\mathcal{V}, \mathcal{C})$.*

Thus, a linear form on $\mathcal{V}$ is a scalar-valued function f defined on $\mathcal{V}$, such that the relations $f(x + y) = f(x) + f(y)$ and $f(\lambda x) = \lambda f(x)$ hold identically. In the context of normed vector spaces, one may speak of continuous linear forms:

Definition 2. *If $\mathcal{E}$ is a normed space, the normed space* **dual** *of $\mathcal{E}$ is the set $\mathcal{L}_c(\mathcal{E},\mathcal{C})$ of all continuous linear forms $f\colon \mathcal{E} \to \mathcal{C}$. Notation: $\mathcal{E}' = \mathcal{L}_c(\mathcal{E},\mathcal{C})$.*

Theorem 1. *If $\mathcal{E}$ is any normed space, $\mathcal{E}'$ is a Banach space relative to the definitions*

$$(f + g)(x) = f(x) + g(x)$$
$$(\lambda f)(x) = \lambda f(x)$$
$$\| f \| = \mathrm{LUB}\,\{\,|f(x)| : \| x \| \leq 1\}.$$

Proof.

Since $\mathcal{C}$ is a Banach space, *Theorem 8.2* applies. ∎

Examples

1. Each vector y in a pre-Hilbert space $\mathcal{P}$ determines a continuous linear form $y'\colon \mathcal{P} \to \mathcal{C}$, namely $y'(x) = (x\,|\,y)$, and one has $\| y' \| = \| y \|$ (see *Example 7.4*). The abundance of continuous linear forms on $\mathcal{P}$ is expressed in the following result: given any non-zero vector $z \in \mathcal{P}$, there exists an $f \in \mathcal{P}'$ such that $\| f \| = 1$ and $f(z) = \| z \|$. For, setting $f = \| z \|^{-1}z'$, one has $f(z) = \| z \|^{-1}z'(z) = \| z \|^{-1}(z\,|\,z) = \| z \|$. This illustrates the following:

*2. If $\mathcal{E}$ is any normed space, and z is a non-zero vector of $\mathcal{E}$, it can be shown, using the "Hahn-Banach theorem," that there exists at least one continuous linear form f on $\mathcal{E}$ such that $\| f \| = 1$ and $f(z) = \| z \|$. In particular, $\mathcal{E} \neq \{\theta\}$ implies $\mathcal{E}' \neq \{0\}$. In the sequel, this example will be referred to only in the exercises.

Theorem 2. *Let $\mathcal{P}$ be a pre-Hilbert space. For each $y \in \mathcal{P}$, define $y' \in \mathcal{P}'$ as in Example 1. Then, the mapping $y \to y'$ of $\mathcal{P}$ into $\mathcal{P}'$ is*

(1)   *conjugate-linear: $(y + z)' = y' + z'$*

$$(\lambda y)' = \lambda^* y',$$

and

(2)   *isometric: $\| y' \| = \| y \|$.*

If this mapping is surjective, $\mathcal{P}$ is necessarily a Hilbert space.

Proof.

For all $x \in \mathcal{P}$, $(y + z)'(x) = (x\,|\,y + z) = (x\,|\,y) + (x\,|\,z) = y'(x) + z'(x) = (y' + z')(x)$, and $(\lambda y)'(x) = (x\,|\,\lambda y) = \lambda^*(x\,|\,y) = \lambda^* y'(x) = (\lambda^* y')(x)$.

It follows that $(y - z)' = y' - z'$; as shown in *Example 1*, $\| (y - z)' \| = \| y - z \|$, thus $\| y' - z' \| = \| y - z \|$, so that the mapping $y \rightarrow y'$ is isometric in the sense of *Definition 7.3*.

Suppose the mapping $y \rightarrow y'$ is surjective. Given a sequence $y_n \in \mathcal{P}$ such that $\| y_m - y_n \| \rightarrow 0$; since $\| y_m' - y_n' \| = \| y_m - y_n \| \rightarrow 0$, y_n' is a Cauchy sequence in $\mathcal{P}'$. By *Theorem 1*, there exists an $f \in \mathcal{P}'$ such that $\| y_n' - f \| \rightarrow 0$. By assumption, $f = y'$ for suitable $y \in \mathcal{P}$, thus $\| y_n - y \| = \| y_n' - y' \| = \| y_n' - f \| \rightarrow 0$. In other words, $y_n \rightarrow y$, and it has been shown that every Cauchy sequence in $\mathcal{P}$ has a limit in $\mathcal{P}$. See also *Exercise 7.3*. ∎

Conversely, it will be shown in *Theorem V.1.1* that if $\mathcal{K}$ is a Hilbert space, the mapping $y \rightarrow y'$ described in *Theorem 2* is a surjective mapping of $\mathcal{K}$ onto $\mathcal{K}'$.

Suppose $\mathcal{E}$ is a normed space, $\mathcal{E}'$ its dual space. Since $\mathcal{E}'$ is itself a normed space, one can in turn form its dual space $(\mathcal{E}')'$. This is called the *bidual* of $\mathcal{E}$, and is denoted $\mathcal{E}''$; it is, of course, a Banach space (*Theorem 1*). There exists a natural mapping of $\mathcal{E}$ into $\mathcal{E}''$, defined as follows. Given any $x \in \mathcal{E}$, define a mapping x'': $\mathcal{E}' \rightarrow \mathcal{C}$ by the formula $x''(f) = f(x)$ $(f \in \mathcal{E}')$. Then, x'' is a continuous linear form on $\mathcal{E}'$, as is shown by the calculations $x''(f + g) = (f + g)(x) = f(x) + g(x) = x''(f) + x''(g)$, $x''(\lambda f) = (\lambda f)(x) = \lambda f(x) = \lambda x''(f)$, and $|x''(f)| = |f(x)| \leq \| f \| \| x \|$. Thus, $x'' \in \mathcal{E}''$, and $\| x'' \| \leq \| x \|$ (see *Exercise 5*). Moreover, the mapping $x \rightarrow x''$ is a linear mapping of $\mathcal{E}$ into $\mathcal{E}''$, that is, $(x + y)'' = x'' + y''$ and $(\lambda x)'' = \lambda x''$; for, $(x + y)''(f) = f(x + y) = f(x) + f(y) = x''(f) + y''(f) = (x'' + y'')(f)$, and $(\lambda x)''(f) = f(\lambda x) = \lambda f(x) = \lambda x''(f) = (\lambda x'')(f)$. In the next chapter we shall be concerned with the following special case:

Theorem 3. *If $\mathcal{P}$ is a pre-Hilbert space, the natural mapping $x \rightarrow x''$ of $\mathcal{P}$ into $\mathcal{P}''$, described above, is*

    (1)   *linear:* $(x + y)'' = x'' + y''$

$$(\lambda x)'' = \lambda x'',$$

and

    (2)   *isometric:* $\| x'' \| = \| x \|$.

Moreover,

    (3) $x''(y') = y'(x) = (x | y)$, *for all* $x, y \in \mathcal{P}$.

Proof.

(1) is proved in the preliminary remarks, and (3) is immediate from the definitions of x'' and y'.

(2): $\| x'' \| \leq \| x \|$ was established in the preliminary remarks. Moreover, $\| x \|^2 = (x|x) = x''(x') \leq \| x'' \| \, \| x' \| = \| x'' \| \, \| x \|$, hence $\| x \| \leq \| x'' \|$ (even if $x = \theta$). ∎

Exercises

1. If $\mathfrak{N}$ is a dense linear subspace of the normed space $\mathcal{E}$, and g is a continuous linear form on $\mathfrak{N}$, there exists one and only one continuous linear form $\tilde{g}$ on $\mathcal{E}$ such that $\tilde{g}\,(x) = g(x)$ for all $x \in \mathfrak{N}$. The mapping $g \rightarrow \tilde{g}$ is an isometric vector space isomorphism of $\mathfrak{N}'$ onto $\mathcal{E}'$.

2. If $\mathcal{E}$ is a normed space of finite dimension n, then every linear form on $\mathcal{E}$ is continuous, thus $\mathcal{E}' = \mathcal{L}(\mathcal{E},\mathcal{C})$. The dimension of $\mathcal{E}'$ is also n.

3. If $\mathcal{K}$ is a Hilbert space of finite dimension n, the mapping $y \rightarrow y'$ described in *Theorem 2* is surjective; that is, given any $f \in \mathcal{K}'$, there exists a (unique) vector $y \in \mathcal{K}$ such that $y' = f$. This result is generalized to arbitrary Hilbert spaces in the next chapter (see *Theorem V.1.1*).

*4. If x and y are distinct vectors of a normed spaced $\mathcal{E}$, there exists an $f \in \mathcal{E}'$ such that $f(x) \neq f(y)$.

*5. If $\mathcal{E}$ is any normed space, the mapping $x \rightarrow x''$ of $\mathcal{E}$ into $\mathcal{E}''$, described above, is isometric: $\| x'' \| = \| x \|$.

6. A normed space $\mathcal{E}$, for which the mapping $x \rightarrow x''$ of $\mathcal{E}$ into $\mathcal{E}''$ is surjective, is said to be *reflexive*. It will be shown in the next chapter that every Hilbert space is reflexive (see *Exercise V.2.2*). Prove:
   (i)   Every finite-dimensional Hilbert space is reflexive.
   (ii) Every finite-dimensional normed space is reflexive.
   *(iii) Every reflexive normed space is a Banach space.

7. Let $\mathcal{E}$ and $\mathcal{F}$ be normed spaces, $T: \mathcal{E} \rightarrow \mathcal{F}$ a continuous linear mapping. Prove:
   (i) For each $g \in \mathcal{F}'$, the mapping $x \rightarrow g(Tx)$ is a continuous linear form on $\mathcal{E}$, hence defines an element of $\mathcal{E}'$.

(ii) For each $g \in \mathfrak{F}'$, denote by $T'g$ the continuous linear form described in part (i). Then, $T' : \mathfrak{F}' \to \mathcal{E}'$ is a continuous linear mapping, and $\| T' \| \leq \| T \|$.

(iii) If also $S \in \mathcal{L}_c(\mathcal{E}, \mathfrak{F})$ and λ is scalar, $(S + T)' = S' + T'$ and $(\lambda T)' = \lambda T'$. Thus, $T \to T'$ is a (continuous) linear mapping of $\mathcal{L}_c(\mathcal{E}, \mathfrak{F})$ into $\mathcal{L}_c(\mathfrak{F}', \mathcal{E}')$.

(iv) By (ii), one can in turn form $(T')' : \mathcal{E}'' \to \mathfrak{F}''$. Write $T'' = (T')'$. Then, $T''x'' = (Tx)''$ for all $x \in \mathcal{E}$.

*(v) $\| T' \| = \| T \|$.

8. If $\mathcal{E}, \mathfrak{F}, \mathcal{G}$ are normed spaces, and $T : \mathcal{E} \to \mathfrak{F}$, $S : \mathfrak{F} \to \mathcal{G}$ are continuous linear mappings, then $(ST)' = T'S'$ (see *Exercise 7* for the notation).

9. Let $\mathcal{E}$ be a normed space, and $x_n, x \in \mathcal{E}$. One says that "$x_n \to x$ *weakly*" in case $f(x_n) \to f(x)$ for each $f \in \mathcal{E}'$. Prove: if $x_n \to x$, then $x_n \to x$ weakly. [However, weak convergence does not imply convergence; see *Exercise V.1.7.*]

10. Let $\mathcal{E}$ and $\mathfrak{F}$ be normed spaces, $T : \mathcal{E} \to \mathfrak{F}$ a continuous linear mapping. Prove: if $x_n, x \in \mathcal{E}$, and $x_n \to x$ weakly, then $Tx_n \to Tx$ weakly [See *Exercise 9* for the terminology.]

11. Let $\mathcal{E}, \mathfrak{F}$ be normed spaces, and $T_n, T \in \mathcal{L}_c(\mathcal{E}, \mathfrak{F})$. One says that "$T_n \to T$ *weakly*" in case $T_n x \to Tx$ weakly, for each $x \in \mathcal{E}$, in the sense of *Exercise 9*. Consider the statements

(i) $T_n \to T$ uniformly (see *Exercise 8.2*)

(ii) $T_n \to T$ strongly

(iii) $T_n \to T$ weakly.

Then: (i) implies (ii), and (ii) implies (iii).

Observe that in the normed space $\mathcal{L}_c(\mathcal{E}, \mathfrak{F})$, "$T_n \to T$ weakly" has another possible meaning, namely $f(T_n) \to f(T)$ for each $f \in [\mathcal{L}_c(\mathcal{E}, \mathfrak{F})]'$ (see *Exercise 9*). The distinction between this, and the concept in (iii), has to be determined from the context.

*12. If $\mathcal{E}$ and $\mathfrak{F}$ are normed spaces, $\mathcal{E} \neq \{\theta\}$, and $\mathcal{L}_c(\mathcal{E}, \mathfrak{F})$ is complete, then $\mathfrak{F}$ is necessarily complete.

Continuous Linear Forms in Hilbert Space

§ 1. RIESZ-FRECHET THEOREM

Chapters VI onward are concerned with the study of continuous linear mappings $T: \mathcal{H} \to \mathcal{H}$ of a Hilbert space into itself. This study is flavored, so to speak, by the circumstance that the dual space $\mathcal{H}'$ can in a natural way be identified with $\mathcal{H}$ (see *Theorem 2* below); it is this "self-duality" of Hilbert space which distinguishes the theory of continuous linear mappings in Hilbert space from the theory of such mappings in Banach space.

If $\mathcal{P}$ is any pre-Hilbert space, each vector $y \in \mathcal{P}$ determines a continuous linear form y' on $\mathcal{P}$, namely $y'(x) = (x \,|\, y)$. This gives rise to a mapping $y \to y'$, of $\mathcal{P}$ into its dual space $\mathcal{P}'$, which is *conjugate-linear* and *isometric* (see *Theorem IV.10.2*). If this mapping is surjective, $\mathcal{P}$ is necessarily complete; we are concerned here with the converse, which is the heart of the whole chapter (see *Theorem 7.2*):

Theorem 1. (Riesz-Frechet theorem) *If f is a continuous linear form on a Hilbert space $\mathcal{H}$, there exists one and only one vector $y \in \mathcal{H}$ such that $f(x) = (x \,|\, y)$ for all $x \in \mathcal{H}$.*

Proof.

That is, given $f \in \mathcal{K}'$, the problem is to find a vector $y \in \mathcal{K}$ such that $y' = f$.

Let $\mathfrak{N}$ be the null space of f; it is a closed linear subspace of $\mathcal{K}$, by *Theorem IV.7.2*. If $\mathfrak{N} = \mathcal{K}$, then $f = 0$, and one takes $y = \theta$. Assuming $f \neq 0$, $\mathfrak{N} \neq \mathcal{K}$; since $\mathfrak{N}^{\perp\perp} = \mathfrak{N}$ by *Theorem III.6.2*, it follows that $\mathfrak{N}^{\perp} \neq \{\theta\}$. Let $z \in \mathfrak{N}^{\perp}$, $z \neq \theta$. Since $\mathfrak{N}$ and $\mathfrak{N}^{\perp}$ have only the vector θ in common, necessarily $f(z) \neq 0$; replacing z by $[f(z)]^{-1}z$, we may suppose $f(z) = 1$.

Given any $x \in \mathcal{K}$; one has $x - f(x)z \in \mathfrak{N}$, since $f[x - f(x)z] = f(x) - f(x)f(z) = f(x) - f(x) = 0$. Since $z \perp \mathfrak{N}$, $0 = (x - f(x)z|z) = (x|z) - f(x)(z|z)$. Thus, $f(x) = (z|z)^{-1}(x|z) = (x|y)$, where $y = (z|z)^{-1}z$ is independent of x. That is, $f = y'$.

If also $f = w'$, $(x|y) = (x|w)$ for all x; $y = w$ results from *Theorem II.2.1*. ∎

Combining *Theorem 1* and *Theorem IV.10.2*,

Theorem 2. *Let $\mathcal{P}$ be a pre-Hilbert space, $y \to y'$ the mapping of $\mathcal{P}$ into $\mathcal{P}'$ described in Theorem IV.10.2. This mapping is surjective if and only if $\mathcal{P}$ is a Hilbert space.*

Exercises

1. Let f be a linear form on the vector space $\mathcal{V}$, $f \neq 0$, and $\mathfrak{N}$ the null space of f. Show that there exists a vector y with the following property: every $x \in \mathcal{V}$ has a unique representation $x = \lambda y + z$, where $z \in \mathfrak{N}$ and λ is a suitable scalar.

2. Let $\mathcal{V}, f, \mathfrak{N}$ be as in *Exercise 1*. Suppose $\mathfrak{M}$ is a linear subspace of $\mathcal{V}$ such that (1) $\mathfrak{M} \neq \{\theta\}$, and (2) $\mathfrak{M}$ and $\mathfrak{N}$ have only the vector θ in common. Prove that $\mathfrak{M}$ is one-dimensional, and every $x \in \mathcal{V}$ has a unique representation $x = y + z$ with $y \in \mathfrak{M}$ and $z \in \mathfrak{N}$.

3. If $\mathcal{P}$ is a pre-Hilbert space such that $\mathfrak{N}^{\perp\perp} = \mathfrak{N}$ for every closed linear subspace $\mathfrak{N}$ of $\mathcal{P}$, then $\mathcal{P}$ is a Hilbert space.

4. Let f be a linear form on the Hilbert space $\mathcal{K}$, $\mathfrak{N}$ the null space of f. If f is not continuous, show that $\mathfrak{N}$ is a dense linear subspace of $\mathcal{K}$.

5. If f is a linear form on a Hilbert space $\mathcal{K}$, and $\mathfrak{N}$ is the null space of f, then f is continuous if and only if $\mathfrak{N}$ is a closed linear subspace.

6. If $\mathfrak{N}$ is a complete linear subspace of a pre-Hilbert space $\mathcal{P}$, then $\mathcal{P} = \mathfrak{N} \oplus \mathfrak{N}^\perp$ (this is *Theorem III.6.1*). Another (admittedly circular) proof of this can be based on *Theorem 1*.

7. Terminology as in *Exercise IV.10.9*. Prove:
    (i) In a pre-Hilbert space $\mathcal{P}$, if $x_n \to x$ weakly, then $(x_n|y) \to (x|y)$ for each $y \in \mathcal{P}$.
    (ii) In a Hilbert space $\mathfrak{IC}$, $x_n \to x$ weakly, if and only if $(x_n|y) \to (x|y)$ for each $y \in \mathfrak{IC}$.
    (iii) If x_n is an orthonormal sequence in a Hilbert space, then $x_n \to \theta$ weakly, but one does not have $x_n \to \theta$.

8. Let $\mathcal{E}$ be a normed space, $\mathfrak{IC}$ a Hilbert space, and $T_n, T \in \mathcal{L}_c(\mathcal{E}, \mathfrak{IC})$. Then, $T_n \to T$ weakly, in the sense of *Exercise IV.10.11*, if and only if $(T_n x|y) \to (Tx|y)$ for each pair $x \in \mathcal{E}$, $y \in \mathfrak{IC}$.

9. If $\mathfrak{IC}$ is a Hilbert space, the mapping $x \to x''$ of $\mathfrak{IC}$ into $\mathfrak{IC}''$ is surjective, hence $\mathfrak{IC}$ is reflexive.

§ 2. COMPLETION

This section is presented as an application of the Riesz-Frechet theorem. It may be considered "optional" and highly omissible.

One knows that the pre-Hilbert space of finitely non-zero sequences (*Example II.1.3*) can be enlarged to a Hilbert space, namely l^2 (*Example II.5.1*). In what sense does this hold for an arbitrary pre-Hilbert space $\mathcal{P}$? In any case, there is a mapping $x \to x''$, of $\mathcal{P}$ into its bidual $\mathcal{P}''$, which preserves sums, scalar multiples, and norms (see *Theorem IV.10.3*). Let us denote this mapping by U; thus, $U: \mathcal{P} \to \mathcal{P}''$, $Ux = x''$. The linear subspace $U(\mathcal{P})$ of $\mathcal{P}''$ is a normed space which is in a sense "equal" to the normed space $\mathcal{P}$; more precisely, U defines an isometric vector space isomorphism of $\mathcal{P}$ with $U(\mathcal{P})$. Since $\mathcal{P}''$ is a Banach space, the closure $\overline{U(\mathcal{P})}$ is also a Banach space (see *Example IV.7.8* and *Exercise IV.7.1*). Thus, after "identifying" $\mathcal{P}$ with $U(\mathcal{P})$, we may think of the normed space $\mathcal{P}$ as having been enlarged to the Banach space $\overline{U(\mathcal{P})}$. There remains the problem of providing every pair of vectors in $\overline{U(\mathcal{P})}$ with a scalar product satisfying the axioms in *Definition II.1.1*, in such a way that the norm deduced from the scalar product is the same as the given Banach space norm on $\overline{U(\mathcal{P})}$. This is done in the following theorem, in which, incidentally, it is shown that $\overline{U(\mathcal{P})} = \mathcal{P}''$.

Theorem 1. (Completion) *If $\mathcal{P}$ is any pre-Hilbert space, there exists a Hilbert space $\mathcal{K}$, and a mapping $U: \mathcal{P} \to \mathcal{K}$, such that:*

(1)   *U is linear.*

(2)   *$(Ux \mid Uy) = (x \mid y)$ for all $x,y \in \mathcal{P}$.*

(3)   *$U(\mathcal{P})$ is a dense linear subspace of $\mathcal{K}$.*

In fact, the norm in the bidual $\mathcal{P}''$ can be deduced from a suitable scalar product, and one can take $\mathcal{K} = \mathcal{P}''$, $Ux = x''$.

Proof.

One knows that $\mathcal{P}''$ is a Banach space (*Theorem IV.10.1*), and that the mapping $U: \mathcal{P} \to \mathcal{P}''$ defined by $Ux = x''$ is linear and isometric (*Theorem IV.10.3*). Moreover, $x''(y') = y'(x) = (x \mid y)$ for all $x,y \in \mathcal{P}$, where $y \to y'$ is the isometric conjugate linear mapping of $\mathcal{P}$ into $\mathcal{P}'$, described in *Theorem IV.10.2*.

Let $\mathcal{K}$ be the closure of $U(\mathcal{P})$ in $\mathcal{P}''$; that is, $\mathcal{K} = \overline{U(\mathcal{P})}$. $\mathcal{K}$ is a closed linear subspace of $\mathcal{P}''$ (see the proof of *Theorem III.3.2*), and is a Banach space (*Example IV.7.8*). Later in the proof, it will be seen that $\mathcal{K} = \mathcal{P}''$.

We now have a linear isometric mapping $U: \mathcal{P} \to \mathcal{K}$, where $\mathcal{K}$ is a Banach space and $U(\mathcal{P})$ is dense in $\mathcal{K}$.

A scalar product is introduced in $\mathcal{K}$ as follows. Given $u,v \in \mathcal{K}$, the problem is to define $(u \mid v)$. Choose sequences $x_n \in \mathcal{P}$, $y_n \in \mathcal{P}$, such that $Ux_n \to u$ and $Uy_n \to v$. Since $\| x_m - x_n \| = \| U(x_m - x_n) \| = \| Ux_m - Ux_n \| \to 0$, x_n is a Cauchy sequence in $\mathcal{P}$; similarly for the sequence y_n. It follows from *Theorem II.5.1* that $(x_n \mid y_n)$ is a convergent sequence of scalars. We wish to define

$$(*) \qquad\qquad (u \mid v) = \lim \, (x_n \mid y_n),$$

hence must check that this limit is independent of the particular sequences approximating u and v. Suppose also $\bar{x}_n \in \mathcal{P}$, $\bar{y}_n \in \mathcal{P}$, with $U\bar{x}_n \to u$ and $U\bar{y}_n \to v$. Then, $\| \bar{x}_n - x_n \| = \| U\bar{x}_n - Ux_n \| \leq \| U\bar{x}_n - u \| + \| u - Ux_n \| \to 0$, and similarly $\| \bar{y}_n - y_n \| \to 0$. The desired equality $\lim \, (x_n \mid y_n) = \lim \, (\bar{x}_n \mid \bar{y}_n)$ results from the identity $(\bar{x}_n \mid \bar{y}_n) - (x_n \mid y_n) = (\bar{x}_n - x_n \mid \bar{y}_n - y_n) + (x_n \mid \bar{y}_n - y_n) + (\bar{x}_n - x_n \mid y_n)$ (see the proof of *Theorem II.5.1*). Thus, $(u \mid v)$ is unambiguously defined by the formula $(*)$. Since $Ux_n \to u$, one has $\| Ux_n \| \to \| u \|$, hence $(u \mid u) = \lim \, (x_n \mid x_n) = \lim \| x_n \|^2 = \lim \| Ux_n \|^2 = \| u \|^2$; from this it is clear that

(i) $(u|u) \geq 0$, $(u|u) = 0$ if and only if $u = \theta$.

Moreover,

(ii) $(v|u)^* = (u|v)$

(iii) $(u + v|w) = (u|w) + (v|w)$

(iv) $(\lambda u|v) = \lambda(u|v)$;

the proofs are left to the reader.

Thus, the scalar products $(u|v)$ satisfy the axioms for a pre-Hilbert space, and the relation $(u|u) = \|u\|^2$ shows that the given notion of $\|u\|$ (calculated as in *Theorem IV.10.1*) coincides with the norm $(u|u)^{\frac{1}{2}}$ deduced from the scalar product (via *Definition II.3.1*); these two (equal) norms will not be distinguished notationally. Since $\mathfrak{IC}$ was already a Banach space, the scalar product $(u|v)$ makes $\mathfrak{IC}$ into a Hilbert space.

One has $(Ux|Uy) = (x|y)$ for all $x,y \in \mathcal{P}$; for, with the notation of formula (*), one can take $x_n = x$ and $y_n = y$ for all n. Thus, the Hilbert space $\mathfrak{IC}$ and the mapping $U\colon \mathcal{P} \to \mathfrak{IC}$ fulfill the desired conditions (1),(2),(3).

It remains only to show that $\mathfrak{IC} = \mathcal{P}''$. The proof will be broken up into a series of remarks:

1. *If* $u \in \mathfrak{IC}$, *then* $(u|x'') = u(x')$ *for all* $x \in \mathcal{P}$.

For, let $x_n \in \mathcal{P}$ with $x_n'' \to u$. Since $x_n''(x') = (x_n|x)$, one has $(u|x'') = \lim (x_n''|x'') = \lim (x_n|x) = \lim x_n''(x') = u(x')$ (for the last equality, see *Exercise IV.8.2*).

2. *If* $f \in \mathcal{P}'$, *there is a unique vector* $u \in \mathfrak{IC}$ *such that* $f(x) = (x''|u)$ *for all* $x \in \mathcal{P}$.

For, let g be the linear form on $U(\mathcal{P})$ defined by $g(x'') = f(x)$. Since $|g(x'')| = |f(x)| \leq \|f\| \|x\| = \|f\| \|x''\|$, g is continuous. Since $U(\mathcal{P})$ is dense in $\mathfrak{IC}$, by *Theorem IV.7.6* there is a continuous linear form h on $\mathfrak{IC}$ such that $h(x'') = g(x'')$ for all $x \in \mathcal{P}$. By *Theorem 1.1*, there exists a vector $u \in \mathfrak{IC}$ such that $h(v) = (v|u)$ for all $v \in \mathfrak{IC}$. In particular, $(x''|u) = h(x'') = g(x'') = f(x)$ for all $x \in \mathcal{P}$.

Suppose also $w \in \mathfrak{IC}$ satisfies $f(x) = (x''|w)$ for all $x \in \mathcal{P}$. Then, $(x''|u - w) = f(x) - f(x) = 0$ for all $x \in \mathcal{P}$. Choose a sequence $x_n \in \mathcal{P}$ such that $x_n'' \to u - w$; then, $(u - w|u - w) = \lim (x_n''|u - w) = \lim 0 = 0$, hence $u - w = \theta$.

3. $\mathfrak{R} = \{y'\colon y \in \mathcal{P}\}$ *is a dense linear subspace of* $\mathcal{P}'$.

$\mathfrak{N}$ is the range of the conjugate-linear mapping $y \rightarrow y'$ of $\mathcal{P}$ into $\mathcal{P}'$; it is clearly a linear subspace of $\mathcal{P}'$. Suppose $f \in \mathcal{P}'$, and $\epsilon > 0$ is given; the problem is to find a vector $y \in \mathcal{P}$ such that $\| f - y' \| \leq \epsilon$ (see *Exercise III.2.1*). By Remark 2, there is a vector $u \in \mathcal{K}$ such that $f(x) = (x''|u)$ for all $x \in \mathcal{P}$. Choose any $y \in \mathcal{P}$ such that $\| u - y'' \| \leq \epsilon$; this is possible because $U(\mathcal{P})$ is dense in $\mathcal{K}$. For any $x \in \mathcal{P}$, $|(f - y')(x)| = |f(x) - y'(x)| = |(x''|u) - (x|y)| = |(x''|u) - (x''|y'')| = |(x''|u - y'')| \leq \| x'' \| \| u - y'' \| = \| x \| \| u - y'' \| \leq \epsilon \| x \|$, hence $\| f - y' \| \leq \epsilon$ by *Theorem IV.7.4*. Finally,

4. $\mathcal{K} = \mathcal{P}''$.

Given $F \in \mathcal{P}''$, let us show that $F \in \mathcal{K}$. For all $y \in \mathcal{P}$, one has $|F(y')| \leq \| F \| \| y' \| = \| F \| \| y \| = \| F \| \| y'' \|$. Defining $G(y'') = [F(y')]^*$, G is a continuous linear form on $U(\mathcal{P})$. Repeating the argument in Remark 2, there is a vector $u \in \mathcal{K}$ such that $G(y'') = (y''|u)$ for all $y \in \mathcal{P}$, hence $(u|y'') = [G(y'')]^* = F(y')$. Quoting Remark 1, $u(y') = F(y')$ for all $y \in \mathcal{P}$. That is, $u(f) = F(f)$ for all $f \in \mathfrak{N}$, where $\mathfrak{N}$ is the dense linear subspace of $\mathcal{P}'$ described in Remark 3; $u = F$ results from *Theorem IV.7.6* (see also *Exercise IV.6.1*). Thus, $F = u \in \mathcal{K}$. ∎

Exercises

1. If x_n is an orthonormal sequence in a pre-Hilbert space $\mathcal{P}$, then $x_n \rightarrow \theta$ weakly (see also *Exercise 1.7*).

2. If $\mathcal{K}$ is a Hilbert space, the mapping $x \rightarrow x''$ of $\mathcal{K}$ into $\mathcal{K}''$ is surjective, hence $\mathcal{K}$ is reflexive.

3. If $\mathcal{E}$ is a normed space, call a linear subspace $\mathfrak{N}$ *quadratic* in case there exists a scalar product $(x|y)$ defined for $x,y \in \mathfrak{N}$, such that (1) $\mathfrak{N}$ is a pre-Hilbert space, and (2) $(x|x)^{1/2}$ coincides with the given norm $\| x \|$ for $x \in \mathfrak{N}$. Then:

*(i) A linear subspace $\mathfrak{N}$ of $\mathcal{E}$ is quadratic if and only if $\| x + y \|^2 + \| x - y \|^2 = 2 \| x \|^2 + 2 \| y \|^2$ for all $x,y \in \mathfrak{N}$.

(ii) If $\mathfrak{N}$ is a quadratic linear subspace of $\mathcal{E}$, its closure $\overline{\mathfrak{N}}$ is also quadratic.

4. Notation as in the proof of *Theorem 1;* in particular $\mathfrak{N}$ is the dense linear subspace of $\mathcal{P}'$ described in Remark 3 of the proof. Prove:
(i) $\mathfrak{N}$ is quadratic in the sense of *Exercise 3*.
(ii) The Banach space $\mathcal{P}'$ is a Hilbert space.
(iii) Hence, in turn, $\mathcal{P}''$ is a Hilbert space. Let $\mathcal{K} = \mathcal{P}'$ be the Hilbert

space described in (ii). There is a mapping $f \to f'$ of $\mathfrak{K}$ *onto* $\mathfrak{K}' = \mathcal{O}''$ by *Theorem 1.2*. Show: if $x \in \mathcal{O}$, then $(x')' = x''$.

5. Let $\mathcal{E}$ be a normed space. A *completion* for $\mathcal{E}$ is a pair $(\mathcal{B}, U)$, where
   (1) $\mathcal{B}$ is a Banach space,
   (2) $U: \mathcal{E} \to \mathcal{B}$ is a linear mapping,
   (3) U is isometric,
   (4) $U(\mathcal{E})$ is dense in $\mathcal{B}$.
Then:
   *(i) It can be shown that every normed space $\mathcal{E}$ has a completion. Specifically, the mapping $Ux = x''$ of $\mathcal{E}$ into $\mathcal{E}''$ can be shown to be isometric, and one can take for $\mathcal{B}$ the closure in $\mathcal{E}''$ of the linear subspace $U(\mathcal{E})$.

   (ii) Suppose $(\mathcal{B}, U)$ is a completion for $\mathcal{E}$. If $\mathcal{F}$ is a Banach space, and $S: \mathcal{E} \to \mathcal{F}$ is a continuous linear mapping, there is one and only one continuous linear mapping $T: \mathcal{B} \to \mathcal{F}$ such that $TU = S$. Moreover, $\| T \| = \| S \|$.

   (iii) If $(\mathcal{B}_1, U_1)$ and $(\mathcal{B}_2, U_2)$ are two completions for $\mathcal{E}$, there exists a unique mapping $T: \mathcal{B}_1 \to \mathcal{B}_2$ such that: (1) T is a vector space isomorphism, (2) T is isometric, and (3) $U_2 = TU_1$. In this sense, a completion for $\mathcal{E}$ is unique.

6. If $\mathcal{O}$ is a pre-Hilbert space, a *completion* for $\mathcal{O}$ is a pair $(\mathfrak{K}, U)$, where
   (1) $\mathfrak{K}$ is a Hilbert space,
   (2) $U: \mathcal{O} \to \mathfrak{K}$ is a linear mapping,
   (3) $(Ux \,|\, Uy) = (x \,|\, y)$ for all $x, y \in \mathcal{O}$,
   (4) $U(\mathcal{O})$ is dense in $\mathfrak{K}$.
Then:
   (i) According to *Theorem 1*, every pre-Hilbert space has a completion.

   (ii) Discuss the analogs of parts (ii) and (iii) of *Exercise 5*.

   (iii) Regarding $\mathcal{O}$ as a normed space, any completion for $\mathcal{O}$, in the sense of *Exercise 5*, leads to a completion of the pre-Hilbert space $\mathcal{O}$.

*7. Let $\mathfrak{X}$ be a metric space. A *completion* for $\mathfrak{X}$ is a pair $(\mathcal{Y}, U)$, where
   (1) $\mathcal{Y}$ is a complete metric space,
   (2) $U: \mathfrak{X} \to \mathcal{Y}$,
   (3) $d(Ux, Uy) = d(x, y)$ for all $x, y \in \mathfrak{X}$ (i.e. U is isometric),
   (4) $U(\mathfrak{X})$ is dense in $\mathcal{Y}$.
It can be shown that every metric space $\mathfrak{X}$ has a completion $(\mathcal{Y}, U)$.

8. Let $\mathcal{O} = \mathfrak{M} \oplus \mathfrak{N}$ in the sense of *Definition III.2.5.* Viewing $\mathcal{O}$ as a linear subspace of its completion $\mathcal{K}$, one has $\mathcal{K} = \overline{\mathfrak{M}} \oplus \overline{\mathfrak{N}}$.

§3. BILINEAR MAPPINGS

If $\mathfrak{X}$ and $\mathfrak{Y}$ are non-empty sets, the *Cartesian product* of $\mathfrak{X}$ and $\mathfrak{Y}$ is the set of all symbols (x,y), called *ordered pairs*, where $x \in \mathfrak{X}$ and $y \in \mathfrak{Y}$. If (x_1,y_1) and (x_2,y_2) are ordered pairs, the relation $(x_1,y_1) = (x_2,y_2)$ means that both $x_1 = x_2$ and $y_1 = y_2$. The Cartesian product of $\mathfrak{X}$ and $\mathfrak{Y}$ is denoted $\mathfrak{X} \times \mathfrak{Y}$. If $u = (x,y) \in \mathfrak{X} \times \mathfrak{Y}$, x is the *first coordinate* of u, y is the *second coordinate* of u. Observe that $\mathfrak{Y} \times \mathfrak{X}$ is conceptually distinct from $\mathfrak{X} \times \mathfrak{Y}$.

Examples

1. If $\mathfrak{R}$ is the set of all real numbers, $\mathfrak{R} \times \mathfrak{R}$ is the "Cartesian plane." Any mapping $T: \mathfrak{R} \times \mathfrak{R} \to \mathfrak{R}$ is called a "real-valued function of two independent real variables"; for example, $T(x,y) = x^2 - y^2$.

2. If $\mathcal{O}$ is any pre-Hilbert space, the scalar product in $\mathcal{O}$ can be thought of as a mapping $T: \mathcal{O} \times \mathcal{O} \to \mathcal{C}$, namely $T(x,y) = (x|y)$.

Definition 1. *If* $\mathfrak{U},\mathfrak{V},\mathfrak{W}$ *are vector spaces, a mapping* $\varphi: \mathfrak{U} \times \mathfrak{V} \to \mathfrak{W}$ *is said to be* **bilinear** *in case the relations*

$$\varphi(x_1 + x_2,y) = \varphi(x_1,y) + \varphi(x_2,y)$$
$$\varphi(\lambda x,y) = \lambda\varphi(x,y)$$
$$\varphi(x,y_1 + y_2) = \varphi(x,y_1) + \varphi(x,y_2)$$
$$\varphi(x,\lambda y) = \lambda\varphi(x,y)$$

hold identically. If moreover $\mathfrak{W} = \mathcal{C}$, φ *is called a* **bilinear form** *on* $\mathfrak{U} \times \mathfrak{V}$.

Thus, φ is a bilinear mapping of $\mathfrak{U} \times \mathfrak{V}$ into $\mathfrak{W}$, if and only if: (1) for each fixed $y \in \mathfrak{V}$, $x \to \varphi(x,y)$ is a linear mapping of $\mathfrak{U}$ into $\mathfrak{W}$, and (2) for each fixed $x \in \mathfrak{U}$, $y \to \varphi(x,y)$ is a linear mapping of $\mathfrak{V}$ into $\mathfrak{W}$. Briefly, φ is linear in each coordinate. Clearly $\varphi(x,\theta) = \varphi(\theta,y) = \theta$.

Examples

3. Let $\mathfrak{U}$ be the vector space of n-ples $x = (\lambda_1, \cdots, \lambda_n), y = (\mu_1, \cdots, \mu_n)$, $\cdots$, and define $\varphi(x,y) = \sum_1^n \lambda_k\mu_k$. Then, φ is a bilinear form on $\mathfrak{U} \times \mathfrak{U}$.

4. Let $\mathcal{U}$ and $\mathcal{W}$ be vector spaces, $T: \mathcal{U} \to \mathcal{W}$ a linear mapping. Let $\mathcal{V} = \mathcal{L}(\mathcal{W}, \mathbb{C})$ be the vector space of all linear forms on $\mathcal{W}$, and define $\varphi: \mathcal{U} \times \mathcal{V} \to \mathbb{C}$ by the formula $\varphi(x,f) = f(Tx)$. Then, φ is a bilinear form on $\mathcal{U} \times \mathcal{V}$.

5. Let $\mathcal{U}, \mathcal{V}, \mathcal{W}$ be vector spaces, f a linear form on $\mathcal{U}$, and $T: \mathcal{V} \to \mathcal{W}$ a linear mapping. Define $\varphi: \mathcal{U} \times \mathcal{V} \to \mathcal{W}$ by the formula $\varphi(x,y) = f(x)(Ty)$. Then, φ is a bilinear mapping of $\mathcal{U} \times \mathcal{V}$ into $\mathcal{W}$.

6. If $\mathcal{C}$ is an algebra, the mapping $\varphi: \mathcal{C} \times \mathcal{C} \to \mathcal{C}$ defined by $\varphi(a,b) = ab$ is bilinear. In particular, if $\mathcal{V}$ is any vector space, the mapping $(S,T) \to ST$ of $\mathcal{L}(\mathcal{V}) \times \mathcal{L}(\mathcal{V})$ into $\mathcal{L}(\mathcal{V})$ is bilinear (see *Theorem IV.5.1*).

Exercises

1. If $\mathcal{X}$ and $\mathcal{Y}$ are non-empty sets, there exists a natural bijective mapping $T: \mathcal{X} \times \mathcal{Y} \to \mathcal{Y} \times \mathcal{X}$.

2. If $\mathcal{X}, \mathcal{Y}, \mathcal{Z}$ are non-empty sets, there exists a natural bijective mapping $T: \mathcal{X} \times (\mathcal{Y} \times \mathcal{Z}) \to (\mathcal{X} \times \mathcal{Y}) \times \mathcal{Z}$.

3. Any mapping $T: \mathcal{X} \to \mathcal{Y}$ determines a subset of $\mathcal{X} \times \mathcal{Y}$, namely the set of ordered pairs $\mathcal{G}_T = \{(x,Tx) : x \in \mathcal{X}\}$, called the *graph* of T. Prove:
   (i) If $S: \mathcal{X} \to \mathcal{Y}$ and $T: \mathcal{X} \to \mathcal{Y}$, then $S = T$ if and only if $\mathcal{G}_S = \mathcal{G}_T$.
   (ii) Given $\mathcal{G} \subset \mathcal{X} \times \mathcal{Y}$. There exists a mapping $T: \mathcal{X} \to \mathcal{Y}$ whose graph is $\mathcal{G}$, if and only if: (1) $\mathcal{G} \neq \varnothing$, and (2) given $(x,y_1) \in \mathcal{G}$ and $(x,y_2) \in \mathcal{G}$, necessarily $y_1 = y_2$.

4. If $\mathcal{U}, \mathcal{V}, \mathcal{W}$ are vector spaces, denote by $\mathcal{B}(\mathcal{U}, \mathcal{V}; \mathcal{W})$ the set of all bilinear mappings $\varphi: \mathcal{U} \times \mathcal{V} \to \mathcal{W}$. For two such mappings φ, ψ, write $\varphi = \psi$ in case $\varphi(x,y) = \psi(x,y)$ for all $x \in \mathcal{U}$ and $y \in \mathcal{V}$. Then, $\mathcal{B}(\mathcal{U}, \mathcal{V}; \mathcal{W})$ is a vector space, relative to the operations

$$(\varphi + \psi)(x,y) = \varphi(x,y) + \psi(x,y)$$

$$(\lambda\varphi)(x,y) = \lambda\varphi(x,y).$$

5. Notation as in *Exercise 4*. Suppose $\varphi \in \mathcal{B}(\mathcal{U}, \mathcal{V}; \mathcal{W})$. Each $x \in \mathcal{U}$ determines a linear mapping $\varphi_x: \mathcal{V} \to \mathcal{W}$, defined by $\varphi_x(y) = \varphi(x,y)$. Each $y \in \mathcal{V}$ determines a linear mapping $\varphi^y: \mathcal{U} \to \mathcal{W}$, defined by $\varphi^y(x) = \varphi(x,y)$. Prove:
   (i) For each fixed $\varphi \in \mathcal{B}(\mathcal{U}, \mathcal{V}; \mathcal{W})$, $x \to \varphi_x$ is a linear mapping of $\mathcal{U}$ into $\mathcal{L}(\mathcal{V}, \mathcal{W})$.

(ii) For each fixed $\varphi \in \mathcal{B}(\mathcal{U},\mathcal{V};\mathcal{W})$, $y \rightarrow \varphi^y$ is a linear mapping of $\mathcal{V}$ into $\mathcal{L}(\mathcal{U},\mathcal{W})$.

(iii) For each fixed $x \in \mathcal{U}$, $\varphi \rightarrow \varphi_x$ is a linear mapping of $\mathcal{B}(\mathcal{U},\mathcal{V};\mathcal{W})$ into $\mathcal{L}(\mathcal{V},\mathcal{W})$.

(iv) For each fixed $y \in \mathcal{V}$, $\varphi \rightarrow \varphi^y$ is a linear mapping of $\mathcal{B}(\mathcal{U},\mathcal{V};\mathcal{W})$ into $\mathcal{L}(\mathcal{U},\mathcal{W})$.

(v) For each fixed pair $(x,y) \in \mathcal{U} \times \mathcal{V}$, $\varphi \rightarrow \varphi(x,y)$ is a linear mapping of $\mathcal{B}(\mathcal{U},\mathcal{V};\mathcal{W})$ into $\mathcal{W}$.

6. Notation as in *Exercise 5*. Suppose $\varphi \in \mathcal{B}(\mathcal{U},\mathcal{V};\mathcal{W})$. The mapping $x \rightarrow \varphi_x$ is a linear mapping of $\mathcal{U}$ into $\mathcal{L}(\mathcal{V},\mathcal{W})$; denote it by $\hat{\varphi}$, that is, $\hat{\varphi}(x) = \varphi_x$. Thus, $\hat{\varphi} \in \mathcal{L}[\mathcal{U},\mathcal{L}(\mathcal{V},\mathcal{W})]$. Prove: $\varphi \rightarrow \hat{\varphi}$ is a vector space isomorphism of $\mathcal{B}(\mathcal{U},\mathcal{V};\mathcal{W})$ with $\mathcal{L}[\mathcal{U},\mathcal{L}(\mathcal{V},\mathcal{W})]$.

7. Notation as in *Exercise 5*. Using the techniques of *Exercise 6*, obtain a vector space isomorphism $\varphi \rightarrow \tilde{\varphi}$ of $\mathcal{B}(\mathcal{U},\mathcal{V};\mathcal{W})$ with $\mathcal{L}[\mathcal{V},\mathcal{L}(\mathcal{U},\mathcal{W})]$.

8. Let $\mathcal{U},\mathcal{W}$ be vector spaces, $\mathcal{V} = \mathcal{L}(\mathcal{U},\mathcal{C})$ the vector space of linear forms f on $\mathcal{U}$. Prove:

(i) For each fixed $z \in \mathcal{W}$, $(x,f) \rightarrow f(x)z$ is a bilinear mapping of $\mathcal{U} \times \mathcal{V}$ into $\mathcal{W}$.

(ii) For each fixed $f \in \mathcal{V}$, $(x,z) \rightarrow f(x)z$ is a bilinear mapping of $\mathcal{U} \times \mathcal{W}$ into $\mathcal{W}$.

(iii) For each fixed $x \in \mathcal{U}$, $(f,z) \rightarrow f(x)z$ is a bilinear mapping of $\mathcal{V} \times \mathcal{W}$ into $\mathcal{W}$.

9. Given a fixed bilinear mapping φ of $\mathcal{U} \times \mathcal{V}$ into $\mathcal{W}$. For subsets $\mathcal{S} \subset \mathcal{U}$ and $\mathcal{J} \subset \mathcal{V}$, define

$$\mathcal{S}^\perp = \{y \in \mathcal{V}: \varphi(x,y) = \theta \text{ for all } x \in \mathcal{S}\}$$
$$^\perp\mathcal{J} = \{x \in \mathcal{U}: \varphi(x,y) = \theta \text{ for all } y \in \mathcal{J}\}.$$

Prove:

(i) $\mathcal{S}^\perp$ and $^\perp\mathcal{J}$ are linear subspaces of $\mathcal{V}$ and $\mathcal{U}$, respectively.

(ii) $\mathcal{S} \subset {}^\perp(\mathcal{S}^\perp)$, and $\mathcal{J} \subset (^\perp\mathcal{J})^\perp$.

(iii) If $\mathcal{S}_1 \subset \mathcal{S}_2$, then $\mathcal{S}_1{}^\perp \supset \mathcal{S}_2{}^\perp$; if $\mathcal{J}_1 \subset \mathcal{J}_2$, then $^\perp\mathcal{J}_1 \supset {}^\perp\mathcal{J}_2$.

(iv) $(^\perp(\mathcal{S}^\perp))^\perp = \mathcal{S}^\perp$, and $^\perp((^\perp\mathcal{J})^\perp) = {}^\perp\mathcal{J}$.

10. Let $\mathcal{V}$ and $\mathcal{W}$ be vector spaces. Prove:

(i) $\mathcal{V} \times \mathcal{W}$ becomes a vector space, on defining $(x_1,y_1) + (x_2,y_2) = (x_1 + x_2, y_1 + y_2)$ and $\lambda(x,y) = (\lambda x, \lambda y)$, with zero element (θ,θ), and $-(x,y) = (-x, -y)$. $\mathcal{V} \times \mathcal{W}$ is called the *vector space direct product* of $\mathcal{V}$ and $\mathcal{W}$.

(ii) A mapping $T: \mathcal{V} \to \mathcal{W}$ is linear if and only if its graph $\mathcal{G}_T$ is a linear subspace of $\mathcal{V} \times \mathcal{W}$ (see *Exercise 3*).

(iii) $x \to (x,\theta)$ is an injective linear mapping of $\mathcal{V}$ into $\mathcal{V} \times \mathcal{W}$; denote its range by $\mathcal{V}_o$. Similarly $y \to (\theta,y)$ is an injective linear mapping of $\mathcal{W}$ into $\mathcal{V} \times \mathcal{W}$; denote its range by $\mathcal{W}_o$. Then: $\mathcal{V}_o$ and $\mathcal{W}_o$ are linear subspaces of $\mathcal{V} \times \mathcal{W}$, and every vector in $\mathcal{V} \times \mathcal{W}$ has a unique representation in the form $v_o + w_o$, with $v_o \in \mathcal{V}_o$ and $w_o \in \mathcal{W}_o$.

(iv) Suppose $\mathfrak{M}$ and $\mathfrak{N}$ are linear subspaces of a vector space $\mathcal{U}$, such that (1) $\mathfrak{M} + \mathfrak{N} = \mathcal{U}$, and (2) the only vector common to $\mathfrak{M}$ and $\mathfrak{N}$ is θ. Then, there is a natural vector space isomorphism of $\mathcal{U}$ with the direct product vector space $\mathfrak{M} \times \mathfrak{N}$.

11. Let $\mathcal{P},\mathcal{Q}$ be pre-Hilbert spaces, and let $\mathcal{P} \times \mathcal{Q}$ be their vector space direct product, as defined in *Exercise 10*. Prove:

(i) $\mathcal{P} \times \mathcal{Q}$ becomes a pre-Hilbert space, on defining $((x_1,y_1) \mid (x_2,y_2)) = (x_1 \mid x_2) + (y_1 \mid y_2)$. $\mathcal{P} \times \mathcal{Q}$ is called the *pre-Hilbert space direct product* of $\mathcal{P}$ and $\mathcal{Q}$.

(ii) One has $\| (x,y) \|^2 = \| x \|^2 + \| y \|^2$.

(iii) Let $\mathcal{P}_o$ be the range of the isometric linear mapping $x \to (x,\theta)$ of $\mathcal{P}$ into $\mathcal{P} \times \mathcal{Q}$, and $\mathcal{Q}_o$ the range of $y \to (\theta,y)$. Then $\mathcal{P}_o = \mathcal{Q}_o{}^\perp$, $\mathcal{Q}_o = \mathcal{P}_o{}^\perp$, and $\mathcal{P} \times \mathcal{Q} = \mathcal{P}_o \oplus \mathcal{Q}_o$ in the sense of *Definition III.2.5*.

(iv) One has $(x_n,y_n) \to (x,y)$ if and only if both $x_n \to x$ and $y_n \to y$.

(v) $\mathcal{P} \times \mathcal{Q}$ is a Hilbert space if and only if both $\mathcal{P}$ and $\mathcal{Q}$ are Hilbert spaces.

12. Let $\mathcal{X}$ and $\mathcal{Y}$ be metric spaces. Prove:

(i) $\mathcal{X} \times \mathcal{Y}$ becomes a metric space, on defining $d((x_1,y_1),(x_2,y_2)) = d(x_1,x_2) + d(y_1,y_2)$. $\mathcal{X} \times \mathcal{Y}$ is called *a* metric space *direct product* of $\mathcal{X}$ and $\mathcal{Y}$ (there are other natural ways of defining distances in $\mathcal{X} \times \mathcal{Y}$).

(ii) One has $(x_n,y_n) \to (x,y)$ if and only if both $x_n \to x$ and $y_n \to y$.

(iii) If $T: \mathcal{X} \to \mathcal{Y}$ is a continuous mapping, its graph $\mathcal{G}_T$ is a closed subset of $\mathcal{X} \times \mathcal{Y}$.

(iv) For each fixed $y_o \in \mathcal{Y}$, $x \to (x,y_o)$ is an isometric mapping of $\mathcal{X}$ onto a closed subset $\mathcal{X}_o$ of $\mathcal{X} \times \mathcal{Y}$. Similarly for the mapping $y \to (x_o,y)$, where $x_o \in \mathcal{X}$ is fixed.

(v) $\mathcal{X} \times \mathcal{Y}$ is complete if and only if both $\mathcal{X}$ and $\mathcal{Y}$ are complete.

(vi) Given completions for $\mathcal{X}$ and $\mathcal{Y}$, in the sense of *Exercise 2.7*, there is a natural way of obtaining a completion for $\mathcal{X} \times \mathcal{Y}$.

13. Let $\mathcal{E}$ and $\mathcal{F}$ be normed spaces, and let $\mathcal{E} \times \mathcal{F}$ be their vector space direct product, as defined in *Exercise 10*. Prove:

(i) $\mathcal{E} \times \mathcal{F}$ becomes a normed space, on defining $\| (x,y) \| = \| x \| + \| y \|$.

(ii) $x \rightarrow (x,\theta)$ and $y \rightarrow (\theta,y)$ are isometric linear mappings.

(iii) If distances in $\mathcal{E}, \mathcal{F}$, and $\mathcal{E} \times \mathcal{F}$ are defined as in § 7 of Chapter IV, $\mathcal{E} \times \mathcal{F}$ is the metric space direct product of $\mathcal{E}$ and $\mathcal{F}$, in the sense of *Exercise 12*.

(iv) If $T: \mathcal{E} \rightarrow \mathcal{F}$ is a continuous linear mapping, its graph $\mathcal{G}_T$ is a closed linear subspace of $\mathcal{E} \times \mathcal{F}$.

(v) $\mathcal{E} \times \mathcal{F}$ is a Banach space if and only if both $\mathcal{E}$ and $\mathcal{F}$ are Banach spaces.

(vi) If $\mathcal{E}$ and $\mathcal{F}$ happen to be pre-Hilbert spaces, $(x_n, y_n) \rightarrow (x,y)$ in the above sense if and only if $(x_n, y_n) \rightarrow (x,y)$ in the sense of *Exercise 11*.

14. If $\mathcal{X}$ and $\mathcal{Y}$ are metric spaces, $T: \mathcal{X} \rightarrow \mathcal{Y}$ is a bijective mapping, $S = T^{-1}$, and $\mathcal{G}_T$ is a closed subset of $\mathcal{X} \times \mathcal{Y}$ (see *Exercise 12*), then $\mathcal{G}_S$ is also closed.

15. (i) If $\mathcal{E}$ is a Banach space, $\mathcal{F}$ is a normed space, and $T: \mathcal{E} \rightarrow \mathcal{F}$ is a continuous linear mapping, then the normed space $\mathcal{G}_T$ (see *Exercise 13*) is a Banach space.

*(ii) If $\mathcal{E}$ and $\mathcal{F}$ are Banach spaces, and $T: \mathcal{E} \rightarrow \mathcal{F}$ is a continuous vector space isomorphism, it can be shown that T^{-1} is also continuous.

*(iii) If $\mathcal{E}$ and $\mathcal{F}$ are Banach spaces, and $T: \mathcal{E} \rightarrow \mathcal{F}$ is a linear mapping such that $\mathcal{G}_T$ is closed, it can be shown that T is continuous.

§ 4. BOUNDED BILINEAR MAPPINGS

Definition 1. *If $\mathcal{E}, \mathcal{F}, \mathcal{G}$ are normed spaces, a bilinear mapping $\varphi: \mathcal{E} \times \mathcal{F} \rightarrow \mathcal{G}$ is said to be* **bounded** *in case there exists a constant M such that $\| \varphi(x,y) \| \leq M \| x \| \| y \|$ for all $x \in \mathcal{E}$ and $y \in \mathcal{F}$. If moreover $\mathcal{G} = \mathcal{C}$, φ is called a* **bounded bilinear form** *on $\mathcal{E} \times \mathcal{F}$.*

Examples

1. Let $\mathcal{E}$ and $\mathcal{G}$ be normed spaces, $T: \mathcal{E} \rightarrow \mathcal{G}$ a continuous linear mapping, and $\mathcal{F} = \mathcal{G}'$ the dual space of $\mathcal{G}$. Define $\varphi: \mathcal{E} \times \mathcal{F} \rightarrow \mathcal{C}$ by the formula $\varphi(x,f) = f(Tx)$. Then, φ is a bilinear form on $\mathcal{E} \times \mathcal{F}$ (see also *Example 3.4*), and $| \varphi(x,f) | = |f(Tx)| \leq \| f \| \| Tx \| \leq \| T \| (\| x \| \| f \|)$ shows that φ is bounded.

2. If $\mathcal{A}$ is any normed algebra, then the bilinear mapping $\varphi: \mathcal{A} \times \mathcal{A} \to \mathcal{A}$ defined by $\varphi(a,b) = ab$ is bounded: $\| \varphi(a,b) \| \leq \| a \| \| b \|$. In particular, if $\mathcal{E}$ is a normed space, $(S,T) \to ST$ defines a bounded bilinear mapping of $\mathcal{L}_c(\mathcal{E}) \times \mathcal{L}_c(\mathcal{E})$ into $\mathcal{L}_c(\mathcal{E})$ (see *Theorem IV.9.1*). ∎

Using arguments similar to those in *Theorems IV.7.3* and *IV.7.4*, the condition for boundedness of a bilinear mapping can be reformulated as follows:

Theorem 1. *If $\mathcal{E}, \mathcal{F}, \mathcal{G}$ are normed spaces, and $\varphi: \mathcal{E} \times \mathcal{F} \to \mathcal{G}$ is a bilinear mapping, the following conditions on φ are equivalent:*

(a)   *φ is bounded.*

(b)   *$M_1 = \text{LUB} \{ \| \varphi(x,y) \| : \| x \| \leq 1, \| y \| \leq 1 \}$ is finite.*

(c)   *$M_2 = \text{LUB} \{ \| \varphi(x,y) \| : \| x \| < 1, \| y \| < 1 \}$ is finite.*

(d)   *$M_3 = \text{LUB} \{ \| \varphi(x,y) \| : \| x \| = 1, \| y \| = 1 \}$ is finite.*

If φ is bounded, $M_1 = M_2 = M_3$; denoting the common value by $\| \varphi \|$, one has

(1)   *$\| \varphi(x,y) \| \leq \| \varphi \| \| x \| \| y \|$ for all $x \in \mathcal{E}, y \in \mathcal{F}$.*

Moreover, $\| \varphi \|$ is minimal in this property:

(2) *If $M \geq 0$ and $\| \varphi(x,y) \| \leq M \| x \| \| y \|$ for all $x \in \mathcal{E}$ and $y \in \mathcal{F}$, necessarily $\| \varphi \| \leq M$.*

Definition 2. *Notation as in Theorem 1. The number $\| \varphi \|$ is called the* **norm** *of the bounded bilinear mapping $\varphi: \mathcal{E} \times \mathcal{F} \to \mathcal{G}$. Thus,*

$$\| \varphi \| = \text{LUB} \{ \| \varphi(x,y) \| : \| x \| \leq 1, \| y \| \leq 1 \}.$$

Clearly $\| \varphi \| = 0$ if and only if $\varphi(x,y) = \theta$ for all $x \in \mathcal{E}, y \in \mathcal{F}$; otherwise, $\| \varphi \| > 0$. In condition (d) of *Theorem 1*, one assumes $\mathcal{E} \neq \{\theta\}, \mathcal{F} \neq \{\theta\}$, so as to have a supply of unit vectors.

Exercises

1. If $\mathcal{E}, \mathcal{F}, \mathcal{G}$ are normed spaces, and $\varphi: \mathcal{E} \times \mathcal{F} \to \mathcal{G}$ is a bilinear mapping, the following conditions on φ are equivalent:
(a) φ is bounded.
(b) If $x_n \to x$ and $y_n \to y$, then $\varphi(x_n,y_n) \to \varphi(x,y)$.
(c) If $x_n \to \theta$ and $y_n \to \theta$, then $\varphi(x_n,y_n) \to \theta$.

2. There is a normed space analog for *Exercise 3.8*.

3. There is a normed space analog for *Exercise 3.9:* assuming φ bounded, $S^{\perp}$ and $^{\perp}\mathcal{J}$ are *closed* linear subspaces.

4. If $\mathcal{E},\mathcal{F},\mathcal{G}$ are normed spaces, denote by $\mathcal{B}_c(\mathcal{E},\mathcal{F};\mathcal{G})$ the set of all bounded bilinear mappings $\varphi\colon \mathcal{E}\times\mathcal{F}\to\mathcal{G}$. Then, $\mathcal{B}_c(\mathcal{E},\mathcal{F};\mathcal{G})$ is a linear subspace of $\mathcal{B}(\mathcal{E},\mathcal{F};\mathcal{G})$ (see *Exercise 3.4*), and becomes a normed space when $\|\varphi\|$ is defined as in *Definition 2*.

5. Let $\mathcal{E},\mathcal{F},\mathcal{G}$ be normed spaces, $\varphi\colon \mathcal{E}\times\mathcal{F}\to\mathcal{G}$ a bounded bilinear mapping. Show:

(i) For each fixed $x\in\mathcal{E}$, $y\to\varphi_x(y)=\varphi(x,y)$ is a continuous linear mapping of $\mathcal{F}$ into $\mathcal{G}$, and $\|\varphi_x\|\le\|\varphi\|\,\|x\|$. Thus, $\varphi_x\in\mathcal{L}_c(\mathcal{F},\mathcal{G})$.

(ii) For each fixed $y\in\mathcal{F}$, $x\to\varphi^y(x)=\varphi(x,y)$ is a continuous linear mapping of $\mathcal{E}$ into $\mathcal{G}$, and $\|\varphi^y\|\le\|\varphi\|\,\|y\|$. Thus, $\varphi^y\in\mathcal{L}_c(\mathcal{E},\mathcal{G})$.

(iii) The mapping $x\to\hat\varphi(x)=\varphi_x$ is a continuous linear mapping of $\mathcal{E}$ into $\mathcal{L}_c(\mathcal{F},\mathcal{G})$, and $\|\hat\varphi\|\le\|\varphi\|$. Thus, $\hat\varphi\in\mathcal{L}_c[\mathcal{E},\mathcal{L}_c(\mathcal{F},\mathcal{G})]$.

(iv) The mapping $y\to\tilde\varphi(y)=\varphi^y$ is a continuous linear mapping of $\mathcal{F}$ into $\mathcal{L}_c(\mathcal{E},\mathcal{G})$, and $\|\tilde\varphi\|\le\|\varphi\|$. Thus, $\tilde\varphi\in\mathcal{L}_c[\mathcal{F},\mathcal{L}_c(\mathcal{E},\mathcal{G})]$.

(v) In fact, $\|\hat\varphi\|=\|\varphi\|=\|\tilde\varphi\|$.

6. Notation as in *Exercise 5*. Prove:

(i) The mapping $\varphi\to\hat\varphi$ is an isometric vector space isomorphism of $\mathcal{B}_c(\mathcal{E},\mathcal{F};\mathcal{G})$ with $\mathcal{L}_c[\mathcal{E},\mathcal{L}_c(\mathcal{F},\mathcal{G})]$.

(ii) The mapping $\varphi\to\tilde\varphi$ is an isometric vector space isomorphism of $\mathcal{B}_c(\mathcal{E},\mathcal{F};\mathcal{G})$ with $\mathcal{L}_c[\mathcal{F},\mathcal{L}_c(\mathcal{E},\mathcal{G})]$.

7. Let $\mathcal{E}$ and $\mathcal{F}$ be normed spaces, $\mathcal{B}$ a Banach space. If $\mathcal{M}$ is a dense linear subspace of $\mathcal{E}$, $\mathcal{N}$ is a dense linear subspace of $\mathcal{F}$, and $\varphi\colon \mathcal{M}\times\mathcal{N}\to\mathcal{B}$ is a bounded bilinear mapping, there exists one and only one bounded bilinear mapping $\psi\colon \mathcal{E}\times\mathcal{F}\to\mathcal{B}$ such that $\psi(x,y)=\varphi(x,y)$ for all $x\in\mathcal{M}$ and $y\in\mathcal{N}$.

*8. Let $\mathcal{E},\mathcal{F},\mathcal{G}$ be normed spaces, and $\varphi\colon \mathcal{E}\times\mathcal{F}\to\mathcal{G}$ a bilinear mapping. Suppose that for each $x\in\mathcal{E}$, $y\to\varphi(x,y)$ is continuous, and that for each $y\in\mathcal{F}$, $x\to\varphi(x,y)$ is continuous. Assuming either $\mathcal{E}$ or $\mathcal{F}$ is a Banach space, it can be shown that φ is bounded.

*9. Let $\mathcal{E}$ and $\mathcal{G}$ be normed spaces, $\mathcal{F}=\mathcal{G}'$ the normed space dual of $\mathcal{G}$. Each $T\in\mathcal{L}_c(\mathcal{E},\mathcal{G})$ determines a bounded bilinear form $\varphi_T\colon \mathcal{E}\times\mathcal{F}\to\mathcal{C}$, namely $\varphi_T(x,f)=f(Tx)$ (see *Example 1*), and one has $\|\varphi_T\|\le\|T\|$.

(i) It can be shown that $\|\varphi_T\|=\|T\|$.

(ii) $T \to \varphi_T$ is an isometric linear mapping of $\mathcal{L}_c(\mathcal{E},\mathcal{G})$ into $\mathcal{B}_c(\mathcal{E},\mathcal{F}; \mathcal{C})$.

(iii) If moreover $\mathcal{G}$ is reflexive, the mapping $T \to \varphi_T$ is surjective, hence is an isometric vector space isomorphism.

10. The following is a specialization of *Exercise 9* which can be worked out using material in the text.

Let $\mathcal{K}$ be a Hilbert space. Each $T \in \mathcal{L}_c(\mathcal{K})$ determines a bounded bilinear form $\varphi_T \colon \mathcal{K} \times \mathcal{K}' \to \mathcal{C}$, namely $\varphi_T(x,f) = f(Tx)$. In view of *Theorem 1.1*, this means $\varphi_T(x,y') = y'(Tx) = (Tx \,|\, y)$ for all $x,y \in \mathcal{K}$. The relation $\| \varphi_T \| = \| T \|$ is elementary (see *Example IV.7.5*). Moreover, $\mathcal{K}$ is reflexive, that is, the mapping $x \to x''$ of $\mathcal{K}$ into $\mathcal{K}''$ is surjective (*Exercise 1.9*). It follows that $T \to \varphi_T$ is an isometric vector space isomorphism of $\mathcal{L}_c(\mathcal{K})$ with $\mathcal{B}_c(\mathcal{K},\mathcal{K}'; \mathcal{C})$.

11. If $\mathcal{E}$ is a normed space, and $\mathcal{K}$ is a Hilbert space, there exists an isometric vector space isomorphism $T \to \varphi_T$ of $\mathcal{L}_c(\mathcal{E},\mathcal{K})$ with $\mathcal{B}_c(\mathcal{E},\mathcal{K}'; \mathcal{C})$.

12. If $\mathcal{E}$ and $\mathcal{F}$ are normed spaces, and $\mathcal{G}$ is a Banach space, then $\mathcal{B}_c(\mathcal{E},\mathcal{F}; \mathcal{G})$ is a Banach space. In particular, $\mathcal{B}_c(\mathcal{E},\mathcal{F}; \mathcal{C})$ is a Banach space.

§ 5. SESQUILINEAR MAPPINGS

Definition 1. *If* $\mathcal{U},\mathcal{V},\mathcal{W}$ *are vector spaces, a mapping* $\varphi \colon \mathcal{U} \times \mathcal{V} \to \mathcal{W}$ *is said to be* **sesquilinear** *in case the relations*

$$\varphi(x_1 + x_2, y) = \varphi(x_1, y) + \varphi(x_2, y)$$

$$\varphi(\lambda x, y) = \lambda \varphi(x, y)$$

$$\varphi(x, y_1 + y_2) = \varphi(x, y_1) + \varphi(x, y_2)$$

$$\varphi(x, \lambda y) = \lambda^* \varphi(x, y)$$

hold identically. If moreover $\mathcal{W} = \mathcal{C}$, φ *is called a* **sesquilinear form** *on* $\mathcal{U} \times \mathcal{V}$.

Thus, φ is a sesquilinear mapping of $\mathcal{U} \times \mathcal{V}$ into $\mathcal{W}$, if and only if: (1) for each fixed $y \in \mathcal{V}$, $x \to \varphi(x,y)$ is a linear mapping of $\mathcal{U}$ into $\mathcal{W}$, and (2) for each fixed $x \in \mathcal{U}$, $y \to \varphi(x,y)$ is a semilinear mapping of $\mathcal{V}$ into $\mathcal{W}$ (see *Definition IV.1.3*). Briefly, φ is linear in the first coordinate, semilinear in the second coordinate. Clearly $\varphi(\theta,y) = \varphi(x,\theta) = \theta$.

Examples

1. If $\mathcal{P}$ is any pre-Hilbert space, the mapping φ: $\mathcal{P} \times \mathcal{P} \to \mathbb{C}$ defined by $\varphi(x,y) = (x\,|\,y)$ is a sesquilinear form on $\mathcal{P} \times \mathcal{P}$.

2. If $\mathcal{U}$ is a vector space, $\mathcal{P}$ is a pre-Hilbert space, and $T\colon \mathcal{U} \to \mathcal{P}$ is a linear mapping, then $\varphi(x,y) = (Tx\,|\,y)$ defines a sesquilinear form on $\mathcal{U} \times \mathcal{P}$.

3. If φ: $\mathcal{U} \times \mathcal{V} \to \mathbb{C}$ is a sesquilinear form, then the mapping ψ: $\mathcal{V} \times \mathcal{U} \to \mathbb{C}$ defined by $\psi(y,x) = [\varphi(x,y)]^*$ is sesquilinear. ∎

Obviously, one could paraphrase the results of the preceding two sections for sesquilinear mappings. However, there is a simple way of deducing the theory of sesquilinear mappings from the theory of bilinear mappings, via the concept of the *complex-conjugate* of a vector space:

Definition 2. *Let* $\mathcal{V}$ *be a vector space, with sums denoted* $x + y$, *and scalar multiples denoted* λx. *The* **complex-conjugate** *of* $\mathcal{V}$ *is the vector space* $\mathcal{V}^*$ *obtained as follows:*

(1)   *The set* $\mathcal{V}^*$ *is the same as the set* $\mathcal{V}$.

(2)   *If* $x,y \in \mathcal{V}^*$, *the* **sum** *of* x *and* y *is defined to be* $x + y$ (*as calculated in* $\mathcal{V}$).

(3)   *If* λ *is a scalar, and* $x \in \mathcal{V}^*$, *the* **multiple** *of* x *by* λ *is defined to be* $\lambda^* x$ (*as calculated in* $\mathcal{V}$); *this will be denoted* $\lambda o x$.

It is easy to check that $\mathcal{V}^*$ satisfies the axioms for a vector space listed in *Definition I.1.1*. For example: $(\lambda\mu)ox = (\lambda\mu)^*x = (\lambda^*\mu^*)x = \lambda^*(\mu^*x) = \lambda^*(\mu o x) = \lambda o(\mu o x)$. It is clear that $\mathcal{V}^*$ is the only vector space structure which can be defined on the set $\mathcal{V}$ in such a way that the identity mapping I: $\mathcal{V} \to \mathcal{V}^*$ is *conjugate*-linear.

Examples

4. If $\mathcal{P}$ is any pre-Hilbert space, the mapping $y \to y'$ of $\mathcal{P}$ into $(\mathcal{P}')^*$ is *linear*; for, $(y + z)' = y' + z'$, and $(\lambda y)' = \lambda^* y' = \lambda o y'$ (see *Theorem IV.10.2*).

5. If $\mathcal{V}$ and $\mathcal{W}$ are vector spaces, a mapping T: $\mathcal{V} \to \mathcal{W}$ is conjugate-linear if and only if T : $\mathcal{V}^* \to \mathcal{W}$ is linear (if and only if T: $\mathcal{V} \to \mathcal{W}^*$ is linear).

6. If $\mathcal{E}$ is a normed space, then $\mathcal{E}^*$ is also a normed space with $\| x \|$ defined the same as in $\mathcal{E}$. The point is that $\| \lambda o x \| = \| \lambda^* x \| = |\lambda^*| \cdot \| x \| = |\lambda| \cdot \| x \|$. The identity mapping $I: \mathcal{E} \to \mathcal{E}^*$ is then isometric and conjugate-linear; $\mathcal{E}$ is a Banach space if and only if $\mathcal{E}^*$ is a Banach space.

7. Combining *Examples 4* and *6*, $y \to y'$ is an isometric linear mapping of $\mathcal{P}$ into the normed space $(\mathcal{P}')^*$.

8. If $\mathcal{P}$ is a pre-Hilbert space with scalar products denoted $(x|y)$, the vector space $\mathcal{P}^*$ becomes a pre-Hilbert space on defining scalar products $[x|y]$ by the formula $[x|y] = (x|y)^* = (y|x)$. For instance, $[\lambda o x|y] = [\lambda^* x|y] = (y|\lambda^* x) = \lambda(y|x) = \lambda[x|y]$. Thus, $\mathcal{P}^*$ acquires a norm from its scalar product, as well as the norm inherited from $\mathcal{P}$ via *Example 6;* these norms coincide: $[x|x]^{\frac{1}{2}} = (x|x)^{\frac{1}{2}}$. $\mathcal{P}$ is a Hilbert space if and only if $\mathcal{P}^*$ is a Hilbert space. $\blacksquare$

The reason for introducing the space $\mathcal{V}^*$ is the following theorem, whose proof is immediate from *Example 5:*

Theorem 1. *Let* $\mathcal{U}, \mathcal{V}, \mathcal{W}$ *be vector spaces, and* $\varphi: \mathcal{U} \times \mathcal{V} \to \mathcal{W}$. *Then,* φ *is a sesquilinear mapping of* $\mathcal{U} \times \mathcal{V}$ *into* $\mathcal{W}$ *if and only if it is a bilinear mapping of* $\mathcal{U} \times \mathcal{V}^*$ *into* $\mathcal{W}$.

The "polarization identity" (see *Theorem II.3.3*) has a generalization for sesquilinear mappings:

Theorem 2. *If* $\mathcal{V}$ *and* $\mathcal{W}$ *are vector spaces, and* $\varphi: \mathcal{V} \times \mathcal{V} \to \mathcal{W}$ *is sesquilinear, then*

$$\varphi(x,y) = \tfrac{1}{4}\{\varphi(x + y, x + y) - \varphi(x - y, x - y)$$
$$+ i\varphi(x + iy, x + iy) - i\varphi(x - iy, x - iy)\}$$

for all $x, y \in \mathcal{V}$.

Proof.
One has $\varphi(x + y, x + y) = \varphi(x,x) + \varphi(y,y) + \varphi(x,y) + \varphi(y,x)$. The proof proceeds as in *Theorem II.3.3*. $\blacksquare$

An immediate consequence of *Theorem 2* is the following:

Theorem 3. *If* $\varphi: \mathcal{V} \times \mathcal{V} \to \mathcal{W}$ *and* $\psi: \mathcal{V} \times \mathcal{V} \to \mathcal{W}$ *are sesquilinear mappings such that* $\varphi(x,x) = \psi(x,x)$ *for all* $x \in \mathcal{V}$, *then* $\varphi = \psi$, *that is,* $\varphi(x,y) = \psi(x,y)$ *for all* $x, y \in \mathcal{V}$.

Definition 3. *Let* $\mathcal{U}$ *be a vector space,* $\varphi\colon \mathcal{U} \times \mathcal{U} \to \mathcal{C}$ *a sesquilinear form.* φ *is said to be* **Hermitian** *in case* $\varphi(y,x) = [\varphi(x,y)]^*$ *for all* $x,y \in \mathcal{U}.$

Theorem 4. *A sesquilinear form* $\varphi\colon \mathcal{U} \times \mathcal{U} \to \mathcal{C}$ *is Hermitian if and only if* $\varphi(x,x)$ *is* **real,** *for all* $x \in \mathcal{U}.$

Proof.

If φ is Hermitian, $\varphi(x,x) = [\varphi(x,x)]^*$, hence $\varphi(x,x)$ is real.

Suppose, conversely, that $\varphi(x,x)$ is real for all x. Define $\psi(x,y) = [\varphi(y,x)]^*$; as noted in *Example 3,* ψ is a sesquilinear form on $\mathcal{U} \times \mathcal{U}$. By assumption, $\psi(x,x) = \varphi(x,x)$ for all x, hence $\psi = \varphi$ by *Theorem 3.* In other words, φ is Hermitian. ∎

Definition 4. *Let* $\mathcal{U}$ *be a vector space,* $\varphi\colon \mathcal{U} \times \mathcal{U} \to \mathcal{C}$ *a sesquilinear form.* φ *is said to be* **positive** *in case* $\varphi(x,x) \geq 0$ *for all* $x \in \mathcal{U}.$

In particular, a positive sesquilinear form is Hermitian, by *Theorem 4*. There is a "Cauchy-Schwarz inequality" for positive sesquilinear forms:

Theorem 5. *If* φ *is a positive sesquilinear form on* $\mathcal{U} \times \mathcal{U}$, *then* $|\varphi(x,y)|^2 \leq \varphi(x,x)\varphi(y,y)$ *for all* $x,y \in \mathcal{U}.$

Proof.

By analogy with scalar products, write $\| z \| = \sqrt{\varphi(z,z)}$, only for convenience in the present proof.

If $\varphi(x,x) > 0$ or $\varphi(y,y) > 0$, the proof proceeds as in *Theorem II.3.4.*

Suppose $\varphi(x,x) = \varphi(y,y) = 0$. For all scalar λ, one has $0 \leq \varphi(x + \lambda y, x + \lambda y) = \varphi(x,x) + \lambda^*\varphi(x,y) + \lambda\varphi(y,x) + |\lambda|^2\,\varphi(y,y) = \lambda^*\varphi(x,y) + \lambda\varphi(y,x)$. In particular, for $\lambda = -\varphi(x,y)$, $0 \leq -2|\varphi(x,y)|^2$. Thus, $\varphi(x,y) = 0$, and the desired inequality is obvious. ∎

Exercises

1. Let $\mathcal{P},\mathcal{Q}$ be pre-Hilbert spaces, and suppose the pre-Hilbert spaces $\mathcal{P}^*$ and $\mathcal{Q}^*$ are constructed as in *Example 8*. The following conditions are equivalent:

(a) $J\colon \mathcal{P} \to \mathcal{Q}$ is conjugate-linear, and $(Jx|Jy) = (y|x)$ for all $x,y \in \mathcal{P}.$

(b) $J\colon \mathcal{P} \to \mathcal{Q}^*$ is linear, and $[Jx|Jy] = (x|y)$ for all $x,y \in \mathcal{P}.$

(c) $J\colon \mathcal{P}^* \to \mathcal{Q}$ is linear, and $(Jx|Jy) = [x|y]$ for all $x,y \in \mathcal{P}^*.$

If $\mathcal{P} = \mathcal{Q}$, a surjective mapping J satisfying condition (a) is called a *conjugation* of the pre-Hilbert space $\mathcal{P}$. For example, $J(\lambda_k) = (\lambda_k{}^*)$ is a conjugation in the Hilbert space l^2.

2. Let $\mathcal{H}$ be a Hilbert space. Show:

(i) The mapping $U \colon \mathcal{H} \to (\mathcal{H}')^*$ defined by $Ux = x'$ is a vector space isomorphism.

(ii) The Banach space $\mathcal{H}'$ becomes a Hilbert space, on defining $(x'|y') = (y|x)$.

(iii) If $\mathcal{H}'$ is the Hilbert space described in (ii), $(\mathcal{H}')^*$ becomes a Hilbert space on setting $[x'|y'] = (y'|x')$. The mapping $J \colon \mathcal{H} \to \mathcal{H}'$, defined by $Jx = x'$, satisfies condition (a) of *Exercise 1*.

(iv) With the Hilbert space structure of $(\mathcal{H}')^*$ defined as in (iii), the mapping U of part (i) is a Hilbert space isomorphism.

3. If $\mathcal{V}$ is a vector space, the vector space $(\mathcal{V}^*)^*$ is entitled to be called *equal* to the vector space $\mathcal{V}$. Analogously for normed spaces and pre-Hilbert spaces (see *Examples 6* and *8*).

4. If $\varphi \colon \mathcal{V} \times \mathcal{V} \to \mathcal{W}$ is bilinear or sesquilinear, the "parallelogram law" holds:

$$\varphi(x + y, x + y) + \varphi(x - y, x - y) = 2\varphi(x,x) + 2\varphi(y,y).$$

5. If $\varphi \colon \mathcal{V} \times \mathcal{V} \to \mathcal{W}$ is bilinear, then

$$\varphi(x + y, x + y) - \varphi(x - y, x - y) +$$
$$i\varphi(x + iy, x + iy) - i\varphi(x - iy, x - iy) = \theta.$$

6. If $\mathcal{U}, \mathcal{V}, \mathcal{W}$ are vector spaces, the set $\mathcal{S}(\mathcal{U}, \mathcal{V}; \mathcal{W})$ of all sesquilinear mappings $\varphi \colon \mathcal{U} \times \mathcal{V} \to \mathcal{W}$ is a vector space relative to the operations

$$(\varphi + \psi)(x,y) = \varphi(x,y) + \psi(x,y)$$

$$(\lambda\varphi)(x,y) = \lambda\varphi(x,y).$$

The identity mapping $\varphi \to \varphi$ is a vector space isomorphism of $\mathcal{S}(\mathcal{U}, \mathcal{V}; \mathcal{W})$ with $\mathcal{B}(\mathcal{U}, \mathcal{V}^*; \mathcal{W})$. [See *Exercise 3.4*.]

7. Let $\mathcal{V}$ be the vector space of 2-ples $x = (\lambda_1, \lambda_2)$, $y = (\mu_1, \mu_2), \cdots$. Define $\varphi(x,y) = \lambda_1\mu_2$, $\psi(x,y) = \lambda_2\mu_1$. Then, φ and ψ are bilinear forms, $\varphi(x,x) = \psi(x,x)$ for all x, but $\varphi \neq \psi$.

8. Let $\mathcal{U}, \mathcal{V}$ be vector spaces. If $\varphi \colon \mathcal{U} \times \mathcal{V} \to \mathcal{C}$ is a sesquilinear form, define $\varphi^\# \colon \mathcal{V} \times \mathcal{U} \to \mathcal{C}$ by the formula $\varphi^\#(y,x) = [\varphi(x,y)]^*$.

Then:

(i) $\varphi^{\#}$ is a sesquilinear form on $\mathcal{V} \times \mathcal{U}$.

(ii) $\varphi \to \varphi^{\#}$ is a bijective conjugate-linear mapping of $\mathcal{S}(\mathcal{U},\mathcal{V}; \mathcal{C})$ onto $\mathcal{S}(\mathcal{V},\mathcal{U}; \mathcal{C})$.

(iii) If $\mathcal{V} = \mathcal{U}$, $\varphi^{\#} = \varphi$ if and only if φ is Hermitian.

9. Let $\mathcal{P}$ and $\mathcal{Q}$ be pre-Hilbert spaces, $J: \mathcal{P} \to \mathcal{Q}$ a mapping such that $(Jx|Jy) = (y|x)$ for all $x,y \in \mathcal{P}$. Prove:

(i) If $J(\mathcal{P})$ is a linear subspace of $\mathcal{Q}$, then J is conjugate-linear.

(ii) In particular, if $\mathcal{P} = \mathcal{Q}$ and J is surjective, then J is a conjugation of $\mathcal{P}$ in the sense of *Exercise 1*.

(iii) If $\mathcal{P} = \mathcal{3C}$ is a Hilbert space, and $J(\mathcal{3C})$ is a total subset of $\mathcal{Q}$, then J is surjective.

10. Let φ be a positive sesquilinear form on $\mathcal{V} \times \mathcal{V}$, and let $\mathfrak{N} = \{x \in \mathcal{V}: \varphi(x,x) = 0\}$. Then, $\mathfrak{N} = \{x \in \mathcal{V}: \varphi(x,y) = 0 \text{ for all } y \in \mathcal{V}\}$, hence $\mathfrak{N}$ is a linear subspace of $\mathcal{V}$.

11. If φ is a positive sesquilinear form, under what conditions on x and y does $|\varphi(x,y)|^2 = \varphi(x,x)\varphi(y,y)$ hold?

§6. BOUNDED SESQUILINEAR MAPPINGS

Definition 1. *If $\mathcal{E},\mathcal{F},\mathcal{G}$ are normed spaces, a sesquilinear mapping $\varphi: \mathcal{E} \times \mathcal{F} \to \mathcal{G}$ is said to be* **bounded** *in case there exists a constant M such that $\| \varphi(x,y) \| \leq M \| x \| \| y \|$ for all $x \in \mathcal{E}$, $y \in \mathcal{F}$. If moreover $\mathcal{G} = \mathcal{C}$, φ is called a* **bounded sesquilinear form.**

In other words, φ is a bounded sesquilinear mapping of $\mathcal{E} \times \mathcal{F}$ into $\mathcal{G}$, if and only if it is a bounded bilinear mapping of $\mathcal{E} \times \mathcal{F}^*$ into $\mathcal{G}$ (see *Definition 4.1, Example 5.6,* and *Theorem 5.1*). The number

$$\text{LUB } \{\| \varphi(x,y) \|: \| x \| \leq 1, \| y \| \leq 1\}$$

is denoted $\| \varphi \|$, and is called the *norm* of φ. By *Theorem 4.1,*

Theorem 1. *If $\varphi: \mathcal{E} \times \mathcal{F} \to \mathcal{G}$ is a bounded sesquilinear mapping,*

(1) $\| \varphi \| = \text{LUB } \{\| \varphi(x,y) \|: \| x \| < 1, \| y \| < 1\}$

        $= \text{LUB } \{\| \varphi(x,y) \|: \| x \| = 1, \| y \| = 1\}$;

(2) $\| \varphi(x,y) \| \leq \| \varphi \| \| x \| \| y \|$ *for all* $x \in \mathcal{E}$, $y \in \mathcal{F}$;

(3)   *if $M \geq 0$ and $\| \varphi(x,y) \| \leq M \| x \| \| y \|$ for all $x \in \mathcal{E}$ and $y \in \mathcal{F}$, necessarily $\| \varphi \| \leq M$.*

Examples

1. If $\mathcal{P}$ is a pre-Hilbert space, the sesquilinear form $\varphi: \mathcal{P} \times \mathcal{P} \to \mathcal{C}$ defined by $\varphi(x,y) = (x|y)$ is bounded, by the Cauchy-Schwarz inequality. Assuming $\mathcal{P} \neq \{\theta\}$, $\|\varphi\| = 1$.

2. If $\mathcal{E}$ is a normed space, $\mathcal{P}$ is a pre-Hilbert space, and $T: \mathcal{E} \to \mathcal{P}$ is a continuous linear mapping, then $\varphi(x,y) = (Tx|y)$ is a bounded sesquilinear form, with $\|\varphi\| = \|T\|$ (see *Example IV.7.5* or *Exercise IV.7.5*).

3. If $\mathcal{E}, \mathcal{F}$ are normed spaces, and $\varphi: \mathcal{E} \times \mathcal{F} \to \mathcal{C}$ is a bounded sesquilinear form, the sesquilinear form $\psi: \mathcal{F} \times \mathcal{E} \to \mathcal{C}$ defined by $\psi(y,x) = [\varphi(x,y)]^*$ is also bounded, and $\|\psi\| = \|\varphi\|$. ∎

The following result plays an important role in the exposition of spectral theory given in Chapter VIII:

Theorem 2. *If $\mathcal{P}$ is a pre-Hilbert space, the norm of a* **Hermitian** *bounded sesquilinear form $\varphi: \mathcal{P} \times \mathcal{P} \to \mathcal{C}$ is given by the formula*

$$\|\varphi\| = \text{LUB} \{|\varphi(x,x)| : \|x\| \leq 1\}.$$

Proof.

By assumption, $\varphi(x,x)$ is real, for all x (see *Theorem 5.4*).

If $\|x\| \leq 1$, $|\varphi(x,x)| \leq \|\varphi\|$ by the definition of $\|\varphi\|$; hence the indicated LUB is a finite real number M, and $M \leq \|\varphi\|$. Clearly $|\varphi(x,x)| \leq M \|x\| \|x\|$ for all $x \in \mathcal{P}$.

Fix $x,y \in \mathcal{P}$, with $\|x\| \leq 1$, $\|y\| \leq 1$. It will suffice to show that $|\varphi(x,y)| \leq M$.

Case 1. Suppose $\varphi(x,y)$ is a real number. By *Theorem 5.2*, $\varphi(x,y) = \frac{1}{4}\{\varphi(x + y, x + y) - \varphi(x - y, x - y) + i\varphi(x + iy, x + iy) - i\varphi(x - iy, x - iy)\}$. Since $\varphi(z,z)$ is real for all z, and since $\varphi(x,y)$ is by assumption real, necessarily $\varphi(x,y) = \frac{1}{4}\{\varphi(x + y, x + y) - \varphi(x - y, x - y)\}$. Quoting the parallelogram law at the appropriate step, $|\varphi(x,y)| \leq \frac{1}{4}\{|\varphi(x + y, x + y)| + |\varphi(x - y, x - y)|\} \leq \frac{1}{4}\{M \|x + y\|^2 + M \|x - y\|^2\} = \frac{M}{4}\{2 \|x\|^2 + 2 \|y\|^2\} \leq \frac{M}{4}\{2 + 2\} = M$.

Case 2. In general, one can write $|\varphi(x,y)| = \lambda\varphi(x,y)$, where λ is a suitable complex number of absolute value 1. Then, $\varphi(\lambda x, y) = \lambda\varphi(x,y) = |\varphi(x,y)|$ is real; since $\|\lambda x\| = |\lambda| \cdot \|x\| = \|x\| \leq 1$, $|\varphi(\lambda x, y)| \leq M$ by case 1, thus $|\varphi(x,y)| \leq M$. ∎

Exercises

1. If $\mathcal{E}, \mathcal{F}, \mathcal{G}$ are normed spaces, the set $\mathcal{S}_c(\mathcal{E}, \mathcal{F}; \mathcal{G})$ of all bounded sesquilinear mappings $\varphi: \mathcal{E} \times \mathcal{F} \to \mathcal{G}$ is a linear subspace of $\mathcal{S}(\mathcal{E}, \mathcal{F}; \mathcal{G})$, and becomes a normed space on defining $\| \varphi \|$ as above. The identity mapping $\varphi \to \varphi$ is an isometric vector space isomorphism of $\mathcal{S}_c(\mathcal{E}, \mathcal{F}; \mathcal{G})$ with $\mathcal{B}_c(\mathcal{E}, \mathcal{F}^*; \mathcal{G})$. (See *Exercises 5.6* and *4.4*)

2. Let $\mathcal{E}$ be a normed space, $\mathcal{P}$ a pre-Hilbert space. Each continuous linear mapping $T: \mathcal{E} \to \mathcal{P}$ determines a bounded sesquilinear form $\varphi_T: \mathcal{E} \times \mathcal{P} \to \mathcal{C}$, namely $\varphi_T(x,y) = (Tx \,|\, y)$, and one has $\| \varphi_T \| = \| T \|$ (see *Example 2*). Then, $T \to \varphi_T$ is an isometric linear mapping of $\mathcal{L}_c(\mathcal{E}, \mathcal{P})$ into $\mathcal{S}_c(\mathcal{E}, \mathcal{P}; \mathcal{C})$ (see *Exercise 1*).

3. If $\mathcal{P}$ is a pre-Hilbert space, $\mathcal{G}$ is a normed space, and $\varphi: \mathcal{P} \times \mathcal{P} \to \mathcal{G}$ is a bounded bilinear mapping such that $\varphi(y,x) = \varphi(x,y)$, then $\| \varphi \| = \mathrm{LUB}\, \{\| \varphi(x,x)\| : \| x \| \leq 1\}$.

4. Let $\mathcal{P}$ be a pre-Hilbert space, and define $\varphi(x,y) = i(x \,|\, y)$. Then, φ is a bounded sesquilinear form, $\| \varphi \| = \mathrm{LUB}\, \{\, | \varphi(x,x)| : \| x \| \leq 1\}$, but φ is not Hermitian.

5. Let $\mathcal{P}$ be a pre-Hilbert space, and suppose $U: \mathcal{P} \to \mathcal{P}$ is a continuous linear mapping such that $\| U \| = 1$ and $Uz = z$ for some $z \neq \theta$. Define $\varphi_U(x,y) = (Ux \,|\, y)$. Then, $\| \varphi_U \| = \| U \| = 1 = \mathrm{LUB}\, \{\, | \varphi_U(x,x)| : \| x \| \leq 1\}$, but φ_U need not be Hermitian.

§7. BOUNDED SESQUILINEAR FORMS IN HILBERT SPACE

As a special case of *Example 6.2*,

Theorem 1. *If $\mathcal{H}$ and $\mathcal{K}$ are Hilbert spaces, and $T: \mathcal{H} \to \mathcal{K}$ is a continuous linear mapping, the formula $\varphi_T(x,y) = (Tx \,|\, y)$ defines a bounded sesquilinear form φ_T on $\mathcal{H} \times \mathcal{K}$, such that $\| \varphi_T \| = \| T \|$.*

The point of stating *Theorem 1* is that its converse is true:

Theorem 2. *If $\mathcal{H}$ and $\mathcal{K}$ are Hilbert spaces, and $\varphi: \mathcal{H} \times \mathcal{K} \to \mathcal{C}$ is a bounded sesquilinear form, there exists one and only one continuous linear mapping $T: \mathcal{H} \to \mathcal{K}$ such that $\varphi(x,y) = (Tx \,|\, y)$ for all $x \in \mathcal{H}$, $y \in \mathcal{K}$. In the notation of Theorem 1, $\varphi = \varphi_T$, and $\| \varphi \| = \| \varphi_T \| = \| T \|$.*

Proof.

Given $x \in \mathcal{H}$, the problem is to define $Tx \in \mathcal{K}$. Now, $y \to [\varphi(x,y)]^*$ is a linear form f_x on $\mathcal{K}$, and $|f_x(y)| = |[\varphi(x,y)]^*| = |\varphi(x,y)| \leq \| \varphi \| \| x \| \| y \|$ shows that f_x is continuous, and $\| f_x \| \leq \| \varphi \| \| x \|$. By *Theorem 1.1*, there is a unique vector $z \in \mathcal{K}$ such that $f_x(y) = (y|z)$ for all $y \in \mathcal{K}$. Defining $Tx = z$, one has $(y|Tx) = f_x(y) = [\varphi(x,y)]^*$, thus $\varphi(x,y) = (Tx|y)$. Incidentally, $\| Tx \| = \| f_x \|$ by *Example IV.7.4*, thus $\| Tx \| \leq \| \varphi \| \| x \|$. It will now be shown that the mapping $T \colon \mathcal{H} \to \mathcal{K}$ is linear.

T is *additive:* given any $x_1, x_2 \in \mathcal{H}$, $T(x_1 + x_2) = Tx_1 + Tx_2$. For, given any $y \in \mathcal{K}$, $(T(x_1 + x_2)|y) = \varphi(x_1 + x_2, y) = \varphi(x_1, y) + \varphi(x_2, y) = (Tx_1|y) + (Tx_2|y) = (Tx_1 + Tx_2|y)$; see *Theorem II.2.1*.

T is *homogeneous:* If $x \in \mathcal{H}$, λ is scalar, and $y \in \mathcal{K}$, $(T(\lambda x)|y) = \varphi(\lambda x, y) = \lambda \varphi(x, y) = \lambda(Tx|y) = (\lambda(Tx)|y)$, hence $T(\lambda x) = \lambda(Tx)$.

T is *unique:* Suppose $S \colon \mathcal{H} \to \mathcal{K}$ is any mapping such that $(Sx|y) = \varphi(x,y)$ for all $x \in \mathcal{H}$, $y \in \mathcal{K}$. Then, $(Tx - Sx|y) = 0$ for all $x \in \mathcal{H}$, $y \in \mathcal{K}$; hence $Tx - Sx = \theta$ for all $x \in \mathcal{H}$, that is, $T = S$.

Since $\| Tx \| \leq \| \varphi \| \| x \|$, the linear mapping T is continuous. Since $\varphi = \varphi_T$, $\| \varphi \| = \| T \|$ by *Theorem 1*. ∎

Exercises

1. If $\mathcal{H}$ and $\mathcal{K}$ are Hilbert spaces, the correspondence $T \to \varphi_T$ described in *Theorem 1* is an isometric vector space isomorphism of $\mathcal{L}_c(\mathcal{H},\mathcal{K})$ with $\mathcal{S}_c(\mathcal{H},\mathcal{K}; \mathcal{C})$. [See *Exercise 6.2*.]

2. If $\mathcal{E}$ is a normed space, and $\mathcal{K}$ is a Hilbert space, generalize *Theorem 2* and *Exercise 1* for bounded sesquilinear forms $\varphi \colon \mathcal{E} \times \mathcal{K} \to \mathcal{C}$.

§ 8. ADJOINTS

Throughout this section, $\mathcal{H}, \mathcal{K}, \mathcal{L}$ denote Hilbert spaces.

Theorem 1. *If $T \colon \mathcal{H} \to \mathcal{K}$ is a continuous linear mapping, there exists one and only one continuous linear mapping $T^* \colon \mathcal{K} \to \mathcal{H}$ such that $(Tx|y) = (x|T^*y)$ for all $x \in \mathcal{H}$, $y \in \mathcal{K}$. One has $\| T^* \| = \| T \|$.*

Proof.

Define $\psi(y,x) = (y|Tx)$. Clearly ψ is a sesquilinear form on $\mathcal{K} \times \mathcal{H}$, and $|\psi(y,x)| = |(y|Tx)| = |(y|Tx)^*| = |(Tx|y)|$ shows that ψ is bounded and $\| \psi \| = \| T \|$ (see *Theorem 7.1*). By *Theorem 7.2*, there exists a continuous linear mapping $T^*: \mathcal{K} \to \mathcal{H}$, with $\| T^* \| = \| \psi \|$, such that $\psi(y,x) = (T^*y \,|\, x)$ for all $y \in \mathcal{K}$, $x \in \mathcal{H}$. Thus, $(y \,|\, Tx) = (T^*y \,|\, x)$, $(Tx \,|\, y) = (x \,|\, T^*y)$.

If $S: \mathcal{K} \to \mathcal{H}$ is any mapping such that $(Tx \,|\, y) = (x \,|\, Sy)$ for all $x \in \mathcal{H}$, $y \in \mathcal{K}$, then $(x \,|\, Sy - T^*y) = 0$ for all x and y, hence $Sy - T^*y = \theta$ for all y; that is, $S = T^*$. ▌

Definition 1. *Notation as in Theorem 1; T^* is called the* **adjoint** *of T.*

The rest of the section is devoted to proving properties of adjoints which will be used often in the sequel.

Theorem 2. *If $S: \mathcal{H} \to \mathcal{K}$ and $T: \mathcal{H} \to \mathcal{K}$ are continuous linear mappings, and λ is scalar,*

(1) $(S + T)^* = S^* + T^*$

(2) $(\lambda T)^* = \lambda^* T^*$

(3) $(T^*y \,|\, x) = (y \,|\, Tx)$ *for all* $y \in \mathcal{K}$, $x \in \mathcal{H}$

(4) $(T^*)^* = T$

(5) $\| T^*T \| = \| TT^* \| = \| T \|^2$

(6) $T^*T = 0$ *if and only if* $T = 0$.

Proof.

(3): $(T^*y \,|\, x) = (x \,|\, T^*y)^* = (Tx \,|\, y)^* = (y \,|\, Tx)$.

(1): $((S + T)^*y \,|\, x) = (y \,|\, (S + T)x) = (y \,|\, Sx + Tx) = (y \,|\, Sx) + (y \,|\, Tx) = (S^*y \,|\, x) + (T^*y \,|\, x) = (S^*y + T^*y \,|\, x) = ((S^* + T^*)y \,|\, x)$.

(2): $((\lambda T)^*y \,|\, x) = (y \,|\, (\lambda T)x) = (y \,|\, \lambda(Tx)) = \lambda^*(y \,|\, Tx) = \lambda^*(T^*y \,|\, x) = (\lambda^*(T^*y) \,|\, x) = ((\lambda^* T^*)y \,|\, x)$.

(4): $((T^*)^*x \,|\, y) = (x \,|\, T^*y) = (Tx \,|\, y)$.

(5): Observe that the composites $T^*T: \mathcal{H} \to \mathcal{H}$ and $TT^*: \mathcal{K} \to \mathcal{K}$ are defined. If $x \in \mathcal{H}$, $\| x \| \leq 1$, one has $\| Tx \|^2 = (Tx \,|\, Tx) = (T^*Tx \,|\, x) \leq \| T^*Tx \| \, \| x \| \leq \| T^*Tx \| \leq \| T^*T \|$; taking LUB over $\| x \| \leq 1$, $\| T \|^2 \leq \| T^*T \|$. By *Theorem IV.9.1*, $\| T^*T \| \leq \| T^* \| \, \| T \| = \| T \|^2$. Thus, $\| T^*T \|^2 = \| T \|^2$. Replacing T by T^*, $\| (T^*)^*T^* \| = \| T^* \|^2$, thus $\| TT^* \| = \| T \|^2$.

(6): follows at once from (5). ▌

Theorem 3. *If $T: \mathcal{K} \to \mathcal{K}$ and $S: \mathcal{K} \to \mathcal{L}$ are continuous linear mappings, then $(ST)^* = T^*S^*$.*

Proof.

If $z \in \mathcal{L}$ and $x \in \mathcal{K}$, $((ST)^*z \,|\, x) = (z \,|\, (ST)x) = (z \,|\, S(Tx)) = (S^*z \,|\, Tx) = (T^*(S^*z) \,|\, x) = ((T^*S^*)z \,|\, x)$. ∎

Theorem 4. *Let $T: \mathcal{K} \to \mathcal{K}$ be a continuous linear mapping. If $\mathcal{S} \subset \mathcal{K}$, $\mathcal{J} \subset \mathcal{K}$, and $T(\mathcal{S}) \subset \mathcal{J}$, then $T^*(\mathcal{J}^{\perp}) \subset \mathcal{S}^{\perp}$.*

Proof.

Given $z \in \mathcal{K}$ with $z \perp \mathcal{J}$, the problem is to show that $T^*z \perp \mathcal{S}$. If $x \in \mathcal{S}$, then $Tx \in \mathcal{J}$, hence $0 = (z \,|\, Tx) = (T^*z \,|\, x)$. ∎

In particular,

Theorem 5. *Suppose $T: \mathcal{K} \to \mathcal{K}$ is a continuous linear mapping, $\mathfrak{M}$ is a closed linear subspace of $\mathcal{K}$, and $\mathfrak{N}$ is a closed linear subspace of $\mathcal{K}$. Then, $T(\mathfrak{M}) \subset \mathfrak{N}$ if and only if $T^*(\mathfrak{N}^{\perp}) \subset \mathfrak{M}^{\perp}$.*

Proof.

If $T^*(\mathfrak{N}^{\perp}) \subset \mathfrak{M}^{\perp}$, then $(T^*)^*(\mathfrak{M}^{\perp\perp}) \subset \mathfrak{N}^{\perp\perp}$ by *Theorem 4*; quote *Theorem III.6.2* and part (4) of *Theorem 2*. ∎

Theorem 6. *If $T: \mathcal{K} \to \mathcal{K}$ is a continuous linear mapping,*

(1) $\{x: Tx = \theta\} = [T^*(\mathcal{K})]^{\perp}$

(2) $\{x: Tx = \theta\}^{\perp} = \overline{T^*(\mathcal{K})}$

(3) $\{y: T^*y = \theta\} = [T(\mathcal{K})]^{\perp}$

(4) $\{y: T^*y = \theta\}^{\perp} = \overline{T(\mathcal{K})}$.

Thus, the null space of T is the orthogonal complement of the closure of the range of T^*.

Proof.

Let $\mathfrak{M} = \{x: Tx = \theta\}$; $\mathfrak{M}$ is a closed linear subspace of $\mathcal{K}$. Similarly, $\mathfrak{N} = \{y: T^*y = \theta\}$ is a closed linear subspace of $\mathcal{K}$.

Since $T(\mathfrak{M}) \subset \{\theta\}$, one has $T^*(\{\theta\}^{\perp}) \subset \mathfrak{M}^{\perp}$ by *Theorem 4*; thus,

(i) $T^*(\mathcal{K}) \subset \mathfrak{M}^{\perp}$.

Let $\mathcal{S} = \mathcal{K}$, $\mathcal{J} = T(\mathcal{K})$; the relation $T(\mathcal{K}) \subset T(\mathcal{K})$ can be written $T(\mathcal{S}) \subset \mathcal{J}$, hence $T^*(\mathcal{J}^{\perp}) \subset \mathcal{S}^{\perp}$. Since $\mathcal{S}^{\perp} = \mathcal{K}^{\perp} = \{\theta\}$, one has $T^*(\mathcal{J}^{\perp}) = \{\theta\}$, $\mathcal{J}^{\perp} \subset \mathfrak{N}$, thus

(ii) $[T(\mathcal{K})]^{\perp} \subset \mathfrak{N}$.

Applying these results to T^* in place of T, one has

(i*) $T(\mathcal{K}) \subset \mathfrak{n}^\perp$

(ii*) $[T^*(\mathcal{K})]^\perp \subset \mathfrak{m}$.

From (i), $\mathfrak{m} \subset \mathfrak{m}^{\perp\perp} \subset [T^*(\mathcal{K})]^\perp$; combining this with (ii*),

(1) $\mathfrak{m} = [T^*(\mathcal{K})]^\perp$.

[Incidentally, $\mathfrak{m} = \mathfrak{m}^{\perp\perp}$ results formally from these calculations; see also *Theorem III.6.2*.]

From (1), $\mathfrak{m}^\perp = [T^*(\mathcal{K})]^{\perp\perp}$; quoting Corollary 1 of *Theorem III.6.3*,

(2) $\mathfrak{m}^\perp = \overline{T^*(\mathcal{K})}$.

The relations (3) and (4) result on replacing T by T^* in the relations (1) and (2). ∎

Exercises

1. Let $\mathcal{P}$ and $\mathcal{Q}$ be pre-Hilbert spaces, and suppose $T: \mathcal{P} \to \mathcal{Q}$ and $S: \mathcal{Q} \to \mathcal{P}$ are mappings such that $(Tx\,|\,y) = (x\,|\,Sy)$ for all $x \in \mathcal{P}$ and $y \in \mathcal{Q}$. Then, S and T are linear.

2. If $\mathcal{K}$ is a Hilbert space, $(S,T) \to ST^*$ is a bounded sesquilinear mapping of $\mathcal{L}_c(\mathcal{K}) \times \mathcal{L}_c(\mathcal{K})$ into $\mathcal{L}_c(\mathcal{K})$. So is $(S,T) \to T^*S$.

3. Let $\mathcal{K}$ be classical Hilbert space, $T: \mathcal{K} \to \mathcal{K}$ a continuous linear mapping. Given an orthonormal basis e_n for $\mathcal{K}$. Let $Te_k = \sum_j \alpha_{jk} e_j$ be the expansion of Te_k in terms of the given orthonormal basis (see *Theorem II.8.1*). The array (α_{jk}) is called the *matrix* of T relative to the given orthonormal basis (see also *Exercise IV.1.6*). Prove:

(i) $(Te_k\,|\,e_j) = \alpha_{jk}$

(ii) If T^* has matrix (β_{jk}) relative to the same orthonormal basis, then $\beta_{jk} = \alpha_{kj}^*$. So to speak, the matrix (β_{jk}) is the "conjugate transpose" of the matrix (α_{jk}).

4. Let $\mathcal{K}$ and $\mathcal{K}$ be Hilbert spaces, $T: \mathcal{K} \to \mathcal{K}$ a continuous linear mapping. Prove:

(i) $T'y' = (T^*y)'$ for all $y \in \mathcal{K}$ (see *Exercise IV.10.7* for the definition of T').

(ii) If $U: \mathcal{K} \to \mathcal{K}'$ is the conjugate linear isometric mapping $Ux = x'$ described in *Theorem IV.10.2*, and similarly $V: \mathcal{K} \to \mathcal{K}'$ is the mapping $Vy = y'$, then $T^* = U^{-1}T'V$.

(iii) Identifying $\mathcal{H}$ with $(\mathcal{H}')^*$ via the Hilbert space isomorphism $x \to x'$ (see *Exercise 5.2*), and similarly identifying $\mathcal{K}$ with $(\mathcal{K}')^*$, one has $T^* = T'$.

5. Let $\mathcal{H}$ and $\mathcal{K}$ be Hilbert spaces. Form the direct product Hilbert spaces $\mathcal{H} \times \mathcal{K}$ and $\mathcal{K} \times \mathcal{H}$ (see *Exercise 3.11*). Define $W: \mathcal{H} \times \mathcal{K} \to \mathcal{K} \times \mathcal{H}$ by the formula $W(x,y) = (y,-x)$. Prove:

(i) W is a Hilbert space isomorphism.

(ii) If $T: \mathcal{H} \to \mathcal{K}$ is a continuous linear mapping, the graphs of T and T^* satisfy the following relation: $\mathcal{G}_{T^*} = [W(\mathcal{G}_T)]^{\perp}$ (see *Exercises 3.10* and *3.13*).

What is the formula for $W^*(y,x)$?

*6. Let $\mathcal{H}$ be a Hilbert space, $\mathcal{P}$ a pre-Hilbert space, and suppose $T: \mathcal{H} \to \mathcal{P}$ and $S: \mathcal{P} \to \mathcal{H}$ are mappings such that $(Tx|y) = (x|Sy)$ for all $x \in \mathcal{H}$ and $y \in \mathcal{P}$. One knows that S and T are linear by *Exercise 1*. It can be shown that S and T are continuous. If moreover $\mathcal{P} = \mathcal{K}$ is a Hilbert space, then $S = T^*$.

7. Let $\mathcal{P}$ be the pre-Hilbert space of finitely non-zero sequences, and let e_n be the canonical basis for $\mathcal{P}$ (see *Example I.7.2*). There is a unique linear mapping $T: \mathcal{P} \to \mathcal{P}$ such that $Te_k = ke_k$ for all k. Prove: $(Tx|y) = (x|Ty)$ for all $x,y \in \mathcal{P}$, but T is not continuous. Compare this result with *Exercise 6*.

8. This exercise is preliminary to *Exercise 9*. A doubly indexed family of real numbers $\alpha_{jk} \geq 0$ ($j = 1,2,3,\cdots$; $k = 1,2,3,\cdots$) is said to be *summable* in case there is a constant $M \geq 0$ such that

$$\sum_{j=1}^{m} \sum_{k=1}^{n} \alpha_{jk} \leq M$$

for all indices m and n (equivalently, the sum of any finite number of the α_{jk} is $\leq M$). One then writes $\sum_{j,k} \alpha_{jk}$ for the LUB of all such finite sums. If $\alpha_{jk} \geq 0$ is a doubly indexed family, the symbol $\sum_{j,k} \alpha_{jk} < \infty$ signifies that the family is summable.

Show that for a family $\alpha_{jk} \geq 0$, the following conditions are equivalent:

(a) $\sum_{j,k} \alpha_{jk} < \infty$.

(b) For each j, $\sum_k \alpha_{jk} < \infty$, and $\sum_j \left(\sum_k \alpha_{jk} \right) < \infty$.

(c) For each k, $\sum_j \alpha_{jk} < \infty$, and $\sum_k \left(\sum_j \alpha_{jk} \right) < \infty$.

If either (hence all) of these conditions is fulfilled, one has

$$\sum_j \left(\sum_k \alpha_{jk} \right) = \sum_k \left(\sum_j \alpha_{jk} \right) = \sum_{j,k} \alpha_{jk}.$$

9. This exercise is preliminary to *Exercise 11*. Denote by $\mathcal{H}$ the set of all doubly indexed families $x = (\lambda_{jk})$ of complex numbers such that $\sum_{j,k} |\lambda_{jk}|^2 < \infty$ in the sense of *Exercise 8*. If $y = (\mu_{jk})$ is another such family, define $x = y$ in case $\lambda_{jk} = \mu_{jk}$ for all j,k. With operations suitably defined, $\mathcal{H}$ is a Hilbert space.

10. Let $\mathcal{H}$ and $\mathcal{K}$ be classical Hilbert spaces, e_n an orthonormal basis for $\mathcal{H}$, and f_n an orthonormal basis for $\mathcal{K}$. If $T: \mathcal{H} \to \mathcal{K}$ is a continuous linear mapping, one has $\sum_k \| Te_k \|^2 < \infty$ if and only if $\sum_j \| T^*f_j \|^2 < \infty$, and in this case one has

$$\sum_k \| Te_k \|^2 = \sum_j \| T^*f_j \|^2 = \sum_{j,k} |(Te_k|f_j)|^2.$$

11. Let $\mathcal{H}$ and $\mathcal{K}$ be classical Hilbert spaces, e_n a fixed orthonormal basis for $\mathcal{H}$, f_n a fixed orthonormal basis for $\mathcal{K}$. A continuous linear mapping $T: \mathcal{H} \to \mathcal{K}$ is said to be of *Hilbert-Schmidt class* if there exists an orthonormal basis g_n of $\mathcal{H}$ such that $\sum_k \| Tg_k \|^2 < \infty$. Briefly, T is of HS-class. Prove:

(i) If $T: \mathcal{H} \to \mathcal{K}$ is of HS-class, then $\sum_k \| Tg_k \|^2 < \infty$ for *every* orthonormal basis g_n of $\mathcal{H}$, and the value of this sum is independent of the particular orthonormal basis.

(ii) If $S: \mathcal{H} \to \mathcal{K}$ and $T: \mathcal{H} \to \mathcal{K}$ are of HS-class, so are $S + T$ and λT. The continuous linear mappings $T: \mathcal{H} \to \mathcal{K}$ of HS-class form a linear subspace $\mathcal{L}_{hs}(\mathcal{H},\mathcal{K})$ of $\mathcal{L}_c(\mathcal{H},\mathcal{K})$.

(iii) A continuous linear mapping $T: \mathcal{H} \to \mathcal{K}$ is of HS-class if and only if $T^*: \mathcal{K} \to \mathcal{H}$ is of HS-class.

(iv) If $T: \mathcal{H} \to \mathcal{K}$ is of HS-class, and $R: \mathcal{H} \to \mathcal{H}$, $S: \mathcal{K} \to \mathcal{K}$ are continuous linear mappings, then $TR: \mathcal{H} \to \mathcal{K}$ and $ST: \mathcal{H} \to \mathcal{K}$ are of HS-class.

*(v) If $T: \mathcal{H} \to \mathcal{K}$ is of HS-class, define $\alpha_{jk} = (Te_k|f_j)$. The correspondence $T \to (\alpha_{jk})$ is a vector space isomorphism of $\mathcal{L}_{hs}(\mathcal{H},\mathcal{K})$ with the Hilbert space described in *Exercise 9*.

*(vi) If S and T are of HS-class, define $(S|T) = \sum_k (Se_k|Te_k)$. Then, $\mathcal{L}_{hs}(\mathcal{H},\mathcal{K})$ becomes a pre-Hilbert space, and the scalar product $(S|T)$ is independent of the particular orthonormal basis employed in its definition. The mapping $T \to (\alpha_{jk})$ described in (v) is an

isometric vector space isomorphism; it follows that $\mathcal{L}_{hs}(\mathcal{K},\mathcal{K})$ is a Hilbert space, and the mapping $T \rightarrow (\alpha_{jk})$ is a Hilbert space isomorphism.

12. If $\mathcal{Q}$ is an algebra, a mapping $a \rightarrow a^*$ of $\mathcal{Q}$ into $\mathcal{Q}$ is called an *involution* in case: (1) $a^{**} = a$, (2) $(a + b)^* = a^* + b^*$, (3) $(ab)^* = b^*a^*$, and $(\lambda a)^* = \lambda^* a^*$, for all $a,b \in \mathcal{Q}$ and scalar λ. An algebra with involution is also called a **-algebra*. A normed algebra with involution is called a *normed *-algebra*. Prove: if $\mathcal{Q}$ is a normed *-algebra such that $\| a^*a \| = \| a \|^2$ for all $a \in \mathcal{Q}$, then $\| a^* \| = \| a \|$.

13. This exercise is preliminary to *Exercise 14*. If $\mathcal{Q}$ is an algebra, a *subalgebra* of $\mathcal{Q}$ is a linear subspace $\mathcal{S}$ such that: if $a \in \mathcal{S}$ and $b \in \mathcal{S}$, then $ab \in \mathcal{S}$. Prove:

(i) In a normed algebra, the relations $a_n \rightarrow a$ and $b_n \rightarrow b$ imply $a_n b_n \rightarrow ab$.

(ii) If $\mathcal{S}$ is a subalgebra of the normed algebra $\mathcal{Q}$, its closure $\bar{\mathcal{S}}$ is a closed subalgebra of $\mathcal{Q}$.

(iii) If $\mathcal{Q}$ is a Banach algebra, every closed subalgebra of $\mathcal{Q}$ is itself a Banach algebra.

14. If $\mathcal{Q}$ is a *-algebra, a **-subalgebra* of $\mathcal{Q}$ is a subalgebra $\mathcal{S}$ such that $a \in \mathcal{S}$ implies $a^* \in \mathcal{S}$.

(i) Suppose $\mathcal{Q}$ is a normed *-algebra such that $\| a^* \| = \| a \|$ for all $a \in \mathcal{Q}$. Then, $a_n \rightarrow a$ implies $a_n^* \rightarrow a^*$.

(ii) If $\mathcal{Q}$ is as in part (i), and $\mathcal{S}$ is a *-subalgebra of $\mathcal{Q}$, its closure $\bar{\mathcal{S}}$ is also a *-subalgebra of $\mathcal{Q}$.

15. A *B*-algebra* is a Banach *-algebra $\mathcal{Q}$ such that $\| a^*a \| = \| a \|^2$ for all $a \in \mathcal{Q}$. Prove:

(i) If $\mathcal{S}$ is a *-subalgebra of a B*-algebra $\mathcal{Q}$, then $\bar{\mathcal{S}}$ is a B*-algebra.

(ii) If $\mathcal{K}$ is a Hilbert space, and $\mathcal{S}$ is a closed *-subalgebra of $\mathcal{L}_c(\mathcal{K})$, then $\mathcal{S}$ is a B*-algebra.

*16. There exists a converse for part (ii) of *Exercise 15*, known as the "theorem of Gelfand-Neumark": if $\mathcal{Q}$ is any B*-algebra, there exists a Hilbert space $\mathcal{K}$, and a mapping $\varphi: \mathcal{Q} \rightarrow \mathcal{L}_c(\mathcal{K})$, such that

(1) $\varphi(a + b) = \varphi(a) + \varphi(b)$
(2) $\varphi(\lambda a) = \lambda \varphi(a)$
(3) $\varphi(ab) = \varphi(a)\varphi(b)$
(4) $\| \varphi(a) \| = \| a \|$
(5) $\varphi(a^*) = [\varphi(a)]^*$ (= the adjoint of $\varphi(a)$).

It follows that $S = \varphi(\mathcal{Q})$ is a B^*-algebra of the kind described in part (ii) of *Exercise 15;* hence, $\mathcal{Q}$ is essentially "equal" to a B^*-algebra of this kind.

17. Notation as in *Exercise 11*, with $\mathcal{3C} = \mathcal{K}$. Then, $\mathcal{L}_{hs}(\mathcal{3C},\mathcal{3C})$ is a $*$-subalgebra of $\mathcal{L}_c(\mathcal{3C})$.

18. An *involution* in a vector space $\mathcal{U}$ is a mapping $x \to x^\#$ of $\mathcal{U}$ into $\mathcal{U}$ such that: (1) $x^{\#\#} = x$, (2) $(x + y)^\# = x^\# + y^\#$, and (3) $(\lambda x)^\# = \lambda^* x^\#$. Prove:

(i) If $\mathcal{U}$ is a vector space, and $\varphi: \mathcal{U} \times \mathcal{U} \to \mathcal{C}$ is a sesquilinear form, define $\varphi^\#(x,y) = [\varphi(y,x)]^*$. Then, $\varphi \to \varphi^\#$ is an involution in the vector space $S(\mathcal{U},\mathcal{U}; \mathcal{C})$ (see *Exercise 5.8*).

(ii) Let $\mathcal{3C}$ be a Hilbert space. If φ_T is defined as in *Theorem 7.1*, then $(\varphi_T)^\# = \varphi_{T^*}$.

Operators in Hilbert Space

§ 1. MANIFESTO

For the rest of the book, we settle down to the study of various types of continuous linear mappings of a Hilbert space into itself. Generalities are henceforth banished to the exercises, and the reader is invited to assess each definition and proof for its possible level of generality. For example, some statements about Hilbert space will make sense for normed spaces, or vector spaces, and so on; observations of this sort will be found in the exercises. Henceforth:

1. $\mathfrak{IC}$ denotes a Hilbert space $\neq \{\theta\}$.

2. Any continuous linear mapping $T: \mathfrak{IC} \to \mathfrak{IC}$ will be called an **operator.** In particular, I is the *identity operator*, 0 is the *zero operator*, λI is a *scalar operator*.

3. T^* denotes the adjoint of the operator T. Thus,
   (i) T^* is an operator
   (ii) $(Tx|y) = (x|T^*y)$ for all $x,y \in \mathfrak{IC}$
   (iii) $T^{**} = T$
   (iv) $(S + T)^* = S^* + T^*$

(v) $(\lambda T)^* = \lambda^* T^*$
(vi) $(ST)^* = T^* S^*$
(vii) $\| T^* \| = \| T \|$
(viii) $\| T^* T \| = \| T \|^2$
(ix) $T^* T = 0$ if and only if $T = 0$.

These facts about adjoints are assumed to be known to the reader (see § 8 of Chapter V); they will be used in the sequel without explicit reference.

The special types of operators T which will be discussed in this chapter are defined as follows:

isometric operator: $T^* T = I$
unitary operator: $T^* T = TT^* = I$
self-adjoint operator: $T^* = T$
projection operator: $TT = T$ and $T^* = T$
normal operator: $T^* T = TT^*$.

Other types of operators (positive, invertible, etc....) are discussed in the exercises.

§ 2. PRELIMINARIES

The theorems of this section will be used often, and without explicit reference, in the sequel.

Theorem 1. *The null space $\mathfrak{N}$ of an operator T is a closed linear subspace of $\mathfrak{IC}$.*

Proof.
   See *Theorem IV.7.2.* ▮

Theorem 2. *If $\mathcal{S}$ is a total subset of $\mathfrak{IC}$, and S,T are operators such that $Sx = Tx$ for all $x \in \mathcal{S}$, then $S = T$.*

Proof.
   Let $\mathfrak{N}$ be the null space of $S - T$. By assumption, $\mathcal{S} \subset \mathfrak{N}$. Since $\mathcal{S}$ is total, so is $\mathfrak{N}$, hence $\mathfrak{N}^\perp = \{\theta\}$ (see *Example III.2.1*). By *Theorem III.6.2*, $\mathfrak{N} = \mathfrak{N}^{\perp\perp} = \{\theta\}^\perp = \mathfrak{IC}$; that is, $S - T = 0$. ▮

Theorem 3. *If S and T are operators such that $(Sx \,|\, x) = (Tx \,|\, x)$ for all $x \in \mathfrak{IC}$, then $S = T$.*

Proof.

Consider the sesquilinear forms φ and ψ defined by the formulas $\varphi(x,y) = (Sx|y)$, $\psi(x,y) = (Tx|y)$ (see *Example V.5.2*). By assumption $\varphi(x,x) = \psi(x,x)$ for all x, hence $\varphi = \psi$ by *Theorem V.5.3*. Thus, $(Sx|y) = (Tx|y)$ for all x and y; $Sx = Tx$ results from *Theorem II.2.1*. ∎

Exercises

1. If $\mathfrak{X}$ is a set, $\mathcal{P}$ is a pre-Hilbert space, and S,T are mappings of $\mathfrak{X}$ into $\mathcal{P}$ such that $(Sx|y) = (Tx|y)$ for all $x \in \mathfrak{X}$ and $y \in \mathcal{P}$, then $S = T$.

2. If T is an operator such that Tx is orthogonal to x, for every vector x, then $T = 0$.

3. If $S^*S + T^*T = 0$, then $S = T = 0$.

4. Let S and T be operators, $\mathcal{S}$ a total subset of $\mathcal{K}$. Show:
(i) If $(Sx|y) = (Tx|y)$ for all $x,y \in \mathcal{S}$, then $S = T$.
(ii) It can happen that $(Sx|x) = (Tx|x)$ for all $x \in \mathcal{S}$, and yet $S \neq T$.

5. *Theorem 3* holds for (not necessarily continuous) linear mappings in pre-Hilbert space.

6. In a normed space $\mathcal{E}$, call a subset $\mathcal{S}$ *total* in case: the only continuous linear form f on $\mathcal{E}$ such that $f(x) = 0$ for all $x \in \mathcal{S}$, is $f = 0$. Then:
*(i) It can be shown that if $\mathcal{S}$ is a total subset of $\mathcal{E}$, then $\mathcal{E}$ is the smallest closed linear subspace of $\mathcal{E}$ which contains $\mathcal{S}$. *Theorem 2* then generalizes to normed spaces.
(ii) In Hilbert space, a subset $\mathcal{S}$ is total in the above sense, if and only if it is total in the sense of *Definition II.8.1*.

7. Let $\mathcal{S}$ be a subset of a pre-Hilbert space $\mathcal{P}$.
(i) If $\mathcal{S}$ is total in the sense of *Exercise 6*, then it is total in the sense of *Definition II.8.1*.
(ii) The converse of (i) fails.

§3. AN EXAMPLE

The theorem of this section is a useful source of examples of operators. Suppose $\mathcal{K}$ is classical Hilbert space, and x_n is an orthonormal basis for $\mathfrak{IC}$. Thus, every $x \in \mathfrak{IC}$ has a unique representation $x = \sum_1^\infty \lambda_k x_k$, where $\sum_1^\infty |\lambda_k|^2 < \infty$, namely $\lambda_k = (x|x_k)$ (see *Theorem II.8.1*).

Theorem 1. *Let μ_n be a bounded sequence of complex numbers, $M =$ LUB $\{|\mu_k|: k = 1,2,3,\cdots\}$. There exists one and only one operator T such that*

(1) $Tx_k = \mu_k x_k$ *for all* k.

Moreover,

(2) $T\left(\sum_1^\infty \lambda_k x_k\right) = \sum_1^\infty \lambda_k \mu_k x_k$

(3) $\|T\| = M$

(4) $T^* x_k = \mu_k^* x_k$ *for all* k

(5) $T^*\left(\sum_1^\infty \lambda_k x_k\right) = \sum_1^\infty \lambda_k \mu_k^* x_k$

(6) $T^*T = TT^*$.

Proof.

(1),(2),(3): Given $x \in \mathfrak{IC}$, say $x = \sum_1^\infty \lambda_k x_k$; the problem is to define Tx. Since $\sum_1^\infty |\lambda_k \mu_k|^2 \le M^2 \sum_1^\infty |\lambda_k|^2 = M^2 \|x\|^2$ (see *Theorem II.7.2*), one can define $Tx = \sum_1^\infty \lambda_k \mu_k x_k$ (see *Theorem II.7.1*). The linearity of T results from the Lemma to *Theorem III.3.2*. Since $\|Tx\|^2 \le M^2 \|x\|^2$, T is continuous, and $\|T\| \le M$.

Clearly $Tx_k = \mu_k x_k$; since $\|x_k\| = 1$, $\|T\| \ge \|Tx_k\| = \|\mu_k x_k\| = |\mu_k|$ for all k, hence $\|T\| \ge M$.

(4),(5): Suppose $x = \sum_1^\infty \lambda_k x_k$ and $T^*x = \sum_1^\infty \nu_k x_k$; the problem is to show $\nu_k = \lambda_k \mu_k^*$. For all k, $\nu_k = (T^*x|x_k) = (x|Tx_k) = (x|\mu_k x_k) = \mu_k^*(x|x_k) = \mu_k^* \lambda_k$.

(6): Clearly $T^*Tx_k = |\mu_k|^2 x_k = TT^*x_k$; since the x_k are total, $T^*T = TT^*$.

Uniqueness: If S is any operator such that $Sx_k = \mu_k x_k$ for all k, then $Sx_k = Tx_k$ for all k; since the x_k are total, $S = T$.   ∎

Exercises

1. Notation as in *Theorem 1*. For each $n = 1,2,3,\cdots$, let T_n be the unique operator such that $T_n x_k = \mu_k x_k$ for $k \leq n$, and $T_n x_k = \theta$ for $k > n$ (the existence of T_n is a special case of *Theorem 1*). Then, $T_n \to T$ strongly, in the sense of *Exercise IV.8.2*.

2. If $\mathcal{E}$ and $\mathcal{F}$ are normed spaces, $S: \mathcal{E} \to \mathcal{F}$ is a continuous linear mapping, $x \in \mathcal{E}$, and $x = \sum_1^\infty x_k$ in the sense of *Definition II.7.1* (generalized to normed spaces), then $Sx = \sum_1^\infty Sx_k$.

§ 4. ISOMETRIC OPERATORS

According to *Definition IV.7.3*, an operator T is *isometric* in case $\| Tx - Ty \| = \| x - y \|$ for all $x,y \in \mathcal{K}$; by *Theorem IV.7.5*, this is equivalent to the condition $\| Tx \| = \| x \|$ for all x. In Hilbert space,

Theorem 1. *The following conditions on an operator T are equivalent:*

(a) *T is isometric*

(b) *$T^*T = I$*

(c) *$(Tx \,|\, Ty) = (x \,|\, y)$ for all $x,y \in \mathcal{K}$.*

Proof.

(a) *implies* (b): By *Theorem IV.7.5*, $\| Tx \| = \| x \|$ for all x, hence $(T^*Tx \,|\, x) = (Tx \,|\, Tx) = \| Tx \|^2 = \| x \|^2 = (x \,|\, x) = (Ix \,|\, x)$.

(b) *implies* (c): $(Tx \,|\, Ty) = (T^*Tx \,|\, y) = (Ix \,|\, y) = (x \,|\, y)$.

(c) *implies* (a): $\| Tx \|^2 = (Tx \,|\, Tx) = (x \,|\, x) = \| x \|^2$. ∎

If T is isometric, it is clear from the relation $\| Tx - Ty \| = \| x - y \|$ that T is injective.

Theorem 2. *The range $T(\mathcal{K})$ of an isometric operator T is a **closed** linear subspace of $\mathcal{K}$.*

Proof.

$T(\mathcal{K})$ is a linear subspace, by *Theorem IV.1.4*. Suppose y is adherent to $T(\mathcal{K})$; the problem is to show that $y \in T(\mathcal{K})$. Choose any sequence $y_n \in T(\mathcal{K})$ such that $y_n \to y$. Say $y_n = Tx_n$. Since $\| x_m - x_n \| = \| Tx_m - Tx_n \| = \| y_m - y_n \| \to 0$, x_n is a Cauchy sequence. Since

$\mathcal{K}$ is complete, $x_n \to x$ for suitable x. By the continuity of T, $Tx_n \to Tx$, that is, $Tx = \lim y_n = y$. ∎

Example 1. Let $\mathcal{K}$ be classical Hilbert space, and $x_1, x_2, x_3, \cdots$ an orthonormal basis for $\mathcal{K}$. There is a unique operator T such that $Tx_k = x_{k+1}$ for all k. Specifically, every vector x has a unique representation $x = \sum_1^\infty \lambda_k x_k$, and one defines $Tx = \sum_1^\infty \lambda_k x_{k+1}$. Clearly T is linear, and $\| Tx \|^2 = \sum_1^\infty |\lambda_k|^2 = \| x \|^2$ shows that T is isometric. T will be referred to as a *one-sided shift operator*.

The effect of T^* is as follows: $T^* x_1 = \theta$, and $T^* x_k = x_{k-1}$ for $k = 2, 3, 4, \cdots$. For, $(T^* x_1 | x_j) = (x_1 | Tx_j) = (x_1 | x_{j+1}) = 0 = (\theta | x_j)$ for $j = 1, 2, 3, \cdots$. If $k > 1$, $(T^* x_k | x_j) = (x_k | x_{j+1}) = 1$ when $j = k - 1$, and $= 0$ for all other j; thus, $(T^* x_k | x_j) = (x_{k-1} | x_j)$ for $j = 1, 2, 3, \cdots$.

Exercises

1. If S and T are isometric operators, so is ST.

2. Operators S and T are said to be *metrically equivalent* in case $\| Sx \| = \| Tx \|$ for all $x \in \mathcal{K}$. Then, S and T are metrically equivalent if and only if $S^*S = T^*T$.

3. In *Example 1*, if $\mathcal{K} = l^2$, and $x_n = e_n$ is the canonical orthonormal basis, describe the effect of T and T^* on the vector $x = (\lambda_1, \lambda_2, \lambda_3, \cdots)$.

4. Let $Tx_k = x_{k+1}$ be the one-sided shift operator (*Example 1*). The x_k are total, and for each k, Tx_k is orthogonal to x_k. Compare with *Exercises 2.2, 2.4*.

5. Conditions (a) and (c) of *Theorem 1* are equivalent, for a linear mapping in pre-Hilbert space.

6. *Theorem 2* holds for an isometric linear mapping of a Banach space.

7. If $\mathfrak{M}$ and $\mathfrak{N}$ are closed linear subspaces of $\mathcal{K}$, T is an isometric operator, and $T(\mathfrak{M}) = \mathfrak{N}$, then $T(\mathfrak{M}^\perp) \subset \mathfrak{N}^\perp$.

8. Suppose S and T are metrically equivalent operators, in the sense of *Exercise 2*. Prove:
   (i) There exists an isometric vector space isomorphism $V: T(\mathcal{K}) \to S(\mathcal{K})$ such that $VTx = Sx$ for all $x \in \mathcal{K}$.
   (ii) If $T(\mathcal{K})$ is a closed linear subspace, then $S(\mathcal{K})$ is also closed.

9. Let $S: \mathcal{3C} \to \mathcal{3C}$ be a mapping such that $(Sx\,|\,Sy) = (x\,|\,y)$ for all $x,y \in \mathcal{3C}$. Suppose, moreover, that $S(\mathcal{3C})$ is a linear subspace of $\mathcal{3C}$. Then S is an isometric operator.

10. Let $T: \mathcal{3C} \to \mathcal{3C}$ be a mapping such that $(Tx\,|\,Ty) = (y\,|\,x)$ for all $x,y \in \mathcal{3C}$. Suppose, moreover, that $T(\mathcal{3C})$ is a linear subspace of $\mathcal{3C}$. Then TT is an isometric operator.

11. Let $\mathcal{3C}$ be classical Hilbert space, x_n an orthonormal basis for $\mathcal{3C}$. An operator T is isometric if and only if Tx_n is an orthonormal sequence.

§5. UNITARY OPERATORS

Definition 1. *An operator T is said to be* **unitary** *in case $T^*T = TT^* = I$.*

Theorem 1. *The following conditions on an operator T are equivalent:*

(a)   *T is unitary*

(b)   *T^* is unitary*

(c)   *T and T^* are isometric*

(d)   *T is isometric and T^* is injective*

(e)   *T is isometric and surjective*

(f)   *T is bijective, and $T^{-1} = T^*$.*

Proof.
The equivalence of (a),(b),(c) is clear from the definitions, and the relation $T^{**} = T$.

(c) *implies* (d): Isometric operators are injective.

(d) *implies* (e): By *Theorem 4.2*, $T(\mathcal{3C})$ is a closed linear subspace of $\mathcal{3C}$. Also, T^* is injective; quoting *Theorem V.8.6*, $\mathcal{3C} = \{\theta\}^{\perp} = \{y: T^*y = \theta\}^{\perp} = \overline{T(\mathcal{3C})} = T(\mathcal{3C})$.

(e) *implies* (f): By assumption, T is bijective. Let $S = T^{-1}$; according to *Definition IV.2.2*, $ST = TS = I$. Then, $T^* = T^*I = T^*(TS) = (T^*T)S = IS = S$.

(f) *implies* (a): Clear from the definitions. ∎

Examples

1. Notation as in *Theorem 3.1*. Thus, $\mathcal{H}$ is classical Hilbert space, e_n is an orthonormal basis for $\mathcal{H}$, μ_n is a bounded sequence of complex numbers, and T is the unique operator such that $Tx_k = \mu_k x_k$ for all k. One has $T^*Tx_k = |\mu_k|^2 x_k = TT^*x_k$. Clearly, T is unitary if and only if $|\mu_k|^2 x_k = Ix_k$ for all k, in other words, $|\mu_k| = 1$ for all k.

2. Let $\mathcal{H}$, x_n be as in *Example 1*. Define $y_k = x_{2k+1}$ for $k = 0,1,2,3,\cdots$, and $y_{-k} = x_{2k}$ for $k = 1,2,3,\cdots$. Thus, y_n is an orthonormal basis indexed by the set of *all* integers. Every vector x has a unique representation $x = \sum_{-\infty}^{\infty} \lambda_k y_k$ (the sum can be interpreted as the unique vector y such that $(y \mid y_k) = \lambda_k$ for all k). There is a unique operator U such that $Uy_k = y_{k+1}$ for all k; specifically, one defines $U\left(\sum_{-\infty}^{\infty} \lambda_k y_k\right) = \sum_{-\infty}^{\infty} \lambda_k y_{k+1}$. It follows that $U^*y_k = y_{k-1}$ (see the calculation made in *Example 4.1*). Since $U^*Uy_k = UU^*y_k = y_k = Iy_k$, U is unitary; it will be referred to as a *two-sided shift operator*.

Exercises

1. If $\mathcal{H}$ is finite-dimensional, every isometric operator is unitary.

2. An operator T is unitary if and only if T^* is isometric and T is injective.

3. If S and T are unitary operators, so is ST.

4. If T is a unitary operator, $\mathfrak{M}$ and $\mathfrak{N}$ are closed linear subspaces, and $T(\mathfrak{M}) = \mathfrak{N}$, then $T(\mathfrak{M}^\perp) = \mathfrak{N}^\perp$.

5. An operator T is unitary if and only if $T\colon \mathcal{H} \to \mathcal{H}$ is a Hilbert space isomorphism. More generally, if $\mathcal{H}$ and $\mathcal{K}$ are Hilbert spaces, a mapping $T\colon \mathcal{H} \to \mathcal{K}$ is a Hilbert space isomorphism if and only if: T is a continuous linear mapping such that $T^*T = I$ (= identity operator in $\mathcal{H}$) and $TT^* = I$ (= identity operator in $\mathcal{K}$).

6. If $T\colon \mathcal{H} \to \mathcal{H}$ is a surjective mapping such that $(Tx \mid Ty) = (x \mid y)$ for all $x,y \in \mathcal{H}$, then T is a unitary operator.

7. If J and K are conjugations of $\mathcal{H}$, in the sense of *Exercise V.5.1*, then JK is a unitary operator; in particular, JJ is unitary. If J is a conjugation, and U,V are unitary operators, then UJV is a conjugation.

8. Let $\mathcal{3C}$ be classical Hilbert space, x_n an orthonormal basis for $\mathcal{3C}$, and $1',2',3',\cdots$ any rearrangement of the indices $1,2,3,\cdots$. The unique operator T such that $Tx_k = x_{k'}$ for all k, is unitary.

9. (i) If $\mathcal{S}$ is a total subset of $\mathcal{3C}$, and T is an isometric operator, then T is unitary if and only if $T(\mathcal{S})$ is a total subset of $\mathcal{3C}$.

(ii) If $\mathcal{3C}$ is classical Hilbert space, and x_n is an orthonormal basis for $\mathcal{3C}$, an operator T is unitary if and only if Tx_n is an orthonormal basis for $\mathcal{3C}$.

10. An operator S is said to be *unitarily equivalent* to the operator T in case there exists a unitary operator U such that $T = U^*SU$. Notation: $S \cong T$. Prove:

(i) $T \cong T$, for every operator T.

(ii) If $S \cong T$, then $T \cong S$.

(iii) If $R \cong S$ and $S \cong T$, then $R \cong T$. Moreover,

(iv) if $S \cong T$, then $S^* \cong T^*$.

§ 6. SELF-ADJOINT OPERATORS

Definition 1. *An operator T is said to be **self-adjoint** (or "Hermitian") in case $T^* = T$.*

Theorem 1. *The following conditions on an operator T are equivalent:*

(a) T *is self-adjoint*

(b) $(Tx|y) = (x|Ty)$ *for all* $x,y \in \mathcal{3C}$

(c) $(Tx|x) = (x|Tx)$ *for all* $x \in \mathcal{3C}$

(d) $(Tx|x)$ *is real, for all* $x \in \mathcal{3C}$.

Proof.

(a) *implies* (b): $(Tx|y) = (x|T^*y) = (x|Ty)$.

(c) *implies* (d): $(Tx|x)^* = (x|Tx) = (Tx|x)$.

(d) *implies* (a): $(Tx|x) = (Tx|x)^* = (x|Tx) = (T^*x|x)$. ∎

The next theorem follows easily from the properties of adjoints listed in § 1:

Theorem 2.

(1) *If S and T are self-adjoint, so is $S + T$.*

(2) *If T is self-adjoint, and α is real, αT is self-adjoint.*

(3) *If T is* **any** *operator, T^*T and $T + T^*$ are self-adjoint.*

(4) *If S and T are self-adjoint, then ST is self-adjoint if and only if $ST = TS$.*

Example 1. Notation as in *Theorem 3.1.* Thus, $Tx_k = \mu_k x_k$ and $T^*x_k = \mu_k{}^*x_k$. Clearly T is self-adjoint if and only if $\mu_k x_k = \mu_k{}^*x_k$ for all k, in other words, μ_k is *real* for all k. ∎

The decomposition of a complex number λ in the form $\lambda = \alpha + i\beta$, where α and β are real, has a generalization for operators:

Theorem 3. (Cartesian form) *If T is any operator, there exist self-adjoint operators A and B such that $T = A + iB$. Necessarily*

$$A = \frac{1}{2}(T + T^*)$$

$$B = \frac{1}{2i}(T - T^*).$$

Proof.
Define A and B by the above formulas; clearly A and B are self-adjoint, and $A + iB = T$. Suppose also $T = C + iD$, with C and D self-adjoint. Then, $T^* = C^* + i^*D^* = C - iD$, hence $T + T^* = 2C$ and $T - T^* = 2iD$. Thus, $C = A$ and $D = B$. ∎

The following result is important for the discussion of spectral theory in Chapter VIII:

Theorem 4. *If T is a self-adjoint operator,*

$$\| T \| = \text{LUB} \{ |(Tx|x)| : \| x \| \leq 1 \}.$$

Proof.
Define $\varphi(x,y) = (Tx | y)$; φ is a bounded sesquilinear form (see *Theorem V.7.1*), and $\| \varphi \| = \| T \|$. Since $\varphi(y,x) = (Ty|x) = (y | Tx) = (Tx | y)^* = [\varphi(x,y)]^*$, φ is Hermitian, hence $\| \varphi \| = \text{LUB} \{ |\varphi(x,x)| : \| x \| \leq 1 \}$ by *Theorem V.6.2*. ∎

Exercises

1. An operator T is said to be *skew-adjoint* in case $T^* = -T$. Show:
 (i) T is skew-adjoint if and only if iT is self-adjoint.
 (ii) For any operator T, $T - T^*$ is skew-adjoint.

2. If T is a self-adjoint operator, $\mathbb{S}$ and $\mathbb{J}$ are subsets of $\mathcal{K}$, and $T(\mathbb{S}) \subset \mathbb{J}$, then $T(\mathbb{J}^{\perp}) \subset \mathbb{S}^{\perp}$.

3. If T is self-adjoint, $Tx = \theta$ if and only if $TTx = \theta$. Give an example of an operator T such that $T \neq 0$ but $TT = 0$.

4. If T is self-adjoint, and S is any operator, then S^*TS is self-adjoint.

5. If T is self-adjoint, and S is unitarily equivalent to T, then S is self-adjoint.

6. (i) If φ is a bounded sesquilinear form on $\mathcal{K} \times \mathcal{K}$, there exist unique bounded Hermitian sesquilinear forms φ_1 and φ_2 such that $\varphi = \varphi_1 + i\varphi_2$.

(ii) If $\mathcal{V}$ is a vector space, and φ is a sesquilinear form on $\mathcal{V} \times \mathcal{V}$, there exist Hermitian sesquilinear forms φ_1, φ_2 such that $\varphi = \varphi_1 + i\varphi_2$.

(iii) Generalize (i) to bounded sesquilinear forms φ on $\mathcal{E} \times \mathcal{E}$, where $\mathcal{E}$ is a normed space.

7. An operator T is said to be *positive* in case $(Tx|x) \geq 0$ for all $x \in \mathcal{K}$. Notation: $T \geq 0$. Prove:

(i)   If $T \geq 0$, then T is self-adjoint.

(ii)   If $S \geq 0$ and $T \geq 0$, then $S + T \geq 0$.

(iii)   If $T \geq 0$ and $\alpha \geq 0$, then $\alpha T \geq 0$.

(iv)   If $T \geq 0$ and S is any operator, then $S^*TS \geq 0$.

(v)   For any operator T, $T^*T \geq 0$.

(vi)   If $S \geq 0$, $T \geq 0$, and $S + T = 0$, then $S = T = 0$.

(vii)   If $T \geq 0$, then $|(Tx|y)|^2 \leq (Tx|x)(Ty|y)$ for all $x, y \in \mathcal{K}$.

(viii) If $T \geq 0$, then $Tx = \theta$ if and only if $(Tx|x) = 0$.

It can also be shown that:

*(ix) If $T \geq 0$, there exists a unique operator $S \geq 0$, such that $T = SS$; S is called the *positive square root* of T. Notation: $S = \sqrt{T}$.

*(x) Let $T \geq 0$, $S = \sqrt{T}$. For an operator R, $RT = TR$ if and only if $RS = SR$.

*(xi) If $S \geq 0$, $T \geq 0$, then $ST \geq 0$ if and only if $ST = TS$. In this case, $\sqrt{ST} = \sqrt{S}\sqrt{T}$.

*(xii) If T is self-adjoint, there exist positive operators A and B such that $T = A - B$ and $AB = 0$.

8. If S and T are self-adjoint operators, one writes $S \leq T$ (or $T \geq S$) in case $T - S \geq 0$ in the sense of *Exercise 7*. Prove:

(i) $T \leq T$ for every self-adjoint operator T.

(ii)   If $S \leq T$ and $T \leq S$, then $S = T$.

(iii)   If $R \leq S$ and $S \leq T$, then $R \leq T$.

(iv)   If S and T are self-adjoint, then $S \leq T$ if and only if $(Sx\,|\,x) \leq (Tx\,|\,x)$ for all $x \in \mathcal{K}$.

(v)   If T is self-adjoint, $T \leq \| T \| I$, and $T \geq -\| T \| I$. Briefly, $-\| T \| I \leq T \leq \| T \| I$.

(vi)   If $A \leq B$ and $C \leq D$, then $A + C \leq B + D$.

(vii) If $S \leq T$ and $\alpha \geq 0$, then $\alpha S \leq \alpha T$.

(viii) If $S \leq T$, then $-S \geq -T$.

(ix)   If $S \leq T$, and R is any operator, then $R^*SR \leq R^*TR$.

9. An operator T is called a *contraction* in case $\| Tx \| \leq \| x \|$ for all $x \in \mathcal{K}$. For an operator T, the following conditions are equivalent:

(a) T is a contraction

(b) $\| T \| \leq 1$

(c) $T^*T \leq I$ in the sense of *Exercise 8*

(d) $TT^* \leq I$

(e) T^* is a contraction

(f) T^*T is a contraction.

10. If T is a self-adjoint operator, there is a smallest number M, and a largest number m, such that $mI \leq T \leq MI$ in the sense of *Exercise 8*. One has $\| T \| = \max \{|m|, |M|\}$.

11. If T is an operator such that $T^*T \geq I$, then $T(\mathcal{K})$ is a closed linear subspace of $\mathcal{K}$. Such an operator is injective; it is not necessarily surjective.

12. Let T be a self-adjoint operator, and set $R = T + iI$. Prove:

(i) $\| Rx \|^2 = \| Tx \|^2 + \| x \|^2$.

(ii) R is injective, $\| Rx \| \geq \| x \|$.

(iii) $R(\mathcal{K})$ is a closed linear subspace of $\mathcal{K}$.

(iv) $R(\mathcal{K}) = \mathcal{K}$.

(v) R is bijective, R^{-1} is continuous, and $\| R^{-1} \| \leq 1$.

(vi) The operator $U = (T - iI)(T + iI)^{-1}$ is unitary; it is called the *Cayley transform* of T.

13. (i) If T is any operator, then the operator $R = T^*T + I$ is bijective, R^{-1} is continuous, and $\| R^{-1} \| \leq 1$.

(ii) If $T \geq 0$, then the operator $S = T + I$ is bijective, S^{-1} is continuous, and $\| S^{-1} \| \leq 1$.

14. Let $Uy_k = y_{k+1}$ be the two-sided shift operator, and P the projection whose range is the closed linear subspace generated by $y_0, y_1, y_2, \cdots$. Then, $P \geq 0$, $UPU^* \leq P$, but $UPU^* \neq P$.

§7. PROJECTION OPERATORS

Definition 1. *An operator T is called a* **projection** *in case $T^* = T = TT$.*

Thus, a projection operator is a self-adjoint operator which equals its "square."

Example 1. Let $\mathfrak{N}$ be a closed linear subspace of $\mathfrak{K}$, and $T = P_\mathfrak{N}$ the projection of $\mathfrak{K}$ on $\mathfrak{N}$. As shown in *Theorem III.8.1*, T is linear and $\| Tx \| \leq \| x \|$, hence T is an operator; also $T(Tx) = Tx$ and $(Tx|y) = (x|Ty)$, thus T is a projection operator in the sense of *Definition 1*. In fact, every projection operator can be obtained in this way from a suitable closed linear subspace:

Theorem 1. *If T is any projection operator, there is one and only one closed linear subspace $\mathfrak{N}$ such that $T = P_\mathfrak{N}$. Specifically, $\mathfrak{N}$ is the range of T, and $\mathfrak{N}^\perp$ is the null space of T.*

Proof.
   Let $\mathfrak{N} = \{y \in \mathfrak{K} : Ty = y\}$; since $\mathfrak{N}$ is the null space of the operator $T - I$, it is a closed linear subspace of $\mathfrak{K}$.
   The range of T is $\mathfrak{N}$. For, if $y \in \mathfrak{N}$, then $y = Ty \in T(\mathfrak{K})$; if conversely $y \in T(\mathfrak{K})$, say $y = Tx$, then $Ty = T(Tx) = Tx = y$ shows that $y \in \mathfrak{N}$. Thus, $\mathfrak{N} = T(\mathfrak{K})$.
   By *Theorem V.8.6*, the null space of T is $[T^*(\mathfrak{K})]^\perp = [T(\mathfrak{K})]^\perp = \mathfrak{N}^\perp$.
   One has $T = P_\mathfrak{N}$. For, given any $x \in \mathfrak{K}$, write $x = y + z$ with $y \in \mathfrak{N}$ and $z \in \mathfrak{N}^\perp$; quoting *Theorem III.8.1*, $P_\mathfrak{N}x = y = y + \theta = Ty + Tz = T(y + z) = Tx$.
   Uniqueness: if $P_\mathfrak{N} = P_\mathfrak{M}$, then $\mathfrak{N} = P_\mathfrak{N}(\mathfrak{K}) = P_\mathfrak{M}(\mathfrak{K}) = \mathfrak{M}$. ∎

Example 2. Let y be a fixed vector of $\mathfrak{K}$, $\| y \| = 1$, and let $\mathfrak{N} = \{\lambda y : \lambda \text{ scalar}\}$ be the one-dimensional linear subspace generated by y. The operator T defined by $Tx = (x|y)y$ is the projection of $\mathfrak{K}$ on $\mathfrak{N}$. For, if $x \in \mathfrak{K}$, one can write $x = \lambda y + z$ with $z \perp \mathfrak{N}$ and λ a suitable scalar, and one has $Tx = (\lambda y + z|y)y = [\lambda(y|y) + (z|y)]y = [\lambda + 0]y = \lambda y = P_\mathfrak{N}x$.

Example 3. Notation as in *Theorem 3.1*. Let P_k be the projection whose range is the one-dimensional linear subspace generated by x_k; by *Example 2*, $P_k x = (x | x_k) x_k$. Define $T_n = \sum_1^n \mu_k P_k$, for $n = 1, 2, 3, \cdots$.

If $x \in \mathfrak{IC}$, one has $x = \sum_1^\infty (x | x_k) x_k$, hence $Tx = \sum_1^\infty (x | x_k) \mu_k x_k = \sum_1^\infty \mu_k (P_k x) = \lim_n \sum_1^n \mu_k (P_k x) = \lim_n T_n x$. Thus, $T_n x \to Tx$, for each x; that is, $T_n \to T$ strongly, in the sense of *Exercise IV.8.2*.

Theorem 2. *Let $\mathfrak{M}$ and $\mathfrak{N}$ be closed linear subspaces of $\mathfrak{IC}$, P the projection with range $\mathfrak{M}$, and Q the projection with range $\mathfrak{N}$. Then, $\mathfrak{M} \perp \mathfrak{N}$ if and only if $PQ = 0$.*

Proof.

If: Suppose $PQ = 0$. If $x \in \mathfrak{M}$ and $y \in \mathfrak{N}$, then $(x | y) = (Px | Qy)$ $= (x | P^*Qy) = (x | PQy) = (x | \theta) = 0$.

Only if: Suppose $\mathfrak{M} \perp \mathfrak{N}$. If $x \in \mathfrak{IC}$, then $Qx \in \mathfrak{N}$, hence $Qx \in \mathfrak{M}^\perp$, hence $P(Qx) = \theta$. ∎

Example 4. If $P_1, \cdots, P_n$ are projections, and $P_j P_k = 0$ whenever $j \neq k$, then $P = \sum_1^n P_k$ is a projection. For, $P^* = \sum_1^n P_k^* = \sum_1^n P_k = P$, and $PP = \sum_{j,k} P_j P_k = \sum_k P_k P_k = \sum_k P_k = P$. See also *Exercise 6*.

Exercises

1. An operator T is a projection if and only if $T = T^*T$.

2. If P is a projection, and Q is unitarily equivalent to P, then Q is a projection.

3. If P is a projection, then $P \geq 0$ in the sense of *Exercise 6.7*. If P is a non-zero projection, $\| P \| = 1$.

4. If P, Q are projections, and $PQ = QP$, then PQ is a projection. In this case, if $\mathfrak{M}$ is the range of P and $\mathfrak{N}$ is the range of Q, then the range of PQ is the intersection of $\mathfrak{M}$ and $\mathfrak{N}$ (see *Exercise I.5.4*).

5. If P is a projection, with range $\mathfrak{N}$, then $I - P$ is a projection, with range $\mathfrak{N}^\perp$.

6. Let P and Q be projections, with ranges $\mathfrak{M}$ and $\mathfrak{N}$, respectively. If $\mathfrak{M} \perp \mathfrak{N}$, then $P + Q$ is the projection with range $\mathfrak{M} \oplus \mathfrak{N}$ (see *Definition III.2.5*).

7. If P, Q are projections, and $PQ = QP$, then $P + Q - PQ$ is a projection. What is its range?

8. If P, Q, and $P + Q$ are projections, necessarily $PQ = 0$.

9. Let P and Q be projections, with ranges $\mathfrak{M}$ and $\mathfrak{N}$, respectively. The following conditions are equivalent:
  (a) $P - Q$ is a projection.
  (b) $P \geq Q$ in the sense of *Exercise 6.8*.
  (c) $\| Px \| \geq \| Qx \|$ for all $x \in \mathfrak{K}$.
  (d) $\mathfrak{M} \supset \mathfrak{N}$.
In this case, the range of $P - Q$ is the set of all vectors common to $\mathfrak{M}$ and $\mathfrak{N}^{\perp}$.

10. If P, Q are non-zero projections, and $PQ = 0$, then $\| P + Q \| < \| P \| + \| Q \|$.

11. If T is an isometric operator, then TT^* is a projection.

12. An operator T is said to be *partially isometric* in case T^*T is a projection. Suppose T is partially isometric, say $T^*T = P$. Prove:
  (i) $TP = T$.
  (ii) Set $Q = TT^*$. Then Q is a projection, and $QT = T$. Thus, T^* is partially isometric.
  (iii) T maps $P(\mathfrak{K})$ isometrically onto $Q(\mathfrak{K})$, $[P(\mathfrak{K})]^{\perp}$ is the null space of T, and $[Q(\mathfrak{K})]^{\perp}$ is the null space of T^*.
  (iv) For an operator S, $TS = 0$ if and only if $PS = 0$. Similarly, $ST = 0$ if and only if $SQ = 0$.
  (v) If U is unitary, and R is any projection, then UR and RU are partially isometric. If S is isometric and T is partially isometric, then ST is partially isometric. If S and T are partially isometric, ST is not necessarily partially isometric.

13. Suppose $\mathfrak{K}$ is finite-dimensional.
  (i) If T is partially isometric, and $TT^* \leq T^*T$, necessarily $TT^* = T^*T$.
  (ii) If U is unitary, P is a projection, and $UPU^* \leq P$, necessarily $UP = PU$. Compare with *Exercise 6.14*.

14. If T is an operator with one-dimensional range, there exist vectors $y,z \in \mathfrak{K}$ such that $Tx = (x|z)y$ for all $x \in \mathfrak{K}$. Moreover,
  (i) $T^*x = (x|y)z$ for all $x \in \mathfrak{K}$
  (ii) $TT = \mu T$, μ a suitable scalar
  (iii) $\| T \| = \| y \| \, \| z \|$

(iv) $T^* = T$ if and only if $y = \alpha z$ for some real number α. Equivalently, $(y|z) = \pm \| y \| \| z \|$.

(v) What are necessary and sufficient conditions on y and z, in order that T be a projection?

§ 8. NORMAL OPERATORS

Definition 1. *An operator T is said to be* **normal** *in case $T^*T = TT^*$.*

Every unitary operator is normal; so is every self-adjoint operator. An isometric operator is normal if and only if it is unitary.

Theorem 1. *The following conditions on an operator T are equivalent:*

(a) *T is normal*

(b) *T^* is normal*

(c) *$\| T^*x \| = \| Tx \|$ for all $x \in \mathfrak{IC}$.*

Proof.

The equivalence of (a) and (b) results from $T^{**} = T$.

(a) *implies* (c): $\| T^*x \|^2 = (T^*x | T^*x) = (TT^*x | x) = (T^*Tx | x) = (Tx | Tx) = \| Tx \|^2$.

(c) *implies* (a): $(T^*Tx | x) = \| Tx \|^2 = \| T^*x \|^2 = (TT^*x | x)$ for all x. ∎

Theorem 2. *Let $T = A + iB$ be the Cartesian form of the operator T. Then, T is normal if and only if $AB = BA$.*

Proof.

Only if: Assuming T normal, it is clear from the formulas in *Theorem 6.3* that $AB = BA$.

If: Suppose $AB = BA$; since $T^* = A - iB$, clearly $T^*T = TT^* = AA + BB$. ∎

Exercises

1. If T is normal, and S is unitarily equivalent to T, then S is normal.

2. T is normal if and only if T and T^* are metrically equivalent.

3. (i) If T is normal, and $TT = 0$, then $T = 0$.
   (ii) Give an example of an operator $T \neq 0$ such that $TT = 0$.

4. If T is normal, and μ is a scalar, then $\| T^*x - \mu^*x \| = \| Tx - \mu x \|$ for all $x \in \mathfrak{IC}$.

5. If T is normal, then T and T^* have the same null space, and $\overline{T(\mathfrak{IC})} = \overline{T^*(\mathfrak{IC})}$. If $\mathfrak{N}$ is the null space of T, then $\mathfrak{N}^\perp = \overline{T(\mathfrak{IC})}$.

6. If T is normal, there exists a unitary operator U such that $T^* = UT$.

7. More generally, if S and T are metrically equivalent normal operators, there exists a unitary operator U such that $S = UT$.

8. Let T be a normal operator. Prove:
(i) T is surjective if and only if T^* is surjective.
(ii) T is injective if and only if T^* is injective.
(iii) T is bijective if and only if T^* is bijective.
(iv) If T is bijective, then T^*T^{-1} is unitary.

9. An operator T is said to be *invertible* if there exists an operator S such that $ST = TS = I$; in this case, it is clear that T is bijective, and $T^{-1} = S$. Prove:
(i)   If S and T are invertible operators, then ST is invertible, and $(ST)^{-1} = T^{-1}S^{-1}$.
(ii)   If T is an invertible operator, then so is T^*, and $(T^*)^{-1} = (T^{-1})^*$.
(iii) If T is an invertible normal (resp. self-adjoint) operator, then T^{-1} is normal (resp. self-adjoint).
(iv) If T is an invertible operator, then T^*T is invertible. The converse fails.
(v)   If T is normal, then T is invertible if and only if T^*T is invertible.
*(vi) It can be shown that every bijective operator T is invertible (that is, T^{-1} is necessarily continuous). A proof of this is sketched in *Exercises 11* through *13*.

*10. If T is a bijective normal operator, then T^{-1} is continuous (see also *Exercise 13*). A brief proof results from *Exercise 8* and *Exercise V.8.6*.

11. An operator T is said to be *bounded below* in case there exists a constant $N > 0$ such that $\| Tx \| \geq N \| x \|$ for all $x \in \mathfrak{IC}$. Equivalently, there exists a constant $M > 0$ such that $T^*T \geq MI$ in the sense of *Exercise 6.8*. Prove:

(i)   Every invertible operator is bounded below.

(ii) If an operator T is bounded below, then T is injective, and $T(\mathcal{3C})$ is a closed linear subspace of $\mathcal{3C}$. Hence, the mapping $T\colon \mathcal{3C} \to T(\mathcal{3C})$ has a continuous inverse.

(iii) An operator T is invertible if and only if, T is bounded below and $T(\mathcal{3C})$ is dense in $\mathcal{3C}$.

(iv) An operator T is invertible if and only if, T is bounded below and T^* is injective.

(v)   An operator T is invertible if and only if, T is injective and T^* is bounded below.

(vi) An operator T is invertible if and only if both T and T^* are bounded below.

*12. If T is a surjective operator, then T^* is bounded below.

*13. If T is a bijective operator, then T^{-1} is continuous.

14. Let T be an operator.

(i)   If $T^*T \geq I$ in the sense of *Exercise 6.8*, T is not necessarily invertible.

(ii) If $T^*T \geq I$ and $TT^* \geq I$, then T is invertible.

(iii) If T is normal and $T^*T \geq I$, then T is invertible.

(iv) If T is normal and bounded below, then T is invertible.

15. An operator S is said to be *similar* to the operator T in case there exists an invertible operator A such that $T = A^{-1}SA$. Notation: $S \sim T$. Then:

(i) $T \sim T$, for every operator T.

(ii)   If $S \sim T$, then $T \sim S$.

(iii) If $R \sim S$ and $S \sim T$, then $R \sim T$. Moreover,

(iv)   If $S \sim T$, then $S^* \sim T^*$.

(v)   If $S \cong T$ in the sense of *Exercise 5.10*, then $S \sim T$.

*(vi) If S and T are normal operators, it can be shown that $S \cong T$ if and only if $S \sim T$.

§ 9. INVARIANT AND REDUCING SUBSPACES

Definition 1. *A closed linear subspace $\mathfrak{N}$ is said to be* **invariant** *under the operator T in case $T(\mathfrak{N}) \subset \mathfrak{N}$.*

Examples

1. $\{\theta\}$ and $\mathfrak{IC}$ are invariant under every operator T.

2. The null space of an operator T is invariant under T; for, $Tx = \theta$ implies $T(Tx) = \theta$.

3. More generally, if S and T are operators such that $ST = TS$, the null space of T is invariant under S. For, if $Tx = \theta$, then $T(Sx) = (TS)x = (ST)x = S(Tx) = S\theta = \theta$.

Theorem 1. *Let* $\mathcal{S}$ *and* $\mathfrak{I}$ *be subsets of* $\mathfrak{IC}$, $\mathfrak{M} = \mathcal{S}^{\perp\perp}$, $\mathfrak{N} = \mathfrak{I}^{\perp\perp}$. *If* T *is an operator such that* $T(\mathcal{S}) \subset \mathfrak{I}$, *then* $T(\mathfrak{M}) \subset \mathfrak{N}$.

Proof.
Incidentally, $\mathfrak{M}$ (resp. $\mathfrak{N}$) is the smallest closed linear subspace of $\mathfrak{IC}$ which contains $\mathcal{S}$ (resp. $\mathfrak{I}$). By *Theorem V.8.4*, $T^*(\mathfrak{I}^{\perp}) \subset \mathcal{S}^{\perp}$, hence $T^{**}(\mathcal{S}^{\perp\perp}) \subset \mathfrak{I}^{\perp\perp}$. ∎

Examples

4. Let $\mathcal{S}$ be a subset of $\mathfrak{IC}$, $\mathfrak{N}$ the smallest closed linear subspace containing $\mathcal{S}$. If T is an operator such that $T(\mathcal{S}) \subset \mathcal{S}$, then $\mathfrak{N}$ is invariant under T; this follows at once from *Theorem 1*.

5. In particular, if $\mathcal{S}$ is a linear subspace of $\mathfrak{IC}$, $\mathfrak{N} = \bar{\mathcal{S}}$, and T is an operator such that $T(\mathcal{S}) \subset \mathcal{S}$, then $\mathfrak{N}$ is invariant under T. See also *Exercise 1*.

6. For any operator T, $\overline{T(\mathfrak{IC})}$ is invariant under T; this follows from the relation $T[T(\mathfrak{IC})] \subset T(\mathfrak{IC})$, and *Example 5*.

Theorem 2. *Let* T *be an operator,* $\mathfrak{M}$ *and* $\mathfrak{N}$ *closed linear subspaces of* $\mathfrak{IC}$. *The following conditions are equivalent:*

(a) $T(\mathfrak{M}) \subset \mathfrak{N}$

(b) $T^*(\mathfrak{N}^{\perp}) \subset \mathfrak{M}^{\perp}$

(c) $P_{\mathfrak{N}}TP_{\mathfrak{M}} = TP_{\mathfrak{M}}$.

Proof.

(a) and (b) are equivalent by *Theorem V.8.5*.

(a) *implies* (c): Given any $x \in \mathfrak{K}$, one has $P_{\mathfrak{M}}x \in \mathfrak{M}$ (see *Example 7.1*); by condition (a), $TP_{\mathfrak{M}}x \in \mathfrak{M}$, hence $P_{\mathfrak{M}}TP_{\mathfrak{M}}x = TP_{\mathfrak{M}}x$.

(c) *implies* (a): If $y \in \mathfrak{M}$, then $Ty = TP_{\mathfrak{M}}y = P_{\mathfrak{M}}TP_{\mathfrak{M}}y = P_{\mathfrak{M}}Ty$, hence $Ty \in \mathfrak{M}$. ∎

In particular, $\mathfrak{M}$ is invariant under T if and only if $\mathfrak{M}^{\perp}$ is invariant under T^*.

Corollary. *A closed linear subspace $\mathfrak{M}$ is invariant under the operator T if and only if $P_{\mathfrak{M}}TP_{\mathfrak{M}} = TP_{\mathfrak{M}}$.*

Definition 2. *Let $\mathfrak{M}$ be a closed linear subspace invariant under the operator T. The **restriction** of T to $\mathfrak{M}$ is the mapping $T/\mathfrak{M}: \mathfrak{M} \to \mathfrak{M}$ defined by $(T/\mathfrak{M})y = Ty$.*

Thus, $T/\mathfrak{M}$ is the mapping $y \to Ty$, restricted to $\mathfrak{M}$. **The** following is elementary:

Theorem 3. *Let $\mathfrak{M}$ be a closed linear subspace of $\mathfrak{K}$.*

(1) *If $\mathfrak{M}$ is invariant under the operator T, then $T/\mathfrak{M}$ is an operator in the Hilbert space $\mathfrak{M}$, and $\| T/\mathfrak{M} \| \leq \| T \|$.*

(2) *If $\mathfrak{M}$ is invariant under the operators S and T, then it is invariant under $S + T$, ST, and λT; moreover,*

$$(S + T)/\mathfrak{M} = (S/\mathfrak{M}) + (T/\mathfrak{M})$$

$$(ST)/\mathfrak{M} = (S/\mathfrak{M})(T/\mathfrak{M})$$

$$(\lambda T)/\mathfrak{M} = \lambda(T/\mathfrak{M}).$$

Definition 3. *A closed linear subspace $\mathfrak{M}$ is said to **reduce** the operator T in case both $\mathfrak{M}$ and $\mathfrak{M}^{\perp}$ are invariant under T.*

Theorem 4. *If T is an operator, and $\mathfrak{M}$ is a closed linear subspace, the following conditions are equivalent:*

(a)   *$\mathfrak{M}$ reduces T*

(b)   *$\mathfrak{M}^{\perp}$ reduces T*

(c)   *$\mathfrak{M}$ reduces T^**

(d)   *$\mathfrak{M}$ is invariant under both T and T^**

(e)   *$TP_{\mathfrak{M}} = P_{\mathfrak{M}}T$.*

Proof.

The equivalence of (a)–(d) is immediate from *Theorem 2* and the definitions. Let $P = P_{\mathfrak{N}}$.

(d) *implies* (e): By the Corollary of *Theorem 2*, $PTP = TP$ and $PT^*P = T^*P$. Then, $PT = P^*T = (T^*P)^* = (PT^*P)^* = PTP = TP$.

(e) *implies* (d): Assuming $PT = TP$, one has $PTP = TPP = TP$, hence $\mathfrak{N}$ is invariant under T by the cited corollary. Also, $PT^* = (TP)^* = (PT)^* = T^*P$, hence $\mathfrak{N}$ is invariant under T^*. ∎

Examples

7. If T is a normal operator, $\mathfrak{N} = \overline{T(\mathfrak{K})} = \overline{T^*(\mathfrak{K})}$ reduces T; for, $\mathfrak{N}^{\perp}$ is the null space of both T and T^*, hence is invariant under them both.

8. If $Tx_k = x_{k+1}$ is the one-sided shift operator (*Example 4.1*), the only closed linear subspaces which reduce T are $\{\theta\}$ and $\mathfrak{K}$. For, suppose $\mathfrak{N} \neq \{\theta\}$ is a closed linear subspace which reduces T. For a non-zero vector $y = \sum_1^{\infty} \lambda_k x_k$, define the *index* of y to be the smallest subscript k such that $\lambda_k \neq 0$. Let m be the smallest index of any non-zero vector in $\mathfrak{N}$, and choose any non-zero $y \in \mathfrak{N}$ with index m; clearly $y = \sum_m^{\infty} \lambda_k x_k$. Necessarily $m = 1$; otherwise, $\mathfrak{N}$ would contain the non-zero vector $T^*y = \sum_m^{\infty} \lambda_k x_{k-1} = \sum_{m-1}^{\infty} \lambda_{k+1} x_k$, contrary to the minimality of m. We may suppose $\lambda_1 = 1$, thus $y = x_1 + \sum_2^{\infty} \lambda_k x_k$. One has $T^*y = T^*x_1 + \sum_2^{\infty} \lambda_k T^* x_k = \theta + \sum_2^{\infty} \lambda_k x_{k-1}$, hence $TT^*y = \sum_2^{\infty} \lambda_k T x_{k-1} = \sum_2^{\infty} \lambda_k x_k = y - x_1$. Since $x_1 = y - TT^*y$, clearly $x_1 \in \mathfrak{N}$. Then, $\mathfrak{N}$ also contains $Tx_1 = x_2$, $Tx_2 = x_3$, and so on. Evidently $\mathfrak{N}$ is total, $\mathfrak{N}^{\perp} = \{\theta\}$, $\mathfrak{N} = \mathfrak{K}$. ∎

Theorem 5. *If $\mathfrak{N}$ reduces T, then $(T/\mathfrak{N})^* = T^*/\mathfrak{N}$.*

Proof.

Let $R = T/\mathfrak{N}$ and $S = T^*/\mathfrak{N}$; these are both defined, by condition (d) of *Theorem 4*. For all $x,y \in \mathfrak{N}$, $(R^*x\,|\,y) = (x\,|\,Ry) = (x\,|\,Ty) = (T^*x\,|\,y) = (Sx\,|\,y)$; since R^* and S are operators in $\mathfrak{N}$, $R^* = S$. ∎

Corollary 1. *If $\mathfrak{N}$ reduces T, and T is normal (resp. unitary), then $T/\mathfrak{N}$ is normal (resp. unitary).*

Proof.

By *Theorems 3* and *5*, $(T^*T)/\mathfrak{N} = (T^*/\mathfrak{N})(T/\mathfrak{N}) = (T/\mathfrak{N})^*(T/\mathfrak{N})$, and $I/\mathfrak{N}$ is the identity operator of $\mathfrak{N}$. ∎

Corollary 2. *If T is self-adjoint, and $\mathfrak{N}$ is invariant under T, then $T/\mathfrak{N}$ is self-adjoint.*

Proof.

Since $T^* = T$, $\mathfrak{N}$ reduces T by *Theorem 4*. Then, $(T/\mathfrak{N})^* = T^*/\mathfrak{N} = T/\mathfrak{N}$. ∎

Example 9. Suppose T is normal, and $\mathfrak{N}$ is invariant under T. Then, $T/\mathfrak{N}$ is normal if and only if $\mathfrak{N}$ reduces T.

For, if $\mathfrak{N}$ reduces T, $T/\mathfrak{N}$ is normal by Corollary 1 above.

Conversely, suppose $R = T/\mathfrak{N}$ is normal, that is, $R^*R = RR^*$, where R^* is an operator in $\mathfrak{N}$. Given $x \in \mathfrak{N}$, the problem is to show that $T^*x \in \mathfrak{N}$. For any $y \in \mathfrak{N}$, $(T^*x \,|\, y) = (x \,|\, Ty) = (x \,|\, Ry) = (R^*x \,|\, y)$; thus, $(T^*x - R^*x \,|\, y) = 0$ for all $y \in \mathfrak{N}$, $T^*x - R^*x \in \mathfrak{N}^\perp$. Since $R^*x \in \mathfrak{N}$, one has

$$\| T^*x \|^2 = \| (T^*x - R^*x) + R^*x \|^2 = \| T^*x - R^*x \|^2 + \| R^*x \|^2$$

by *Theorem II.6.2*. Since T and R are normal, $\| T^*x \| = \| Tx \|$ and $\| R^*x \| = \| Rx \| = \| Tx \|$, hence the above equation reduces to $\| Tx \|^2 = \| T^*x - R^*x \|^2 + \| Tx \|^2$. Thus, $T^*x - R^*x = \theta$, $T^*x = R^*x \in \mathfrak{N}$.

Exercises

1. Let $\mathfrak{S}$ and $\mathfrak{J}$ be subsets of the metric spaces $\mathfrak{X}$ and $\mathfrak{Y}$, respectively, and let $T: \mathfrak{X} \to \mathfrak{Y}$ be a continuous mapping such that $T(\mathfrak{S}) \subset \mathfrak{J}$. Then, $T(\bar{\mathfrak{S}}) \subset \bar{\mathfrak{J}}$.

2. If T is isometric, and $\mathfrak{N}$ is invariant under T, then $T/\mathfrak{N}$ is isometric.

3. If T has Cartesian form $T = A + iB$, and $\mathfrak{N}$ reduces T, then $T/\mathfrak{N}$ has Cartesian form $(A/\mathfrak{N}) + i(B/\mathfrak{N})$.

4. If $\mathfrak{N}$ is invariant under T, and P is the projection with range $\mathfrak{N}$, then $(T/\mathfrak{N})^* = (PT^*P)/\mathfrak{N}$.

5. Let $Uy_k = y_{k+1}$ be the two-sided shift operator (*Example 5.2*), $\mathfrak{N}$ the smallest closed linear subspace containing $y_1, y_2, y_3, \cdots$. Then $\mathfrak{N}$ is invariant under U, but does not reduce U.

6. If T is unitary, and $\mathfrak{N}$ is invariant under T, then $T/\mathfrak{N}$ is unitary if and only if $\mathfrak{N}$ reduces T.

7. If T is normal, $\mathfrak{N}$ is invariant under T, and $T/\mathfrak{N}$ is a scalar operator, then $\mathfrak{N}$ reduces T.

8. Suppose T is isometric, and $\mathfrak{N}$ is invariant under T. Then:
   (i) If $T(\mathfrak{N}) = \mathfrak{N}$, $\mathfrak{N}$ reduces T.
   (ii) If $T/\mathfrak{N}$ is normal, then $\mathfrak{N}$ reduces T and $T/\mathfrak{N}$ is unitary.

9. Call an operator T *hyponormal* in case $\| T^*x \| \leq \| Tx \|$ for all $x \in \mathfrak{IC}$. Prove:
   (i) T is hyponormal if and only if $TT^* \leq T^*T$ in the sense of *Exercise 6.8*.
   (ii) If T is isometric, then T is hyponormal.
   (iii) If T is hyponormal, $\mathfrak{N}$ is invariant under T, and $T/\mathfrak{N}$ is normal, then $\mathfrak{N}$ reduces T.

10. Let $\mathfrak{N}$ be a closed linear subspace invariant under the operator T. Prove:
   (i) If $R = T/\mathfrak{N}$, $\| R^*x \| \leq \| T^*x \|$ for all $x \in \mathfrak{N}$.
   (ii) If T is hyponormal, so is $T/\mathfrak{N}$.

11. An operator T is hyponormal if and only if there exists an operator V, $\| V \| \leq 1$, such that $T^* = VT$.

12. If T is an invertible hyponormal operator, then T^{-1} is hyponormal.

13. Let $Uy_k = y_{k+1}$ be the two-sided shift operator. Given a bounded sequence of complex numbers μ_n ($n = 0,\pm1,\pm2,\cdots$), let R be the unique operator such that $Ry_k = \mu_k y_k$ for all k. Define $T = RU$. Then, T is hyponormal if and only if $|\mu_k| \leq |\mu_{k+1}|$ for all k. T is normal if and only if all the μ_k lie on the circle in the complex plane with center 0 and radius $|\mu_0|$; equivalently, T is a scalar multiple of a unitary operator.

14. *(i) It can be shown that every hyponormal operator on a finite-dimensional Hilbert space is normal.
   (ii) If T is hyponormal, and $\mathfrak{N}$ is a finite-dimensional subspace invariant under T, then $\mathfrak{N}$ reduces T.

15. Let $T = A + iB$ be the Cartesian form of the operator T. Let $AB = C + iD$ be the Cartesian form of AB. Then, T is hyponormal if and only if $D \leq 0$.

16. Let $Tx_k = x_{k+1}$ be the one-sided shift operator. The only finite-dimensional subspace $\mathfrak{N}$ invariant under T is $\mathfrak{N} = \{\theta\}$.

17. If $Tx_k = x_{k+1}$ is the one-sided shift operator, there exists a linear subspace $\mathcal{S}$, distinct from $\{\theta\}$ and $\mathfrak{IC}$, such that $T(\mathcal{S}) \subset \mathcal{S}$ and $T^*(\mathcal{S}) \subset \mathcal{S}$. Such a linear subspace is necessarily dense in $\mathfrak{IC}$. Among all such $\mathcal{S}$, there is a smallest, that is, one which is contained in every other.

18. Suppose $\mathfrak{N}$ reduces the operator T. Then, T is an isometric operator if and only if both $T/\mathfrak{N}$ and $T/\mathfrak{N}^{\perp}$ are isometric. The word "isometric" can be replaced by "unitary," "normal," "self-adjoint," "projection," "hyponormal," "positive," "invertible."

**19. Given an arbitrary operator T. It is not known whether there exists a closed linear subspace $\mathfrak{N}$ invariant under T, other than $\{\theta\}$ and $\mathfrak{IC}$.

Proper Values

§ 1. PROPER VECTORS, PROPER VALUES

Definition 1. *A vector $x \in \mathcal{K}$ is said to be a* **proper vector** *for the operator T in case:* (1) $x \neq \theta$, *and* (2) $Tx = \mu x$ *for a suitable scalar μ.*

If also $Tx = \nu x$, then $(\mu - \nu)x = \theta$, hence $\mu = \nu$. Thus, a proper vector x determines uniquely the associated scalar μ.

Definition 2. *A scalar μ is said to be a* **proper value** *for the operator T in case there exists a vector $x \neq \theta$ such that $Tx = \mu x$.*

Thus, μ is a proper value for T if and only if the null space of $T - \mu I$ is $\neq \{\theta\}$.

Examples

1. If $T = \mu I$, every non-zero vector of $\mathcal{K}$ is a proper vector for T; the only proper value is μ.

2. Let P be the projection with range $\mathfrak{N}$. Assume $\mathfrak{N} \neq \{\theta\}$, $\mathfrak{N} \neq \mathcal{K}$. If y is any non-zero vector of $\mathfrak{N}$, $Py = y = 1y$ shows that y is a proper vector, with associated proper value 1. Similarly, every non-zero $z \in \mathfrak{N}^\perp$ is a proper vector, with associated proper value 0. The only proper values of P are 0 and 1. Every proper vector of P belongs either to $\mathfrak{N}$ or to $\mathfrak{N}^\perp$.

3. Let x be a proper vector for T, say $Tx = \mu x$. If $\mathfrak{N}$ is the null space of $T - \mu I$, every non-zero vector of $\mathfrak{N}$ is also a proper vector. In particular, $\| x \|^{-1}x$ is a proper vector of norm 1.

4. Given a Hilbert space $\mathfrak{K}$ of finite dimension n, and scalars $\mu_1, \cdots, \mu_n$ (not necessarily distinct). If $x_1, \cdots, x_n$ is any basis of $\mathfrak{K}$, there is a unique linear mapping $T: \mathfrak{K} \to \mathfrak{K}$ such that $Tx_k = \mu_k x_k$ for all k (see *Theorem IV.1.3*). See *Exercise 1*.

Theorem 1. *Let μ be a proper value for T. Then:*

(1) $|\mu| \leq \|T\|$.

(2)   *If T is self-adjoint, μ is real.*

(3)   *If T is isometric, $|\mu| = 1$.*

Proof.

Let x be a non-zero vector such that $Tx = \mu x$; we may suppose $\|x\| = 1$.

(1): $|\mu| = \|\mu x\| = \|Tx\| \leq \|T\|$.

(2): $\mu = \mu(x|x) = (\mu x|x) = (Tx|x)$ is real by *Theorem VI.6.1*.

(3): $|\mu| = \|Tx\| = \|x\| = 1$. ∎

Example 5. Let $\mathfrak{K}$ be classical Hilbert space, x_n an orthonormal basis for $\mathfrak{K}$, μ_n a bounded sequence of scalars, and T the unique operator such that $Tx_k = \mu_k x_k$ for all k (see *Theorem VI.3.1*). Thus, the μ_k are proper values for T. In fact, these are the *only* proper values. For, suppose $Tx = \mu x$, $x \neq \theta$. Say $x = \sum_1^\infty \lambda_k x_k$; then $Tx = \sum_1^\infty \lambda_k \mu_k x_k$, hence $\lambda_k \mu_k = (Tx|x_k) = (\mu x|x_k) = \mu(x|x_k) = \mu \lambda_k$, $\lambda_k(\mu - \mu_k) = 0$ for all k. Since $x \neq 0$, there is an index m such that $\lambda_m \neq 0$; necessarily $\mu - \mu_m = 0$, thus $\mu = \mu_m$. Similarly, the μ_k^* are the proper values for T^*; this is a symptom of normality:

Theorem 2. *If T is a normal operator, x is a vector, and μ is a scalar, then $Tx = \mu x$ if and only if $T^*x = \mu^* x$. In particular:*

(1)   *x is a proper vector for T if and only if it is a proper vector for T^*.*

(2)   *μ is a proper value for T if and only if μ^* is a proper value for T^*.*

Proof.

By assumption, $T^*T = TT^*$. Since $(T - \mu I)^* = T^* - \mu^* I$, clearly $T - \mu I$ is normal, hence $\|(T - \mu I)x\| = \|(T - \mu I)^* x\|$ by *Theorem VI.8.1*. ∎

Examples

6. The one-sided shift operator $Tx_k = x_{k+1}$ (see *Example VI.4.1*) has *no* proper values. For, assuming $Tx = \mu x$, let us show that necessarily $x = \theta$. If $\mu = 0$, $Tx = \mu x = 0x = \theta$; since T is injective, $x = \theta$. Suppose $\mu \neq 0$. If $x = \sum_1^\infty \lambda_k x_k$, then $Tx = \sum_1^\infty \lambda_k x_{k+1} = \sum_2^\infty \lambda_{k-1} x_k$, hence $0 = (Tx \,|\, x_1) = (\mu x \,|\, x_1) = \mu\lambda_1$; thus $\lambda_1 = 0$. Also, for $k > 1$, $\lambda_{k-1} = (Tx \,|\, x_k) = (\mu x \,|\, x_k) = \mu\lambda_k$, hence $\lambda_k = \mu^{-1}\lambda_{k-1}$; since $\lambda_1 = 0$, this implies $\lambda_k = 0$ for all k.

7. If μ is a proper value for the operator S, it does not follow that μ^* is a proper value for S^*. For instance, let $S = T^*$, where T is the one-sided shift operator. As shown in *Example 6*, S^* has no proper values, but $Sx_1 = T^*x_1 = \theta = 0x_1$ shows that 0 is a proper value for S.

8. There exist normal operators having no proper values. For example, let $Uy_k = y_{k+1}$ be the two-sided shift operator (see *Example VI.5.2*). Suppose $Ux = \mu x$, and assume to the contrary that $x \neq \theta$. Since U is isometric, $|\mu| = 1$. If $x = \sum_{-\infty}^\infty \lambda_k y_k$, then

$$Ux = \sum_{-\infty}^\infty \lambda_k y_{k+1} = \sum_{-\infty}^\infty \lambda_{k-1} y_k.$$

For all k, $\lambda_{k-1} = (Ux \,|\, y_k) = \mu(x \,|\, y_k) = \mu\lambda_k$, hence $|\lambda_{k-1}| = |\lambda_k|$. It follows that $|\lambda_k| = |\lambda_0|$ for all k; since $x \neq \theta$, $\lambda_0 \neq 0$. But $\sum_{-\infty}^\infty |\lambda_k|^2 < \infty$, a contradiction.

Exercises

1. Notation as in *Example 4*. T is an operator, and a complex number μ is a proper value for T if and only if $\mu = \mu_k$ for some k.

2. Notation as in *Example 5*. If the μ_k are distinct, a non-zero vector x is a proper vector for T if and only if x is a scalar multiple of some x_k.

3. Let $Tx_k = x_{k+1}$ be the one-sided shift operator, and R the unique operator such that $Rx_k = (1/k)x_k$ for all k $(k = 1,2,3,\cdots)$. Then $S = TR$ has no proper values.

4. If $Tx_k = x_{k+1}$ is the one-sided shift operator, then μ is a proper value for T^* if and only if $|\mu| < 1$.

5. There exists a self-adjoint operator T which has no proper values.

6. If T is a hyponormal operator, and $Tx = \mu x$, then $T^*x = \mu^* x$.

7. Let T be an operator. Then:

(i) A non-zero vector x is a proper vector for T if and only if $|(Tx|x)| = \|Tx\| \|x\|$.

(ii) In order that T have a proper value μ such that $|\mu| = \|T\|$, it is necessary and sufficient that there exist a vector x such that $\|x\| = 1$ and $|(Tx|x)| = \|T\|$.

(iii) If α_n is a sequence of scalars such that $\alpha_k \geq 0$ for all k, and $\sum_1^\infty \alpha_k^2 = 1$, then $\sum_1^\infty \alpha_k \alpha_{k+1} < 1$.

8. Proper vectors and values are definable for a linear mapping of a vector space into itself. If T is a continuous linear mapping in a normed space, and μ is a proper value for T, then $|\mu| \leq \|T\|$.

§ 2. PROPER SUBSPACES

Definition 1. *If T is an operator and μ is a scalar, the null space of the operator $T - \mu I$ is called the μ-th **proper subspace** of T, and is denoted $\mathfrak{N}_T(\mu)$. Thus,*

$$\mathfrak{N}_T(\mu) = \{x \in \mathfrak{IC}: Tx = \mu x\}.$$

*Briefly, $\mathfrak{N}_T(\mu)$ is the μ-**space** of T.*

Thus, $\mathfrak{N}_T(\mu)$ is a closed linear subspace of $\mathfrak{IC}$; it is different from $\{\theta\}$ if and only if μ is a proper value for T. A non-zero vector x is a proper vector for T if and only if x belongs to some μ-space of T.

Theorem 1. *If S and T are operators such that $ST = TS$, then the μ-spaces of T are invariant under S; that is,*

$$S(\mathfrak{N}_T(\mu)) \subset \mathfrak{N}_T(\mu) \text{ for all } \mu.$$

Proof.

If $x \in \mathfrak{N}_T(\mu)$, then $T(Sx) = (TS)x = (ST)x = S(Tx) = S(\mu x) = \mu(Sx)$ shows that $Sx \in \mathfrak{N}_T(\mu)$. $\blacksquare$

Corollary. *The μ-spaces of T are invariant under T.*

Theorem 2. *If T is a **normal** operator,*

(1)   *the μ-spaces of T reduce T;*

(2) $\mathfrak{N}_T(\mu) = \mathfrak{N}_{T*}(\mu^*)$;

(3) $\mathfrak{N}_T(\mu) \perp \mathfrak{N}_T(\nu)$ *whenever $\mu \neq \nu$.*

Proof.

(1): Since $T^*T = TT^*$, $\mathfrak{N}_T(\mu)$ is invariant under T^* by *Theorem 1*. By the *Corollary*, $\mathfrak{N}_T(\mu)$ is also invariant under T, hence $\mathfrak{N}_T(\mu)$ reduces T by *Theorem VI.9.4*.

(2): See *Theorem 1.2*.

(3): Given $x \in \mathfrak{N}_T(\mu)$, $y \in \mathfrak{N}_T(\nu)$, and $\mu - \nu \neq 0$, the problem is to show that $x \perp y$. By (2), $T^*y = \nu^*y$. Then, $(Tx\,|\,y) = (x\,|\,T^*y)$, $(\mu x\,|\,y) = (x\,|\,\nu^*y)$, $\mu(x\,|\,y) = \nu(x\,|\,y)$, $(\mu - \nu)(x\,|\,y) = 0$, hence $(x\,|\,y) = 0$. ∎

Theorem 1 has a converse, provided T has "sufficiently many" proper vectors:

Theorem 3. *Suppose T is an operator such that the only vector x which is orthogonal to every μ-space of T is $x = \theta$. Then, the following conditions on an operator S are equivalent:*

(a) $ST = TS$

(b)   *Every μ-space of T is invariant under S.*

Proof.

(b) *implies* (a): Let $\mathfrak{N}$ be the null space of $TS - ST$; the problem is to show that $\mathfrak{N} = \mathcal{K}$, or, equivalently, that $\mathfrak{N}^\perp = \{\theta\}$.

One has $\mathfrak{N}_T(\mu) \subset \mathfrak{N}$; for, if $x \in \mathfrak{N}_T(\mu)$, by assumption $Sx \in \mathfrak{N}_T(\mu)$, hence $T(Sx) = \mu(Sx) = S(\mu x) = S(Tx)$, $(TS - ST)x = \theta$. It follows that if $x \perp \mathfrak{N}$, then $x \perp \mathfrak{N}_T(\mu)$ for all μ, hence $x = \theta$ by the hypothesis on T.

(a) implies (b) by *Theorem 1*. ∎

The hypothesis on the μ-spaces of T in *Theorem 3* is conveniently expressed in terms of the following:

Definition 2. *A family of closed linear subspaces is said to be **total** in case the only vector x which is orthogonal to every subspace $\mathfrak{N}$ belonging to the family is $x = \theta$.*

Thus, the condition on T in *Theorem 3* is that the μ-spaces are a total family. It will be shown in § 4 of Chapter VIII that the μ-spaces of any "completely continuous" normal operator are a total family; this is the essence of the "spectral theorem" for such operators.

Exercises

1. If T is any operator, and P_μ is the projection whose range is $\mathfrak{N}_T(\mu)$, then $P_\mu T P_\mu = T P_\mu = \mu P_\mu$.

2. Let $T x_k = \mu_k x_k$, with notation as in *Example 1.5*.
(i)   Describe the μ-spaces of T.
(ii) If S is an operator, $ST = TS$ if and only if every μ-space of T is invariant under S.
(iii) If S is an operator such that $ST = TS$, then $S^*T = TS^*$.
(iv) If S is an operator, $ST = TS$ if and only if the μ-spaces of T reduce S.

3. Suppose T is a normal operator whose μ-spaces are a total family. If S is an operator such that $ST = TS$, then $ST^* = T^*S$.

4. If the μ-spaces of an operator T are a total family, and $\mathfrak{N}_T(\mu) \subset \mathfrak{N}_{T^*}(\mu^*)$ for all μ, then T is normal.

5. Let T be a hyponormal operator.
(i)   For every scalar μ, $\mathfrak{N}_T(\mu) \subset \mathfrak{N}_{T^*}(\mu^*)$.
(ii) For a fixed scalar μ, let $\mathfrak{N} = \mathfrak{N}_T(\mu)$. Then, $\mathfrak{N}$ reduces T, and $T/\mathfrak{N}$ is normal.
(iii) $\mathfrak{N}_T(\mu) \perp \mathfrak{N}_T(\nu)$ whenever $\mu \neq \nu$.
(iv) If the μ-spaces of T are a total family, then T is normal.

*6. If $\mathfrak{IC}$ is finite-dimensional, every hyponormal operator T is normal.

7. *Definition 1* makes sense, and *Theorem 1* is true, for linear mappings in a vector space. For a continuous linear mapping in a normed space, the μ-spaces are closed linear subspaces.

8. Suppose $x_1, \cdots, x_n$ are proper vectors for T, $T x_k = \mu_k x_k$. If $\mu_1, \cdots, \mu_n$ are distinct, then $x_1, \cdots, x_n$ are linearly independent.

9. If the μ-spaces of T reduce T, and are a total family, then T is normal.

§ 3. APPROXIMATE PROPER VALUES

A scalar μ is a proper value for the operator T if and only if there exists a vector x such that $\| x \| = 1$ and $\| Tx - \mu x \| = 0$. An operator may not have any proper values at all, even if it is normal (see

Example 1.8). A less stringent condition on μ would be the following: given any $\epsilon > 0$, there exists a vector x such that $\| x \| = 1$ and $\| Tx - \mu x \| < \epsilon$; equivalently,

Definition 1. *A scalar μ is said to be an* **approximate proper value** *for the operator T in case there exists a sequence of vectors x_n such that* $\| x_n \| = 1$ *and* $\| Tx_n - \mu x_n \| \to 0$. *Briefly, μ is an AP-**value** for T.*

Examples

1. Every proper value for T is obviously also an AP-value.

2. Let $Tx_k = \mu_k x_k$, with notation as in *Example 1.5*. Assume moreover that the sequence μ_k converges to a limit μ, distinct from every μ_k. As shown in *Example 1.5*, μ is not a proper value for T; however, $\| Tx_k - \mu x_k \| = \| \mu_k x_k - \mu x_k \| = \| (\mu_k - \mu) x_k \| = | \mu_k - \mu | \to 0$, hence μ is an AP-value for T.

3. Let μ be an AP-value for T, and suppose $\| Tx_n - \mu x_n \| \to 0$, where $\| x_n \| = 1$. Then, $| (Tx_n | x_n) - \mu | = | (Tx_n | x_n) - \mu (x_n | x_n) | = | (Tx_n - \mu x_n | x_n) | \leq \| Tx_n - \mu x_n \| \to 0$, hence $(Tx_n | x_n) \to \mu$, $| (Tx_n | x_n) | \to | \mu |$. Clearly $| \mu | \leq \text{LUB} \{ | (Tx | x) | : \| x \| \leq 1 \} \leq \| T \|$.

Theorem 1. *The following conditions on an operator T are equivalent:*

(a) *T has an AP-value μ such that $| \mu | = \| T \|$.*

(b) $\text{LUB} \{ | (Tx | x) | : \| x \| \leq 1 \} = \| T \|$.

Proof.

(a) *implies* (b): Suppose $| \mu | = \| T \|$, $\| x_n \| = 1$, and $\| Tx_n - \mu x_n \| \to 0$. As shown in *Example 3*, $| (Tx_n | x_n) | \to | \mu | = \| T \|$. If M denotes the indicated LUB, one has $\| T \| \geq M \geq | (Tx_n | x_n) | \to \| T \|$ as $n \to \infty$, hence $M = \| T \|$.

(b) *implies* (a): Choose a sequence of vectors x_n such that $\| x_n \| = 1$ and $| (Tx_n | x_n) | \to \| T \|$. Passing to a subsequence, we may assume $(Tx_n | x_n) \to \mu$ for a suitable scalar μ, hence $| \mu | = \| T \|$. Then, $0 \leq \| Tx_n - \mu x_n \|^2 = \| Tx_n \|^2 - (Tx_n | \mu x_n) - (\mu x_n | Tx_n) + | \mu |^2 = \| Tx_n \|^2 - (Tx_n | \mu x_n) - (Tx_n | \mu x_n)^* + | \mu |^2 \leq \| T \|^2 - (Tx_n | \mu x_n) - (Tx_n | \mu x_n)^* + | \mu |^2 = | \mu |^2 - \mu^* (Tx_n | x_n) - \mu (Tx_n | x_n)^* + | \mu |^2 \to | \mu |^2 - \mu^* \mu - \mu \mu^* + | \mu |^2 = 0$ as $n \to \infty$. Thus, $\| Tx_n - \mu x_n \| \to 0$, and μ is an AP-value for T. ∎

There exist self-adjoint operators having no proper values at all (see *Exercise 1.5*). However, it can be shown that *every* operator has at least one AP-value. For our purposes, the following result will suffice:

Theorem 2. *If T is a self-adjoint operator, either* $\| T \|$ *or* $-\| T \|$ *is an AP-value for T.*

Proof.

Condition (b) of *Theorem 1* holds for T, by *Theorem VI.6.4*. Let $(Tx_n | x_n) \rightarrow \mu$, with notation as in the proof of *Theorem 1*. Since $(Tx_n | x_n)$ is real for all n, μ is real. Since $|\mu| = \| T \|$, one has $\mu^2 = \| T \|^2$. ∎

Exercises

1. AP-values are definable for a linear mapping in a normed space. If T is a continuous linear mapping, and μ is an AP-value for T, then $|\mu| \leq \| T \|$.

2. If μ is an AP-value for T, then $\mu + \lambda$ is an AP-value for $T + \lambda I$, and $\lambda\mu$ is an AP-value for λT.

3. If T is isometric, and μ is an AP-value for T, then $|\mu| = 1$.

4. If T is self-adjoint, every AP-value for T is real.

5. If T is normal, and μ is an AP-value for T, then μ^* is an AP-value for T^*.

6. Let T be a hyponormal operator.
   (i) If μ is an AP-value for T, then μ^* is an AP-value for T^*.
   (ii) Let μ and ν be AP-values for T, $\mu \neq \nu$. If x_n and y_n are sequences of unit vectors such that $\| Tx_n - \mu x_n \| \rightarrow 0$ and $\| Ty_n - \nu y_n \| \rightarrow 0$, then $(x_n | y_n) \rightarrow 0$.

7. If μ is an AP-value for the operator S, it does not follow that μ^* is an AP-value for S^*.

8. (i) μ is an AP-value for T if and only if $T - \mu I$ fails to be bounded below in the sense of *Exercise VI.8.11*.
   (ii) If μ is an AP-value for T, $T - \mu I$ cannot be invertible.
   (iii) If $Tx_k = x_{k+1}$ is the one-sided shift operator, then $T = T - 0I$ is not invertible, but 0 is not an AP-value for T.

*9. It can be shown that every normal operator T has an AP-value μ such that $|\mu| = \| T \|$, hence $\| T \| = $ LUB $\{ | (Tx|x) | : \| x \| \leq 1 \}$. It would be nice to have a proof in the reverse order.

10. Let T be an operator, μ a scalar. The following conditions are equivalent:

(a) μ is an AP-value for T.

(b) There exists a sequence of operators S_n such that $\| S_n \| = 1$ and $\| (T - \mu I)S_n \| \to 0$.

*11. *Exercise 10* can be generalized to normed spaces.

12. The *spectrum* of an operator T is defined to be the set of all scalars μ such that $T - \mu I$ fails to be invertible in the sense of *Exercise VI.8.9;* it will be denoted $s(T)$. Then:

(i)   If μ is an AP-value for T, $\mu \in s(T)$.

(ii) $\mu \in s(T)$ if and only if $\mu^* \in s(T^*)$.

(iii) $s(T + \lambda I) = \{ \mu + \lambda : \mu \in s(T) \}$.

(iv) $s(\lambda T) = \{ \lambda \mu : \mu \in s(T) \}$.

(v) T is invertible if and only if 0 is not in $s(T)$.

(vi)   If T is invertible, $s(T^{-1}) = \{ \mu^{-1} : \mu \in s(T) \}$.

(vii)   If T is self-adjoint, every $\mu \in s(T)$ is real.

(viii)   If T is positive, every $\mu \in s(T)$ is ≥ 0.

*(ix)   It can be shown that for every operator T, $s(T)$ is a *non-empty* and *closed* set of complex numbers, and $|\mu| \leq \| T \|$ for all $\mu \in s(T)$.

(x)   If T is normal, $\mu \in s(T)$ if and only if μ is an AP-value for T.

(xi)   If T is unitary, then $|\mu| = 1$ for every $\mu \in s(T)$.

*(xii)   If $Tx_k = x_{k+1}$ is the one-sided shift operator, $s(T)$ is the entire disc $|\mu| \leq 1$.

*13. If Λ is any non-empty closed and bounded set of complex numbers, and $\mathcal{3C}$ is classical Hilbert space, there exists a normal operator T such that (1) Λ is the spectrum of T, and (2) $\mu \in \Lambda$ if and only if μ is an AP-value for T.

Completely Continuous Operators

§ 1. COMPLETELY CONTINUOUS OPERATORS

If the μ-spaces of an operator T are a total family, and S is any operator, $ST = TS$ if and only if the μ-spaces of T are invariant under S; this shows the power of proper values. However, the μ-spaces of an operator, even a self-adjoint one, may all be $\{\theta\}$; this shows their weakness.

Every self-adjoint operator T does have an AP-value μ, in fact, one for which $|\mu| = \| T \|$. Happily, there is an important class of operators for which AP-values are nearly always proper (see *Theorem 3.2*); these are the completely continuous operators:

Definition 1. *An operator T is said to be* **completely continuous** *in case: given any sequence of vectors x_n such that $\| x_n \|$ is bounded, Tx_n has a convergent subsequence. Briefly, T is a CC-***operator.**

Clearly, an operator T is CC if and only if: $\| x_n \| \leq 1$ implies Tx_n has a convergent subsequence.

Examples

1. The zero operator is CC.

2. If y and z are fixed vectors, the operator T defined by the formula $Tx = (x|y)z$ is CC. For, suppose $\| x_n \| \leq 1$. Since $|(x_n|y)| \leq \| y \|$,

$(x_n|y)$ has a convergent subsequence, say $(x_{n_k}|y) \to \lambda$; then $Tx_{n_k} = (x_{n_k}|y)z \to \lambda z$.

3. If $\mathcal{H}$ is infinite-dimensional, the identity operator is *not* CC. For, if $x_1,x_2,x_3,\cdots$ is any orthonormal sequence (see *Theorems I.7.3 and II.6.4*), $\| Ix_m - Ix_n \|^2 = \| x_m - x_n \|^2 = 2$ whenever $m \neq n$, hence Ix_n cannot have a convergent subsequence. ∎

The results of this section and the next show that CC-operators exist abundantly; § 3 is preliminary to § 4, in which normal CC-operators are analyzed in detail.

Theorem 1. *If T is a CC-operator, and λ is a scalar, λT is a CC-operator.*

Proof.
  If $Tx_{n_k} \to y$, then $(\lambda T)x_{n_k} \to \lambda y$. ∎

Theorem 2. *If S and T are CC-operators, $S + T$ is a CC-operator.*

Proof.
  Given $\| x_n \| \leq 1$, the problem is to find a convergent subsequence of $Sx_n + Tx_n$. Passing to a subsequence, we may suppose $Sx_n \to u$. For a further subsequence, $Tx_{n_k} \to v$; since also $Sx_{n_k} \to u$, $(S + T)x_{n_k} \to u + v$. ∎

Definition 2. *An operator T is said to be **finite-dimensional** if its range $T(\mathcal{H})$ is a finite-dimensional linear subspace.*

Theorem 3. *Every finite-dimensional operator T is CC.*

Proof.
  Let $z_1,\cdots,z_n$ be an orthonormal basis for $T(\mathcal{H})$. For each $x \in \mathcal{H}$, $Tx = \sum_1^n f_k(x)z_k$, where $f_1(x),\cdots,f_n(x)$ are scalars uniquely determined by x; clearly $f_k(x) = (Tx|z_k) = (x|T^*z_k)$. Define $T_kx = f_k(x)z_k = (x|T^*z_k)z_k$; T_k is a CC-operator by *Example 2*, hence $T = \sum_1^n T_k$ is CC by *Theorem 2*. ∎

Theorem 4. *If T is a CC-operator, and S is **any** operator, then ST and TS are CC-operators.*

Proof.
  Given $\| x_n \| \leq 1$. For a suitable subsequence, $Tx_{n_k} \to u$, hence $STx_{n_k} \to Su$; thus, ST is CC. Also, $\| Sx_n \| \leq \| S \|$, hence $T(Sx_n)$ has a convergent subsequence; thus, TS is CC. ∎

Theorem 5. *If T_n is a sequence of CC-operators, T is an operator, and $\| T - T_n \| \to 0$, then T is a CC-operator.*

Proof. ("diagonal procedure")

Given $\| x_n \| \leq 1$, the problem is to find a convergent subsequence of Tx_n.

Let x_n^1 be a subsequence of x_n for which $T_1 x_n^1$ is convergent. Say, $T_1 x_n^1 \to u_1$.

Let x_n^2 be a subsequence of x_n^1 for which $T_2 x_n^2$ is convergent. Say, $T_2 x_n^2 \to u_2$.

Continuing inductively, one obtains, for each k, a subsequence x_n^k of x_n^{k-1} such that $T_k x_n^k \to u_k$.

The x_n^k may be arranged in a rectangular array, with $x_1^k, x_2^k, x_3^k, \cdots$ as the k'th row. Then, the k'th row is by construction a subsequence of the $(k-1)$'th row. Consider the "diagonal sequence" $x_1^1, x_2^2, x_3^3, \cdots$. For each k, the sequence $x_k^k, x_{k+1}^{k+1}, x_{k+2}^{k+2}, \cdots$ is clearly a subsequence of the k'th row, hence

$$\lim_{n \to \infty} T_k x_n^n = u_k \quad \text{for } k = 1,2,3, \cdots.$$

We assert that Tx_n^n is a Cauchy sequence. For, given any $\epsilon > 0$, fix any index k such that $\| T - T_k \| \leq \epsilon$. For all m and n, $\| T x_m^m - T x_n^n \| \leq \| (T - T_k) x_m^m \| + \| T_k x_m^m - T_k x_n^n \| + \| (T_k - T) x_n^n \| \leq 2\epsilon + \| T_k x_m^m - T_k x_n^n \|$. Since $T_k x_n^n \to u_k$ as $n \to \infty$, there is an index N such that $\| T_k x_m^m - T_k x_n^n \| \leq \epsilon$ whenever $m,n \geq N$. Then, $\| T x_m^m - T x_n^n \| \leq 3\epsilon$ whenever $m,n \geq N$. This shows that the sequence Tx_n^n is Cauchy; since $\mathfrak{IC}$ is complete, it is convergent. ∎

Corollary. *If T_n is a sequence of finite-dimensional operators, T is an operator, and $\| T_n - T \| \to 0$, then T is a CC-operator.*

Proof.

Each T_n is a CC-operator by *Theorem 3*, hence T is CC by *Theorem 5*. ∎

Exercises

1. Let T be an operator, $\mathfrak{N}$ a closed linear subspace of $\mathfrak{IC}$.

(i) If $\mathfrak{N}$ is invariant under T, and T is CC, then $T/\mathfrak{N}$ is CC.

(ii) If $\mathfrak{N}$ reduces T, T is CC if and only if both $T/\mathfrak{N}$ and $T/\mathfrak{N}^\perp$ are CC.

2. If $\mathfrak{IC}$ is finite-dimensional, every linear mapping $T: \mathfrak{IC} \to \mathfrak{IC}$ is a CC-operator.

3. (i) If S and T are metrically equivalent operators, and T is CC, then S is CC.

(ii) In particular, if T is normal and CC, then T^* is CC. See also *Exercise 6*.

4. If T is a CC-operator, and $S^*S \leq T^*T$, then S is a CC-operator. In particular, if T is a hyponormal CC-operator, T^* is CC. See also *Exercise 6*.

5. If $\mathcal{X}$ is infinite-dimensional, a CC-operator cannot be invertible.

6. (i) An operator T is CC if and only if T^*T is CC.
(ii) If T is a CC-operator, then T^* is CC.

7. (i) If $\mathcal{X}$ is infinite-dimensional, and the operator T is bounded below, then T cannot be CC.
  *(ii) If $\mathcal{X}$ is infinite-dimensional, a CC-operator cannot be surjective.

8. (i) If y and z are fixed vectors, and $y \neq \theta$, there exists a CC-operator T such that $Ty = z$.

(ii) More generally, the set of CC-operators is *n-fold transitive* in the following sense: if $y_1, \cdots, y_n$ are linearly independent, and $z_1, \cdots, z_n$ are arbitrary, there exists a CC-operator T such that $Ty_k = z_k$ for all k.

9. If $\mathcal{Q}$ is an algebra, an *ideal* of $\mathcal{Q}$ is a linear subspace $\mathcal{I}$ such that: if $x \in \mathcal{I}$, and $a \in \mathcal{Q}$ is arbitrary, both $ax \in \mathcal{I}$ and $xa \in \mathcal{I}$. Evidently, an ideal of $\mathcal{Q}$ is a subalgebra. The results of this section can be summarized as follows:

(i) The CC-operators form a closed ideal $\mathcal{L}_{cc}(\mathcal{X})$ of the Banach algebra $\mathcal{L}_c(\mathcal{X})$, and this ideal contains every finite-dimensional operator.

(ii) $\mathcal{L}_{cc}(\mathcal{X})$ is itself a Banach algebra.

(iii) One has $I \in \mathcal{L}_{cc}(\mathcal{X})$ if and only if $\mathcal{X}$ is finite-dimensional, and in this case $\mathcal{L}_{cc}(\mathcal{X}) = \mathcal{L}_c(\mathcal{X})$.

(iv) In view of *Exercise 6*, $\mathcal{L}_{cc}(\mathcal{X})$ is a *-subalgebra of $\mathcal{L}_c(\mathcal{X})$, hence is a B^*-algebra.

10. Notation as in *Exercise V.8.11*, with $\mathcal{K} = \mathcal{X}$ a classical Hilbert space. Prove:

(i) The *-algebra $\mathcal{L}_{hs}(\mathcal{X},\mathcal{X})$ of operators of Hilbert-Schmidt class is an ideal of $\mathcal{L}_c(\mathcal{X})$.

(ii) Every finite-dimensional operator is of Hilbert-Schmidt class.

*11. If $\mathfrak{g}$ is an ideal of $\mathfrak{L}_c(\mathfrak{IC})$, different from $\{0\}$, then $\mathfrak{g}$ contains every finite-dimensional operator.

12. If $\mathcal{E}$ and $\mathfrak{F}$ are normed spaces, complete continuity is definable for a linear mapping $T: \mathcal{E} \to \mathfrak{F}$. If T is CC, it is necessarily continuous.

13. Let $\mathcal{E}$ and $\mathfrak{F}$ be normed spaces, and denote by $\mathfrak{L}_{cc}(\mathcal{E},\mathfrak{F})$ the set of all CC linear mappings $T: \mathcal{E} \to \mathfrak{F}$. Then:

(i) $\mathfrak{L}_{cc}(\mathcal{E},\mathfrak{F})$ is a linear subspace of $\mathfrak{L}_c(\mathcal{E},\mathfrak{F})$.

(ii) $\mathfrak{L}_{cc}(\mathcal{E},\mathcal{E})$ is an ideal in the algebra $\mathfrak{L}_c(\mathcal{E})$, hence is a normed algebra.

(iii) If $\mathfrak{F}$ is a Banach space, $\mathfrak{L}_{cc}(\mathcal{E},\mathfrak{F})$ is a closed linear subspace of the Banach space $\mathfrak{L}_c(\mathcal{E},\mathfrak{F})$, hence is itself a Banach space.

(iv) If $\mathfrak{F}$ is a Banach space, $\mathfrak{L}_{cc}(\mathfrak{F},\mathfrak{F})$ is a closed ideal of the Banach algebra $\mathfrak{L}_c(\mathfrak{F})$, hence is itself a Banach algebra.

*(v) If $T: \mathcal{E} \to \mathfrak{F}$ is a continuous linear mapping such that $T(\mathcal{E})$ is finite-dimensional, then T is CC.

*(vi) It can be shown that the identity mapping $I: \mathcal{E} \to \mathcal{E}$ is CC if and only if $\mathcal{E}$ is finite-dimensional. In this case, every linear mapping $T: \mathcal{E} \to \mathcal{E}$ is CC.

14. If $\mathcal{E}$ and $\mathfrak{F}$ are normed spaces, and $\mathcal{E}$ is finite-dimensional, then every linear mapping $T: \mathcal{E} \to \mathfrak{F}$ is CC.

15. Let $\mathcal{E}$ be a normed space, and $\mathfrak{N}$ a dense linear subspace of $\mathcal{E}$. Prove:

(i) If $x \in \mathcal{E}$, there exists a sequence $y_n \in \mathfrak{N}$ such that $y_n \to x$, and $\| y_n \| = \| x \|$ for all n.

(ii) Let $\mathfrak{B}$ be a Banach space, $S: \mathfrak{N} \to \mathfrak{B}$ a continuous linear mapping. If $T: \mathcal{E} \to \mathfrak{B}$ is the unique continuous linear mapping such that $Ty = Sy$ for all $y \in \mathfrak{N}$ (see *Theorem IV.7.6*), then T is CC if and only if S is CC.

*16. If $\mathcal{E}$ is a normed space, $\mathfrak{B}$ is a Banach space, and $T: \mathcal{E} \to \mathfrak{B}$ is a continuous linear mapping, it can be shown that T is CC if and only if T' is CC.

17. If $\mathcal{E}$ and $\mathfrak{F}$ are normed spaces, consider the set of all linear mappings $T: \mathcal{E} \to \mathfrak{F}$ satisfying the following condition: if $x_n \in \mathcal{E}$, $\| x_n \| \leq 1$, Tx_n has a Cauchy subsequence. Examine the theorems of this section, with complete continuity replaced by this condition.

§2. AN EXAMPLE

Let $\mathcal{K}$ be classical Hilbert space, x_n an orthonormal basis for $\mathcal{K}$, μ_n a bounded sequence of scalars, and T the unique operator such that $Tx_k = \mu_k x_k$ for all k (see *Theorem VI.3.1*). If P_k is the projection whose range is the one-dimensional subspace generated by x_k, and $T_n = \sum_1^n \mu_k P_k$, one has $T_n x \to Tx$ for each $x \in \mathcal{K}$ (see *Example VI.7.3*). It will be shown in §4 that if T is CC, necessarily $\mu_n \to 0$; we are concerned here with the converse:

Theorem 1. *If $\mu_n \to 0$, then $\| T - T_n \| \to 0$ and T is completely continuous.*

Proof.

The range of T_n is contained in the n-dimensional subspace generated by $x_1, \cdots, x_n$, hence T_n is a finite-dimensional operator. In view of the Corollary of *Theorem 1.5*, it will suffice to show that $\| T - T_n \| \to 0$.

Given $\epsilon > 0$, let N be an index such that $|\mu_k| \leq \epsilon$ whenever $k \geq N$. Fix an index $n \geq N$; it will be shown that $\| T - T_n \| \leq \epsilon$. For any vector $x = \sum_1^\infty \lambda_k x_k$, one has $T_n x = \sum_1^n \lambda_k \mu_k x_k$, hence $\| Tx - T_n x \|^2$ $= \| \sum_1^\infty \lambda_k \mu_k x_k - \sum_1^n \lambda_k \mu_k x_k \|^2 = \| \sum_{n+1}^\infty \lambda_k \mu_k x_k \|^2 = \sum_{n+1}^\infty |\lambda_k \mu_k|^2$ $\leq \epsilon^2 \sum_{n+1}^\infty |\lambda_k|^2 \leq \epsilon^2 \sum_1^\infty |\lambda_k|^2 = \epsilon^2 \| x \|^2$. Thus, $\| (T - T_n)x \| \leq \epsilon \cdot \| x \|$; since x is arbitrary, $\| T - T_n \| \leq \epsilon$. ∎

Exercises

1. Let $\mathcal{K}$ be classical Hilbert space, x_n an orthonormal basis for $\mathcal{K}$, and (α_{jk}) an "infinite matrix" of scalars ($j = 1,2,3,\cdots$; $k = 1,2,3,\cdots$) such that $\sum_{j,k} |\alpha_{jk}|^2 < \infty$. Then, there exists one and only one operator T such that $Tx_k = \sum_j \alpha_{jk} x_j$ for all k; this operator is CC. Every operator of Hilbert-Schmidt class is completely continuous.

2. If $\mathcal{K}$ is classical Hilbert space, x_n is an orthonormal basis for $\mathcal{K}$, and β_{jk} are scalars such that $\sum_{j,k} |\beta_{jk}| < \infty$, there exists a unique operator T whose matrix is (β_{jk}) relative to the given basis. This operator is of Hilbert-Schmidt class, hence is CC.

§ 3. PROPER VALUES OF CC-OPERATORS

Recall that if T is an operator and μ is a scalar, $\mathfrak{N}_T(\mu)$ denotes the μ-space of T; it is the closed linear subspace $\{x \in \mathfrak{K} : Tx = \mu x\}$, that is, the null space of the operator $T - \mu I$.

Theorem 1. *If T is a CC-operator, and $\mu \neq 0$, then $\mathfrak{N}_T(\mu)$ is finite-dimensional.*

Proof.

Assume to the contrary; by *Theorem I.7.3*, $\mathfrak{N}_T(\mu)$ contains a linearly independent sequence x_n. By *Theorem II.6.4*, we may suppose the x_n are orthonormal. If $m \neq n$, $\| Tx_m - Tx_n \|^2 = \| \mu x_m - \mu x_n \|^2 = |\mu|^2 \| x_m - x_n \|^2 = 2 |\mu|^2 > 0$, hence Tx_n cannot have a convergent subsequence; since $\| x_n \| = 1$, this is contrary to the complete continuity of T. ∎

Definition 1. *Suppose μ is a proper value for the operator T. If $\mathfrak{N}_T(\mu)$ has finite dimension n, μ is said to be a proper value of **finite multiplicity** n. If $\mathfrak{N}_T(\mu)$ is infinite-dimensional, μ is said to have **infinite multiplicity**. If μ is not a proper value for T, that is, if $\mathfrak{N}_T(\mu) = \{\theta\}$, it is convenient to say that μ is a "proper value of **multiplicity zero**."*

In this terminology, *Theorem 1* asserts that every non-zero proper value of a CC-operator has finite multiplicity. This result is not always helpful, for there exist CC-operators having no proper values at all:

Example 1. Let $Tx_k = x_{k+1}$ be the one-sided shift operator, R the unique operator such that $Rx_k = (1/k)x_k$ for all k, and let $S = TR$. Since R is CC by *Theorem 2.1*, S is CC by *Theorem 1.4*; however, S has no proper values (see *Exercise VII.1.3*). ∎

Every *normal* CC-operator does have at least one proper value, as is shown in *Theorem 3* below. This result is expedited by the following

Theorem 2. *If T is a CC-operator, and μ is a **non-zero** approximate proper value for T, then μ is a proper value.*

Proof.

By assumption, there exists a sequence of vectors x_n such that $\| x_n \| = 1$ and $\| Tx_n - \mu x_n \| \to 0$. Since T is CC, we may suppose, after passing to a subsequence, that Tx_n is convergent, say $Tx_n \to u$. Since $\| u - \mu x_n \| \leq \| u - Tx_n \| + \| Tx_n - \mu x_n \| \to 0$, one has $\mu x_n \to u$. Then, $T(\mu x_n) \to Tu$, thus $Tu = \lim T(\mu x_n) = \lim \mu(Tx_n)$

$= \mu \lim T x_n = \mu u$. Since $\| u \| = \lim \| \mu x_n \| = \lim | \mu | = | \mu | > 0$, u is a proper vector.   ∎

Lemma 1. *If S is any self-adjoint CC-operator, S has a proper value μ such that $| \mu | = \| S \|$.*

Proof.

If $S = 0$, $\mu = 0$ is a proper value (we are assuming $\mathcal{K} \neq \{\theta\}$). If $S \neq 0$, then by *Theorem VII.3.2*, S has an approximate proper value μ such that $| \mu | = \| S \| > 0$; quote *Theorem 2*.   ∎

Lemma 2. *If $\mathcal{K}$ is finite-dimensional, every normal operator T has at least one proper value.*

Proof.

Every operator in $\mathcal{K}$ is CC, by *Theorem 1.3*. Let $T = A + iB$ be the Cartesian form of T (see *Theorem VI.6.3*). By *Lemma 1*, there is a (real) scalar α such that the proper subspace $\mathfrak{N} = \mathfrak{N}_A(\alpha)$ is $\neq \{\theta\}$. Since T is normal, $AB = BA$ (see *Theorem VI.8.2*), hence $\mathfrak{N}$ is invariant under B (see *Theorem VII.2.1*). Let $R = B/\mathfrak{N}$ be the restriction of B to $\mathfrak{N}$; R is self-adjoint operator in $\mathfrak{N}$ (see Corollary 2 of *Theorem VI.9.5*). By *Lemma 1*, there exists a scalar β, and a non-zero vector $x \in \mathfrak{N}$ such that $Rx = \beta x$, that is, $Bx = \beta x$. By the definition of $\mathfrak{N}$, $Ax = \alpha x$, hence $Tx = Ax + iBx = (\alpha + i\beta)x$.   ∎

Theorem 3. *Every normal CC-operator T has at least one proper value; in fact, there exists a proper value μ such that $| \mu | = \| T \|$.*

Proof.

Let $S = T^*T$; S is self-adjoint, and is CC by *Theorem 1.4*. We may suppose $T \neq 0$, hence $\| S \| > 0$.

By the definition of $\| T \|$, there is a sequence of vectors x_n such that $\| x_n \| = 1$ and $\| T x_n \| \to \| T \|$. Then, $\| S \| = \| T^*T \| = \| T \|^2 = \lim \| T x_n \|^2 = \lim (T^* T x_n | x_n) = \lim (S x_n | x_n)$.

Passing to a subsequence, we may suppose, by the complete continuity of T, that $T x_n \to y$ for a suitable vector y.

Let $\alpha = \| S \|$. We assert that α is a proper value for S. For, $\| S x_n - \alpha x_n \|^2 = \| S x_n \|^2 - 2\alpha(S x_n | x_n) + \alpha^2 \leq \alpha^2 - 2\alpha(S x_n | x_n) + \alpha^2 \to \alpha^2 - 2\alpha^2 + \alpha^2 = 0$, thus $S x_n - \alpha x_n \to \theta$. Since $T x_n \to y$, one has $S x_n = T^*(T x_n) \to T^* y$, hence $\alpha x_n = (\alpha x_n - S x_n) + S x_n \to \theta + T^* y$. Thus, $x_n \to \alpha^{-1}(T^* y)$. Setting $z = \alpha^{-1}(T^* y)$, one has $x_n \to z$, $\| z \| = \lim \| x_n \| = \lim 1 = 1$, and $Sz = \lim S x_n = T^* y = \alpha z$. Thus, z is a proper vector for S, with associated proper value α. [One could also have quoted *Lemma 1*, since $S \geq 0$; see the remarks following this theorem.]

Let $\mathfrak{N} = \mathfrak{N}_S(\alpha)$; it has just been shown that $\mathfrak{N} \neq \{\theta\}$. Since $\alpha > 0$, $\mathfrak{N}$ is finite-dimensional by *Theorem 1*. Since T is normal, clearly $TS = ST$ and $T^*S = ST^*$, hence $\mathfrak{N}$ reduces T (see *Theorems VII.2.1* and *VI.9.4*). Let $R = T/\mathfrak{N}$; R is a normal operator in $\mathfrak{N}$ (see Corollary 1 of *Theorem VI.9.5*). By *Lemma 2*, there exists a scalar μ, and a vector $x \in \mathfrak{N}$, such that $\| x \| = 1$ and $Rx = \mu x$, that is, $Tx = \mu x$. By *Theorem VII.1.2*, $T^*x = \mu^*x$, hence $Sx = T^*Tx = |\mu|^2 x$; since $Sx = \alpha x$ by the definition of $\mathfrak{N}$, $|\mu|^2 = \alpha$. Thus, $|\mu|^2 = \| S \| = \| T \|^2$.   ∎

Remarks on Theorem 3

Suppose T is a normal CC-operator. Since $\| T^*x_m - T^*x_n \| = \| T^*(x_m - x_n) \| = \| T(x_m - x_n) \| = \| Tx_m - Tx_n \|$, it is clear that T^* is also CC. Let $T = A + iB$ be the Cartesian form; it is clear from the formulas in *Theorem VI.6.3* that A and B are CC-operators (see *Theorems 1.1* and *1.2*). It follows that the proof of *Lemma 2* is valid for T without the assumption of finite-dimensionality: T has at least one proper value.

Why mention *Lemma 2* at all? The point is that the existence of proper values for a linear mapping in finite-dimensional space is an essentially algebraic fact (see *Exercise 5*) which may be known to the reader from other contexts. Granted *Lemma 2*, one way or another, the proof of *Theorem 3* derives directly from *Lemma 2*, and one need not quote *Theorem 2* and *Lemma 1*; in this way, the concept of AP-value is circumvented, thus emphasizing the algebraic aspects of *Theorem 3* and the spectral theorem to follow.

Exercises

1. (i) If T is a normal CC-operator, there exists a vector x, $\| x \| = 1$, such that $|(Tx|x)| = \| T \|$. Compare this with *Exercise VII.1.7*.

*(ii) It can be shown that for every normal operator T, $\| T \| = $ LUB $\{ |(Tx|x)| : \| x \| = 1\}$.

2. Notation as in the proof of *Theorem 3*. Then, $\mathfrak{N}$ contains all vectors x such that $Tx = \lambda x$ for some scalar λ with $|\lambda| = \| T \|$. One has $\| Tx \| = \| T \| \| x \|$ for every $x \in \mathfrak{N}$.

3. Let $Rx_k = (1/k)x_k$, as in *Example 1*. R is a self-adjoint CC-operator, 0 is an AP-value for R, but 0 is not a proper value.

*4. It can be shown that every operator T has at least one AP-value μ. If moreover T is CC and $\mu \neq 0$, T has a proper value.

*5. It can be shown that if $\mathcal{H}$ is finite-dimensional, every operator T has at least one proper value.

*6. *Theorem 1* holds for a CC linear mapping $T: \mathcal{E} \to \mathcal{E}$, where $\mathcal{E}$ is a normed space.

*7. In the wake of a result such as *Theorem 2*, the reader should be warned of the existence of a stubborn class of operators whose only AP-values are 0. Such an operator is called a *generalized nilpotent*. It can be shown that the following conditions on an operator T are equivalent:
 (a) T is a generalized nilpotent.
 (b) The spectrum of T is $\{0\}$.
 (c) $\lim \| T^n \|^{1/n} = 0$.
[The operators T^n are defined inductively by the formulas $T^1 = T$, $T^{n+1} = T^n T$. Incidentally, T is called a *nilpotent* operator in case $T^n = 0$ for some n.] It can be shown that the only normal generalized nilpotent is the zero operator.

8. The operator S of *Example 1* is a generalized nilpotent.

§ 4. SPECTRAL THEOREM FOR A NORMAL CC-OPERATOR

Throughout this section, T is a fixed normal CC-operator.

Theorem 1. (Spectral Theorem) *The proper subspaces of T are a total family. That is, if $x \perp \mathfrak{N}_T(\mu)$ for every scalar μ, necessarily $x = \theta$.*

Proof.
 Let $\mathcal{S}$ be the smallest subset of $\mathcal{H}$ such that $\mathfrak{N}_T(\mu) \subset \mathcal{S}$ for all μ; clearly $\mathcal{S} = \{x \in \mathcal{H}: x \in \mathfrak{N}_T(\mu)$ for some $\mu\}$. Let $\mathfrak{N} = \mathcal{S}^\perp$; the problem is to show that $\mathfrak{N} = \{\theta\}$.
 Since each $\mathfrak{N}_T(\mu)$ reduces T (*Theorem VII.2.2*), $T(\mathcal{S}) \subset \mathcal{S}$ and $T^*(\mathcal{S}) \subset \mathcal{S}$; by *Theorem V.8.4*, $T^*(\mathfrak{N}) \subset \mathfrak{N}$ and $T(\mathfrak{N}) \subset \mathfrak{N}$, thus $\mathfrak{N}$ reduces T (see *Theorem VI.9.4*).
 Assume to the contrary that $\mathfrak{N} \neq \{\theta\}$, and let $R = T/\mathfrak{N}$; R is a normal operator in $\mathfrak{N}$ (see Corollary 1 of *Theorem VI.9.5*). We assert that R is a CC-operator in the Hilbert space $\mathfrak{N}$. For, if $x_n \in \mathfrak{N}$ and $\| x_n \| \leq 1$, $Rx_n = Tx_n$ has a convergent subsequence, say $Rx_{n_k} \to u \in \mathcal{H}$; since $\mathfrak{N}$ is closed, $u \in \mathfrak{N}$.

Thus, R is a normal CC-operator in the Hilbert space $\mathfrak{N} \neq \{\theta\}$. By *Theorem 3.3*, there exists a non-zero vector $x \in \mathfrak{N}$, and a scalar μ, such that $Rx = \mu x$, that is, $Tx = \mu x$. Then, $x \in \mathfrak{N}_T(\mu) \subset \mathcal{S}$; but $x \in \mathfrak{N} = \mathcal{S}^\perp$, hence $x \perp x$, $x = \theta$, a contradiction. ∎

Let $P(\mu)$ denote the projection with range $\mathfrak{N}_T(\mu)$. [More precisely, $P(\mu) = P_T(\mu)$; thus, $P_{T*}(\mu) = P_T(\mu^*)$.] The following result is essentially an application of the spectral theorem:

Theorem 2. *The following conditions on an operator S are equivalent:*

(a) $ST = TS$

(b) *The μ-spaces of T are invariant under S.*

(c) $ST^* = T^*S$

(d) *The μ-spaces of T reduce S.*

(e) $SP(\mu) = P(\mu)S$ *for all* μ.

Proof.

(a) *implies* (b): See *Theorem VII.2.1*.

(b) *implies* (c): Since $\mathfrak{N}_{T*}(\mu) = \mathfrak{N}_T(\mu^*)$, the μ-spaces of T^* are invariant under S; since they are a total family by the spectral theorem, $ST^* = T^*S$ by *Theorem VII.2.3*.

(c) *implies* (d): The μ-spaces of T^* are invariant under S by *Theorem VII.2.1*; in other words, the μ-spaces of T are invariant under S. Since $S^*T = TS^*$, the μ-spaces of T are also invariant under S^*.

(d) and (e) are equivalent by *Theorem VI.9.4*.

(d) implies (a) by *Theorem VII.2.3* and the spectral theorem. ∎

The next results will show that the proper values of T can be enumerated in a (finite or infinite) sequence.

Theorem 3. *For each $\epsilon > 0$, the annulus $\epsilon \leq |\lambda| \leq \| T \|$ contains at most finitely many proper values of T. Every proper value of T lies in the disc $|\lambda| \leq \| T \|$; that is, $\mathfrak{N}_T(\lambda) = \{\theta\}$ whenever $|\lambda| > \| T \|$.*

Proof.

If μ is a proper value of T, $|\mu| \leq \| T \|$ was shown in *Theorem VII.1.1*; this does not require any special hypotheses on T.

Given $\epsilon > 0$, assume to the contrary that there exists an infinite sequence μ_n of distinct proper values of T such that $\epsilon \leq |\mu_n| \leq \| T \|$.

Passing to a subsequence, we may assume $\mu_n \to \mu$, where $\epsilon \le |\mu| \le \| T \|$. Let $Tx_n = \mu_n x_n$, $\| x_n \| = 1$. Again passing to a subsequence; we may assume $Tx_n \to y$ for a suitable vector y. Thus, $\mu_n x_n \to y$, since $\mu_n^{-1} \to \mu^{-1}$, one has $x_n = \mu_n^{-1}(\mu_n x_n) \to \mu^{-1}y$, hence $\| x_m - x_n \| \to 0$ as $m,n \to \infty$. But x_n is an orthonormal sequence by *Theorem VII.2.2*, hence $\| x_m - x_n \|^2 = 2$ whenever $m \ne n$, a contradiction. ∎

Let us first dispose of a special case:

Theorem 4. *The following conditions on T are equivalent:*

(a)   *T is finite-dimensional.*

(b)   *T has only finitely many distinct proper values* $\mu_1, \cdots, \mu_n$.

In this case, $T = \sum_1^n \mu_k P(\mu_k)$.

Proof.

(a) *implies* (b): Assume to the contrary there is an infinite sequence $\mu_1, \mu_2, \mu_3, \cdots$ of distinct proper values. Let $Tx_k = \mu_k x_k$, $\| x_k \| = 1$; the sequence of vectors x_n is orthonormal, hence linearly independent. Since at most one of the μ_k is 0, $x_k = T(\mu_k^{-1}x_k) \in T(\mathfrak{IC})$ for the remaining k, hence $T(\mathfrak{IC})$ is infinite-dimensional.

(b) *implies* (a): Let $\mathfrak{M}$ be the smallest linear subspace containing $\mathfrak{N}_T(\mu_1), \cdots, \mathfrak{N}_T(\mu_n)$. Evidently, $\mathfrak{M}$ is the set of all vectors x of the form $x = \sum_1^n y_k$, with $y_k \in \mathfrak{N}_T(\mu_k)$ (see *Theorem I.5.1*). Since the $\mathfrak{N}_T(\mu_k)$ are mutually orthogonal, it is appropriate to write $\mathfrak{M} = \mathfrak{N}_T(\mu_1) \oplus \cdots \oplus \mathfrak{N}_T(\mu_n)$, in analogy with *Definition III.2.5*. We assert that $\mathfrak{M} = \mathfrak{IC}$; since $\mathfrak{M}$ is closed (see the Corollary of *Theorem III.4.2*), it will suffice to show that $\mathfrak{M}^\perp = \{\theta\}$. Indeed, let

$$\mathfrak{S} = \{x \in \mathfrak{IC} : x \in \mathfrak{N}_T(\mu) \text{ for some } \mu\};$$

clearly $\mathfrak{M}^\perp = \mathfrak{S}^\perp$. But $\mathfrak{S}^\perp = \{\theta\}$ was shown in the proof of *Theorem 1*.

Thus, given any vector $x \in \mathfrak{IC}$, one can write $x = \sum_1^n y_k$, with $y_k \in \mathfrak{N}_T(\mu_k)$. If $j \ne k$, then $y_k \in [\mathfrak{N}_T(\mu_j)]^\perp$, hence $P(\mu_j)y_k = \theta$; it follows that $P(\mu_j)x = \sum_k P(\mu_j)y_k = y_j$, thus $x = \sum_1^n P(\mu_k)x$. This shows that $\sum_1^n P(\mu_k) = I$. Also,

$$Tx = \sum_1^n Ty_k = \sum_1^n \mu_k y_k = \sum_1^n \mu_k P(\mu_k)x,$$

hence $T = \sum_1^n \mu_k P(\mu_k)$.

Incidentally, if T is also injective, $\mathcal{K}$ is necessarily finite-dimensional. ∎

Assume henceforth that T is not finite-dimensional; that is, T has infinitely many proper values.

Theorem 5. *Assuming T is not a finite-dimensional operator,*

(1) *the distinct proper values of T can be enumerated in an infinite sequence $\mu_1, \mu_2, \mu_3, \cdots$;*

(2) *necessarily $\mu_n \to 0$;*

(3) *one can arrange to have $|\mu_1| \geq |\mu_2| \geq |\mu_3| \geq \cdots$.*

Proof.

(1): For each $n = 1, 2, 3, \cdots$, let Λ_n denote the set (possibly empty) of all proper values μ such that $1/n \leq |\mu| \leq \| T \|$. By *Theorem 3*, each Λ_n contains at most finitely many scalars, and every non-zero proper value belongs to some Λ_n. Since $\Lambda_1 \subset \Lambda_2 \subset \cdots$, the non-zero proper values can be enumerated in a sequence by first writing down those in Λ_1, those in Λ_2 not in Λ_1, and so on.

(2): Suppose λ_n is *any* sequence of distinct proper values of T. Given any $\epsilon > 0$. By *Theorem 3*, $|\lambda_n| \geq \epsilon$ for at most finitely many n, hence there is an index N such that $|\lambda_n| < \epsilon$ whenever $n \geq N$. Thus, $\lambda_n \to 0$.

(3): This is clear from the proof of (1); incidentally, $|\mu_1| = \| T \|$. ∎

Henceforth, $\mu_1, \mu_2, \mu_3, \cdots$ denotes the sequence of distinct non-zero proper values of T, enumerated as in *Theorem 5*. Then, $P(\mu_k)$ denotes the projection whose range is the proper subspace $\mathfrak{N}_T(\mu_k)$; $P(0)$ is the projection whose range is the null space of T. The next results will show that $T = \sum_1^\infty \mu_k P(\mu_k)$ in a suitable sense.

Lemma. *If $\mathfrak{N}_1, \mathfrak{N}_2, \mathfrak{N}_3, \cdots$ is a sequence of closed linear subspaces of $\mathcal{K}$ such that $\mathfrak{N}_j \perp \mathfrak{N}_k$ whenever $j \neq k$, the following conditions are equivalent:*

(a) *The $\mathfrak{N}_k$ are a total family.*

(b) *The smallest closed linear subspace of $\mathcal{K}$ which contains every $\mathfrak{N}_k$ is $\mathcal{K}$ itself.*

(c)   *Every $x \in \mathcal{K}$ is uniquely expressible in the form $x = \sum_1^\infty x_k$, with $x_k \in \mathfrak{N}_k$ and $\sum_1^\infty \| x_k \|^2 < \infty$.*

Proof.

Let $S = \{x \in \mathcal{K}: x \in \mathfrak{N}_k \text{ for some } k\}$; as shown in Corollary 2 of *Theorem III.6.3*, $\mathfrak{M} = S^{\perp\perp}$ is the smallest closed linear subspace containing every $\mathfrak{N}_k$. Since $\mathfrak{M}^\perp = S^{\perp\perp\perp} = S^\perp$, clearly $\mathfrak{M} = \mathcal{K}$ if and only if $S^\perp = \{\theta\}$. This proves the equivalence of (a) and (b).

Let P_k be the projection with range $\mathfrak{N}_k$.

(a) *implies* (c): Suppose first that $x_k \in \mathfrak{N}_k$ and $\sum_1^\infty \| x_k \|^2 < \infty$. It is clear from the Lemma of *Theorem II.7.1* that one can form the vector $x = \sum_1^\infty x_k = \lim_n \sum_1^n x_k$. Since $P_j x_k = \theta$ when $k \neq j$, $P_j \left(\sum_1^n x_k \right) = x_j$ whenever $n \geq j$, hence $P_j x = \lim_n P_j \left(\sum_1^n x_k \right) = x_j$.

Now, given any $x \in \mathcal{K}$, define $x_k = P_k x$. For each n, $Q_n = \sum_1^n P_k$ is a projection (see *Example VI.7.4*); since the x_k are mutually orthogonal, $\sum_1^n \| x_k \|^2 = \| \sum_1^n x_k \|^2 = \| \sum_1^n P_k x \|^2 = \| Q_n x \|^2 \leq \| x \|^2$, hence $\sum_1^\infty \| x_k \|^2 < \infty$. Form the vector $y = \sum_1^\infty x_k$. For each j, $P_j y = x_j = P_j x$, $P_j(y - x) = \theta$, $y - x \in \mathfrak{N}_j{}^\perp$; since the $\mathfrak{N}_j$ are total, $y - x = \theta$, $x = y = \sum_1^\infty x_k$. Since $x_j = P_j \left(\sum_1^\infty x_k \right)$, the uniqueness of such a representation is clear.

(c) *implies* (a): Suppose $x \perp \mathfrak{N}_j$ for all j. By (c), write $x = \sum_1^\infty x_k$ with $x_k \in \mathfrak{N}_k$. Since $x \in \mathfrak{N}_j{}^\perp$, $\theta = P_j x = x_j$ for all j, thus $x = \theta$. ∎

Definition 1. *If the conditions of the Lemma are fulfilled, one writes*

$$\mathcal{K} = \sum_{\oplus 1}^\infty \mathfrak{N}_k = \mathfrak{N}_1 \oplus \mathfrak{N}_2 \oplus \mathfrak{N}_3 \oplus \cdots.$$

More generally, let $\mathfrak{N}_1, \mathfrak{N}_2, \mathfrak{N}_3, \cdots$ be any sequence of closed linear subspaces, and $\mathfrak{N}$ the smallest closed linear subspace containing every $\mathfrak{N}_k$. If $x \perp \mathfrak{N}_k$ for all k, then $x \perp \mathfrak{N}$; for, writing $S = \{x\}$, one has $\mathfrak{N}_k \subset S^\perp$ for all k, hence $\mathfrak{N} \subset S^\perp$. It follows that $\mathfrak{N}_k$ is a total family of subspaces in the Hilbert space $\mathfrak{N}$. If moreover $\mathfrak{N}_j \perp \mathfrak{N}_k$ whenever $j \neq k$, one has $\mathfrak{N} = \sum_{\oplus 1}^\infty \mathfrak{N}_k$ in the sense of *Definition 1*. It is easy to see that $\sum_{\oplus 1}^\infty \mathfrak{N}_k = \mathfrak{N}_1 \oplus \sum_{\oplus 2}^\infty \mathfrak{N}_k$.

Theorem 6. *If μ_n is the sequence of distinct non-zero proper values of T, then*

(1) $\quad \mathfrak{IC} = \mathfrak{N}_T(0) \oplus \sum_{\oplus 1}^{\infty} \mathfrak{N}_T(\mu_k)$

$\qquad = \mathfrak{N}_{T^*}(0) \oplus \sum_{\oplus 1}^{\infty} \mathfrak{N}_{T^*}(\mu_k{}^*)$;

(2) $\quad \mathfrak{N}_T(0) = \mathfrak{N}_{T^*}(0)$ *is the null space of T and T^*, and*

$\qquad \overline{T(\mathfrak{IC})} = \overline{T^*(\mathfrak{IC})} = \sum_{\oplus 1}^{\infty} \mathfrak{N}_T(\mu_k) = \sum_{\oplus 1}^{\infty} \mathfrak{N}_{T^*}(\mu_k{}^*)$;

(3) $\quad \| T - \sum_1^n \mu_k P(\mu_k) \| \to 0$,

$\qquad \| T^* - \sum_1^n \mu_k{}^* P(\mu_k) \| \to 0$.

Proof.

(1) results from *Theorem 1*, the *Lemma*, and the fact that $\mathfrak{N}_{T^*}(\mu^*) = \mathfrak{N}_T(\mu)$.

(2): Let $\mathfrak{N} = \sum_{\oplus 1}^{\infty} \mathfrak{N}_T(\mu_k)$. It is clear from (1) that $\mathfrak{N} = [\mathfrak{N}_T(0)]^\perp = [\mathfrak{N}_{T^*}(0)]^\perp$; thus, $\mathfrak{N} = \overline{T^*(\mathfrak{IC})} = \overline{T(\mathfrak{IC})}$ by *Theorem V.8.6*.

(3): Given $x \in \mathfrak{IC}$, one has $x = P(0)x + \sum_1^{\infty} P(\mu_k)x$ by the proof of the *Lemma*. Then, $Tx = \theta + \sum_1^{\infty} \mu_k P(\mu_k)x = \lim_n \left[\sum_1^n \mu_k P(\mu_k) \right] x$. Since $\mu_n \to 0$, $\| T - \sum_1^n \mu_k P(\mu_k) \| \to 0$ by essentially the same argument as in *Theorem 2.1*. The remaining assertion follows from $\| S^* \| = \| S \|$. ∎

Corollary 1. *If T is a normal CC-operator, there exists a sequence of finite-dimensional operators T_n such that $\| T - T_n \| \to 0$.*

Corollary 2. *Notation as in the theorem. Given any vector $y \in \overline{T(\mathfrak{IC})}$, there exists an expansion $y = \sum_1^{\infty} y_k$, where the y_k are mutually orthogonal, $\sum_1^{\infty} \| y_k \|^2 < \infty$, and $T y_k = \mu_k y_k$.*

Exercises

1. Let $Tx_k = \mu_k x_k$, with notation as in *Example VII.1.5*. Then, T is CC if and only if $\mu_n \to 0$.

2. An operator T is CC if and only if there exists a sequence of finite-dimensional operators T_n such that $\| T_n - T \| \to 0$.

3. Let T and S be operators.
*(i) It can be shown that if T is normal, and $ST = TS$, then $ST^* = T^*S$. Granted this result; if S and T are normal, and $ST = TS$, then $S + T$ and ST are normal.
(ii) If T and S are hyponormal, and $ST^* = T^*S$, then $T - S$ is hyponormal.
(iii) If T is normal, S is hyponormal, and $ST = TS$, then $T - S$ is hyponormal.

4. If S and T are normal operators, $ST = TS$, and T is CC, then $S + T$ and ST are normal.

5. Let S and T be normal CC-operators, and assume, for the sake of simplicity, that both S and T are injective. Then, S and T are unitarily equivalent if and only if: for each scalar μ, the multiplicity of μ for T equals the multiplicity of μ for S.

6. (i) If S and T are similar operators, and $\mathfrak{N}_S(\mu)$ has finite dimension n, then $\mathfrak{N}_T(\mu)$ also has finite dimension n.
(ii) Suppose S and T are normal CC-operators. Assume for the sake of simplicity that S and T are injective. If S and T are similar, there exists a unitary operator U such that $U^*SU = T$; that is, S and T are unitarily equivalent.
*(iii) One can prove (ii) without the hypotheses of complete continuity and injectivity.

7. The most general normal CC-operator in $\mathfrak{K}$ can be obtained as follows. Let $\mathfrak{N}_0, \mathfrak{N}_1, \mathfrak{N}_2, \cdots$ be a total sequence of mutually orthogonal closed linear subspaces, with $\mathfrak{N}_k$ finite-dimensional for $k \geq 1$; let $\mu_1, \mu_2, \cdots$ be a sequence of scalars such that $\mu_n \to 0$; let $\mu_0 = 0$. There is a unique operator T such that $Tx = \mu_k x$ when $x \in \mathfrak{N}_k$, $(k = 0, 1, 2, \cdots)$.

8. Let T_n be a sequence of normal CC-operators such that $T_j T_k = T_k T_j$ for all j and k. Then, there exists a vector z which is proper for every T_k.

*9. *Theorem 3* holds for a CC linear mapping in a normed space.

**10. The analog of *Exercise 2* for Banach space is an open question.

11. Does there exist a hyponormal CC-operator which is not normal?

References, and Hints to the Exercises

[1] BANACH, S., *Théorie des opérations linéaires*, Warsaw, 1932.

[2] HALMOS, P. R., *Finite-dimensional vector spaces*, New York, 1958.

[3] HALMOS, P. R., *Introduction to Hilbert space and the theory of spectral multiplicity*, New York, 1951.

[4] HILLE, E. and R. S. PHILLIPS, *Functional analysis and semigroups*, Providence, 1957.

[5] LANDAU, E., *Differential and integral calculus*, New York, 1951.

[6] LOOMIS, L. H., *An introduction to abstract harmonic analysis*, New York, 1953.

[7] NAIMARK, M. A., *Normed rings*, Groningen, 1959.

[8] RIESZ, F. and B. SZ.-NAGY, *Leçons d'analyse fonctionelle*, Budapest, 1952.

[9] STONE, M. H., *Linear transformations in Hilbert space and their applications to analysis*, New York, 1932.

[10] TAYLOR, A. E., *Introduction to functional analysis*, New York, 1958.

CHAPTER I

§ 1. 2. See *Example 2*.

   3. See *Example 7*.

§ 5. 6. $e^t = \cosh t + \sinh t$.

   8. Show that each vector in $\mathfrak{M} + \mathfrak{N}$ is in [S], and vice versa.

§ 6. 4. Factor theorem.

   5. (ii) See *Exercise 4.4*.

§ 7. 6. See Section 1.72 of [10] for the existence of a basis, also called a *Hamel basis*.

CHAPTER II

§ 1. 1. See Theorem 388 of [5].

§ 3. 3. $x = (x - y) + y$.

4. Suppose the relation holds. Then, in the proof of *Theorem 5*, all $\leq$ signs can be replaced by $=$; cite *Exercise 2*.

5. See *Exercise 4*.

6. *Exercise 4*, and the relation $x = (x - y) + y$.

8. Assuming $\| x \| \leq 1$ and $\| y \| \leq 1$, it suffices to show that $|(x|y)| \leq 1$. If $(x|y)$ is real, $(x|y) = \frac{1}{4}\{\| x + y \|^2 - \| x - y \|^2\}$. In general, one can write $|(x|y)| = \lambda(x|y) = (\lambda x|y)$ for suitable $|\lambda| = 1$.

§ 4. 1. Try $\epsilon = \frac{1}{2}$.

6. For each t, $|x_m(t) - x_n(t)| \leq d(x_m,x_n)$.

§ 5. 5. See *Theorem 4.1* or *Exercise 3.3*.

§ 7. 1. If $|\lambda| \leq 1$, then $|\lambda|^2 \leq |\lambda|$.

2. $\| \sum_m^n x_k \| \leq \sum_m^n \| x_k \|$.

7. Bessel.

8. Assuming to the contrary, produce an infinite orthonormal sequence x_n such that $[x_1,x_2,x_3,\cdots] = [y_1,y_2,y_3,\cdots] = \mathfrak{IC}$, and look at the vector $x = \sum_1^\infty (1/k)x_k$.

§ 8. 1. $\mathcal{S}$ contains the vectors $x_n = (1,0,\cdots,0,-n,0,0,\cdots)$, where $-n$ occurs as the n'th coordinate.

2. Gram-Schmidt.

3, 4, 5. See Theorems 1.4 and 1.14 of [9].

6. See Theorems 155 and 479 of [5]. See also Section 3.22 of [10]. Another approach is via Theorem 4E of [6].

7. See §14 of [3].

CHAPTER III

§ 2. 3. (i) See *Theorem II.8.1*.

(ii) Look at $x = \sum_1^\infty (1/k)x_k$.

6. See *Exercise II.6.1*.

7. See the proof of part (3) of *Theorem 4.3*.

§ 3. 1. See the proof of the Lemma to *Theorem 2*.

2. See *Theorems 2.1* and *2.2*.

3. See *Exercise 2.3*.

§ 4. 2. Calculate $\mathfrak{N}^\perp$.

§ 5.   5. (iii) If y_n is a Cauchy sequence of vectors, and $\| y_n \| \to \alpha > 0$, consider the sequence $x_n = \| y_n \|^{-1} y_n$; see *Exercise 3.1*.

6. If $y = (\lambda_k) \in \mathcal{S}$, then $1 = |\sum_1^n \lambda_k| \le \sum_1^n |\lambda_k| = \sum_1^n 1 \cdot |\lambda_k|$

$$\le \sqrt{n} \left(\sum_1^n |\lambda_k|^2 \right)^{1/2} = \sqrt{n} \parallel y \parallel, \text{ thus } \parallel y \parallel \ge 1/\sqrt{n}.$$

Clearly $y_0 \in \mathcal{S}$ and $\| y_0 \| = 1/\sqrt{n}$. Quote uniqueness.

7. Look at the vectors $y_1 = (1,0,0,\cdots)$, $y_2 = (\frac{1}{2},\frac{1}{2},0,\cdots)$, $y_3 = (\frac{1}{3},\frac{1}{3},\frac{1}{3},0,\cdots),\cdots$.

§ 6.   3. See *Exercise II.8.1*.

4. Assuming to the contrary that such a vector $y_0 \in \mathcal{S}$ exists, one has $x - y_0 \in \mathcal{S}^\perp$ by the argument used in the proof of *Theorem 1*. But, x and y_0 belong to $\mathcal{S}^{\perp\perp}$, hence $x - y_0 \in \mathcal{S}^{\perp\perp}$; in particular, $x - y_0 \perp x - y_0$, $x = y_0 \in \mathcal{S}$, a contradiction.

5. Write $x_n = y_n + z_n$ according to *Theorem 1*.

6. (i) See Theorem 1.18 of [9].

(ii) See also *Exercise 4.1*.

§ 8.   1. Use condition (1′) to show that $T(u + v) = Tu + Tv$ for all $u, v \in \mathcal{K}$.

CHAPTER IV

§ 1.   2. Let $e_1,\cdots,e_n$ be the canonical basis for $\mathbb{C}^n$ (see *Example I.7.1*), $f_1,\cdots,f_m$ the canonical basis for $\mathbb{C}^m$, and express Te_k as a linear combination of the f_j.

7. See Section 1.72 of [10] for the existence of a basis (also called *Hamel basis*).

§ 2.   1. See *Exercise 1.4*.

3. See *Exercise I.6.4*.

4. See *Example I.7.3*.

§ 3.   3. Let $x_1,\cdots,x_n$ be a basis for $\mathcal{V}$, and $y_1,\cdots,y_m$ a basis for $\mathcal{W}$. For each pair of indices j and k ($j = 1,\cdots,m; k = 1,\cdots,n$), there is a unique linear mapping $E_{jk}: \mathcal{V} \to \mathcal{W}$ such that $E_{jk}x_k = y_j$ and $E_{jk}x_i = \theta$ when $i \ne k$. The E_{jk} are a basis for $\mathcal{L}(\mathcal{V},\mathcal{W})$.

6. There is no essential difference between this and the situation in *Exercise 3*. See also *Theorem 1.3* and *Exercise 1.7*.

§ 4.   4. (ii) Suppose T is surjective. For each $y \in \mathcal{Y}$, let $F(y)$ denote the non-empty set $\{x \in \mathcal{X}: Tx = y\}$. The problem is to define a mapping $R: \mathcal{Y} \to \mathcal{X}$ such that $T(Ry) = y$ for all $y \in \mathcal{Y}$, that is, $Ry \in F(y)$ for all $y \in \mathcal{Y}$. This is possible via the *axiom of choice; see* Theorem 1D of [6].

(iii) See *Exercises 2.9* and *2.10*.

§ 5. 2. Show there exists a non-zero vector x_1 in the range of E_{11}, and define $x_k = E_{k1}x_1$.

6. $\frac{1}{2}([a,b] + [b,a]) = \theta$, $\{a,b\} - \{b,a\} = \theta$.

§ 6. 2. For example, see *Exercise 4.5* and *Theorem 1*.

§ 7. 1. See the proof of *Theorem III.3.2*.

3. See *Exercise 2*.

7. See *Example II.4.8*.

9. The uniform limit of a sequence of continuous functions is continuous. See Theorem 229 of [5].

12. T is continuous by *Example 6*. Consider the real-valued mapping $x \to \parallel Tx \parallel$, where $\parallel x \parallel = 1$. This is a continuous mapping defined on a closed and bounded subset of $\mathbb{C}^n$. By the Weierstrass-Bolzano theorem, suitably generalized to $\mathbb{C}^n$, there is a vector $x_o \in \mathbb{C}^n$, $\parallel x_o \parallel = 1$, such that $\parallel Tx \parallel \geq \parallel Tx_o \parallel > 0$ whenever $\parallel x \parallel = 1$. This implies that T^{-1} is continuous. See also Section 3.12 of [10].

13. See *Exercises 12* and *3*.

14. See *Exercise 13* and Remark 3 following *Definition III.4.1*.

15. For the proof of completeness, see the argument used for l^2 in *Example II.5.1*.

17. See the discussion of l^2 in *Example II.5.1*.

18, 19. The inequality which exhibits subadditivity is known as *Minkowski's inequality*. See Section 21 of [8], or Section 14 of [6].

20. Without loss of generality, one can suppose $|\lambda_1| = \cdots = |\lambda_m| = 1$ and $|\lambda_k| < 1$ for $m < k \leq n$. Then $(\parallel x \parallel_p)^p = m + \sum_{m+1}^{n} |\lambda_k|^p$, thus $\parallel x \parallel_p = (m + \alpha_p)^{1/p}$, where $\alpha_p \to 0$ as $p \to \infty$. It follows that $\parallel x \parallel_p \to 1 = \parallel x \parallel_\infty$. See also Theorem 24A of [6].

21. See Section 10A of [6]; the relevant paper of J. von Neumann and P. Jordan is cited in the bibliography of [3].

§ 8. 1. (ii) Suppose $y_n \in \mathcal{F}$, $\parallel y_m - y_n \parallel \to 0$. Choose any $z \in \mathcal{P}$ with $\parallel z \parallel = 1$. Define $T_n: \mathcal{P} \to \mathcal{F}$ by the formula $T_n x = (x|z)y_n$. Clearly $\parallel T_m - T_n \parallel = \parallel y_m - y_n \parallel$.

(iii) See *Exercise 10.12*.

3. (i) If $x_k \in \mathfrak{N}$ and $x_k \to x$, look at $\| T_m x - T_n x \| \leq$ $\| T_m x - T_m x_k \| + \| T_m x_k - T_n x_k \| + \| T_n x_k - T_n x \| \leq$ $K \| x - x_k \| + \| T_m x_k - T_n x_k \| + K \| x_k - x \|$. See Theorem 2.11.4 of [4].

4. See Theorem 2.5.5 of [4].

5. See *Exercise 4*.

6. See *Exercises 3* and *5*.

§ 9. 1. If $\mathcal{E}$ has dimension n, let $S\colon \mathbb{C}^n \to \mathcal{E}$ be any vector space isomorphism. By *Exercise 7.12*, S and S^{-1} are continuous. Since $TS\colon \mathbb{C}^n \to \mathcal{F}$ is continuous by *Example 7.6*, $T = (TS)S^{-1}$ is continuous by *Theorem 1*.

2. See *Example 5.2*.

4. See *Exercise 10.12*.

§ 10. 1. See *Theorem 7.6*.

2. See *Exercises 9.1* and *3.3*.

3. See *Exercise 2*.

4. This is immediate from *Example 2;* see Theorem 2.7.4 of [4].

5. This follows from *Example 2;* see also Theorem 8D of [6].

6. (i) See *Exercise 2* and *Theorem 3*.
   (ii) Part (i), and *Exercise 7.12*.
   (iii) See *Exercise 5*.

7. (v) $\| T' \| \geq \| T \|$ results from *Example 2;* see Section 4.5 of [10].

12. Let $x_0 \in \mathcal{E}$, $\| x_0 \| = 1$. By Theorem 2.7.4 of [4], there exists an $f \in \mathcal{E}'$ such that $\| f \| = 1$ and $f(x_0) = 1$. Define $T_n\colon \mathcal{E} \to \mathcal{F}$ by the formula $T_n x = f(x)y_n$. Clearly $\| T_m - T_n \| = \| y_m - y_n \|$.

CHAPTER V

§ 1. 1. Choose $y \in \mathcal{V}$ with $f(y) = 1$, and look at $x = f(x)y + [x - f(x)y]$.

3. In view of *Theorem IV.10.2*, it suffices to show that given any $f \in \mathcal{P}'$, there is a vector $y \in \mathcal{P}$ such that $f = y'$. See the proof of *Theorem 1*.

4. Assume to the contrary that $\overline{\mathfrak{N}} \neq \mathfrak{K}$, and choose a vector $z \in (\overline{\mathfrak{N}})^{\perp}$ such that $f(z) = 1$. See the proof of *Theorem 1*. Incidentally, two linear forms having the same null space are necessarily scalar multiples of each other.

5. See *Exercise 4*. This result can be generalized to normed spaces; see Theorem 3.5-E of [10], or the Corollary to Theorem 2.6.2 of [4].

6. Given $x \in \mathcal{P}$, the mapping $y \rightarrow (y|x)$ is a continuous linear form on the Hilbert space $\mathfrak{N}$.

7. (iii) See the Corollary of *Theorem II.6.3*.

9. Given $F \in \mathfrak{IC}''$, $x \rightarrow [F(x')]^*$ is a continuous linear form on $\mathfrak{IC}$. By *Theorem 1*, there is a vector $y \in \mathfrak{IC}$ such that $[F(x')]^* = (x|y)$ for all $x \in \mathfrak{IC}$. Thus, $F(x') = (y|x) = y''(x')$. Then, $F = y''$ by *Theorem 1*.

§ 2.
1. See Remark 2 in the proof of *Theorem 1*, and the Corollary of *Theorem II.6.3*.

2. Take $\mathcal{P} = \mathfrak{IC}$ in *Theorem 1*; since U is isometric, and $\mathfrak{IC}$ is complete, $U(\mathfrak{IC})$ is complete.

3. (i) See *Exercise IV.7.21*.
   (ii) See the proof of *Theorem 1*; alternate proof via part (i).

4. (i) If $x',y' \in \mathfrak{N}$, define $(x'|y') = (y|x)$.
   (ii) See *Exercise 3*.

5. (i) See *Exercise IV.10.5*.

6. (iii) See *Exercise 3*.

7. See Subsection 13 of § 2 in Chapter I of [7], or Theorem 2.41-A of [10].

§ 3.
4. In view of *Example I.1.2*, it suffices to show that $\varphi + \psi$ and $\lambda\varphi$ are bilinear.

15. (ii) See Theorem 4.2-H of [10], or the Corollary to Theorem 2.12.1 of [4].
    (iii) This result is known as the *closed graph theorem*. It can be deduced from (ii) by considering the mapping $(x,Tx) \rightarrow x$, which is a continuous vector space isomorphism of the Banach space $\mathcal{G}_T$ onto the Banach space $\mathcal{E}$. See Theorem 4.2-I of [10], or Theorem 2.12.3 of [4].

§ 4.
1. $\varphi(x_n,y_n) - \varphi(x,y) = \varphi(x_n - x,y_n - y) + \varphi(x,y_n - y) + \varphi(x_n - x,y)$. For the proof that (c) implies (a), see the proof of *Theorem IV.7.3*.

7. If $x_n \in \mathfrak{M}$ and $y_n \in \mathfrak{N}$ are Cauchy sequences, then $\varphi(x_n,y_n) \in \mathfrak{B}$ is a Cauchy sequence, by an obvious modification of the identity given in the hint to *Exercise 1*. See also *Theorem IV.7.6*.

8. Say $\mathcal{E}$ is a Banach space. Consider the family of mappings $\mathcal{S} = \{\varphi^y : y \in \mathfrak{F}, \| y \| \leq 1\}$. For each $x \in \mathcal{E}$, $\| \varphi^y(x) \| =$

$\| \varphi(x,y) \| = \| \varphi_x(y) \| \leq \| \varphi_x \| \| y \| \leq \| \varphi_x \|$ whenever $\| y \| \leq 1$. Thus, $\mathcal{S}$ is a "pointwise bounded" family of continuous linear mappings of the Banach space $\mathcal{E}$ into the normed space $\mathcal{G}$. By the principle of uniform boundedness (see *Exercise IV.8.4*), there is a constant M such that $\| \varphi^y \| \leq M$ whenever $\| y \| \leq 1$. It follows that $\| \varphi(x,y) \| \leq M$ whenever $\| x \| \leq 1$ and $\| y \| \leq 1$; thus, φ is bounded, and $\| \varphi \| \leq M$.

9. (i) See *Example IV.10.2*, and Section 8C of [6].
11. See *Exercise 10*.
12. See the proof of *Theorem IV.8.2*; alternate proof via *Exercise 6*.

§ 5. 2. (i) See *Example 4* and *Theorem 1.2*.
   (ii) See *Exercise 2.4*.
   (iii) See *Example 8*.
9. (i) Show that $J(x + y) - (Jx + Jy)$ and $J(\lambda x) - \lambda^*(Jx)$ are orthogonal to $J(\mathcal{P})$; by assumption, they belong to $J(\mathcal{P})$.
   (iii) Show first that J is conjugate-linear and isometric.

§ 6. 3. $\varphi(x + y, x + y) - \varphi(x - y, x - y) = 4\varphi(x,y)$.

§ 8. 3. See Theorem 3.5 of [9].
6. See *Exercise 4.8*.
9. See the discussion of l^2 in *Example II.5.1*.
11. (i) See *Exercise 10*.
   (v) The surjectivity of the correspondence is discussed in *Exercise VIII.2.1*.
   (vi) Apply the polarization identity to the sesquilinear mapping $(S,T) \rightarrow T^*S$.
13. (iii) See *Theorem III.4.1*.
14. (ii) See *Exercise 13*.
15. (i) See *Exercise 14*.
   (ii) See *Theorem IV.9.3*.
16. See Theorem 5 in § 24 of [7].

CHAPTER VI

§ 2. 4. (ii) See *Exercise V.8.3*.
6. (i) One can show that if $\mathfrak{N}$ is a closed linear subspace of a normed space $\mathcal{E}$, $y \in \mathcal{E}$, and y is not in $\mathfrak{N}$, then there exists a continuous linear form f on $\mathcal{E}$ such that $f(x) = 0$ for all $x \in \mathfrak{N}$ but $f(y) \neq 0$. See Theorem 2.7.5 of [4].

(ii) See *Theorem V.1.1.*

7. (i) See *Example IV.10.1.*
   (ii) See *Exercise II.8.1.*

§ 4. 8. (i) $Tx = Ty$ if and only if $Sx = Sy$.
   (ii) See *Theorem 2*.

9. See *Exercise V.5.9.*

10. See *Exercise V.5.9.*

§ 5. 5. See *Theorem V.8.1.*

6. See *Exercise 4.9.*

9. (i) See *Theorem 4.2.*
   (ii) See *Exercise 4.11.*

§ 6. 3. See *Exercise 7.12.*

6. (i) See *Theorem V.7.2* and *Theorem 3*.
   (ii) See the proof of *Theorem 3*. See also *Exercises V.5.8* and *V.8.18*.

7. (vii) See *Theorem V.5.5.*
   (ix), (x), (xi) See Section 104 of [8].
   (xii) See Section 108 of [8].

10. See Section 104 of [8].

11. See *Example 4.1.*

12. (iv) By (iii), it suffices to show that $[R(\mathfrak{K})]^{\perp} = \{\theta\}$. Indeed, since $(Tx\,|\,x)$ is real, $(Rx\,|\,x) = 0$ implies $x = \theta$.

13. The details are similar to those in *Exercise 12*. See also *Exercise 11*.

14. See *Theorem III.8.1.*

§ 7. 6. See *Theorem 2* and *Example 4*.

12. (i) Calculate $(TP - T)^*(TP - T)$.

13. (i) Dimension.

§ 8. 3. (i) Look at $(T^*T)^*(T^*T)$.
   (ii) See *Exercise 7.12.*

4. $T - \mu I$ is normal.

5. See *Theorem V.8.6.*

6. See *Exercises 5* and *4.8.*

7. See *Exercise 4.8.*

8. (i) See *Exercise 6.*

10. T and T^* are both bijective. Let $R = T^{-1}, S = (T^*)^{-1}$. For all x and y, $(Rx\,|\,y) = (Rx\,|\,T^*Sy) = (TRx\,|\,Sy) = (x\,|\,Sy)$.

11. (iv) Part (iii) and *Theorem V.8.6.*
   (v) Apply (iv) to T^*, and quote *Exercise 9* part (ii).

12. T^* is injective by *Theorem V.8.6.* Let $S = \{x \in \mathfrak{K} : \|\,T^*x\,\|$

$\leq 1\}$. Given any $y \in \mathcal{K}$, the numbers $(x|y)$ are bounded as x varies over $\mathcal{S}$; for, supposing $y = Tz$, for all $x \in \mathcal{S}$ one has
$$|(x|y)| = |(x|Tz)| = |(T^*x|z)| \leq \|T^*x\| \|z\| \leq \|z\|.$$
It follows from the principle of uniform boundedness (see *Exercise IV.8.4*) that there is a constant $K > 0$ such that $\|x\| \leq K$ for all $x \in \mathcal{S}$. It follows that $\|T^*y\| \geq K^{-1} \|y\|$ for all $y \in \mathcal{K}$; this is clear if $y = \theta$, and if $y \neq \theta$, then $T^*y \neq \theta$, and the vector $x = \|T^*y\|^{-1}y$ belongs to $\mathcal{S}$.

13. T^* is bounded below by *Exercise 12*. See part (v) of *Exercise 11*.

14. (ii) See part (vi) of *Exercise 11*.

15. (vi) This is a theorem of C. R. Putnam; see the *American Journal of Mathematics*, Vol. 73 (1951), pp. 357-62.

§ 9. 8. (i) See *Exercise 4.7*.
   (ii) See the calculation in *Example 9*.
  9. (ii) See *Exercise 6.9*.
   (iii) See the calculation in *Example 9*.
  10. (i) If $x \in \mathfrak{N}$, $\|R^*x\| = \text{LUB}\{|(R^*x|y)| : y \in \mathfrak{N}, \|y\| \leq 1\}$. Alternate proof via *Exercise 4*.
  11. See *Exercises 4.8* and *6.9*.
  12. See *Exercise 11*.
  14. (i) See *Exercise VII.2.6*. There is also a simple argument using "trace."
   (ii) $T/\mathfrak{N}$ is hyponormal by *Exercise 10*, hence $T/\mathfrak{N}$ is normal by part (i). Quote *Exercise 9*.
  15. Calculate $T^*T - TT^*$.
  16. See *Exercise 8* and *Example 8*; see also *Exercise 14*.
  17. See *Example 8*.

CHAPTER VII

§ 1. 1. See *Example IV.7.6*.
  5. For example, let $T = U + U^*$, where U is any operator such that U^* is isometric and U has no proper values; for instance, U can be the two-sided shift operator (see *Example 8*). Suppose $Tx = \alpha x$. Then, $Ux + U^*x = \alpha x$; applying U, one has $UUx + x = \alpha Ux$, $(UU - \alpha U + I)x = \theta$. Suppose $t^2 - \alpha t + 1 = (t - \lambda)(t - \mu)$. Then $(U - \lambda I)(U - \mu I)x = \theta$. It follows that $x = \theta$.
  6. It is easy to see that $T - \mu I$ is hyponormal, for every scalar

μ. Or, apply part (iii) of *Exercise VI.9.9* to the linear subspace generated by x.

7. (i) See *Exercise II.3.2*.

(iii) Let $Tx_k = x_{k+1}$ be the one-sided shift operator, and set $x = \sum_1^\infty \alpha_k x_k$. By *Example 6*, T has no proper values, hence $|(Tx|x)| < \| T \|$ by part (ii).

§ 2.   1. See the Corollary of *Theorem VI.9.2*.

3. See *Theorems 2* and *3*. It can be shown that if T is *any* normal operator, then $ST = TS$ implies $ST^* = T^*S$; see Theorem 41.2 of [3].

4. Clearly $\mathfrak{N}_T(\mu)$ reduces T; let $S = T^*$ in *Theorem 3*.

5. (i) See *Exercise 1.6*.

(ii) $T/\mathfrak{N}$ and $T^*/\mathfrak{N}$ are scalar operators; see also part (iii) of *Exercise VI.9.9*.

(iii) See part (i) and the proof of *Theorem 2*.

(iv) See *Exercise 4*.

6. There is a simple argument using "trace." Another proof, by induction on the dimension n of $\mathfrak{IC}$, runs as follows. For $n = 1$, every operator is normal. Assume the theorem holds for dimensions $<n$. It can be shown that every linear mapping in a finite-dimensional space has at least one proper value (see § 55 of [2]). Let μ be a proper value for T, and let $\mathfrak{N} = \mathfrak{N}_T(\mu)$. By *Exercise 5*, $\mathfrak{N}$ reduces T, and $T/\mathfrak{N}$ is normal. But, $\mathfrak{N}^\perp$ also reduces T, and $T/\mathfrak{N}^\perp$ is hyponormal by *Exercise VI.9.10*, hence $T/\mathfrak{N}^\perp$ is normal by the inductive assumption. See *Exercise VI.9.18*.

8. Induction on n.

§ 3.   1. $\big| \, \| Tx_n \| - \| \mu x_n \| \, \big| \le \| Tx_n - \mu x_n \|$.

6. (i) $T - \mu I$ is hyponormal.

(ii) $(\mu - \nu)(x_n | y_n) = ((\mu I - T)x_n | y_n) + (x_n | (T^* - \nu^* I)y_n)$.

7. Let $S = T^*$, where $Tx_k = x_{k+1}$ is the one-sided shift operator, and consider $\mu = 0$.

9. See the hint for *Exercise VIII.3.1*.

10. If $\| x_n \| = 1$ and $\| Tx_n - \mu x_n \| \to 0$, define $S_n x = (x | x_n)x_n$, as in *Example VI.7.2*. Conversely, if the operators S_n satisfy condition (b), choose vectors y_n with $\| y_n \| = 1$ and $\| S_n y_n \| \ge \frac{1}{2}$, and set $x_n = \| S_n y_n \|^{-1} S_n y_n$.

11. Suppose $\| x_n \| = 1$ and $\| Tx_n - \mu x_n \| \to 0$. By Section 8C of [6], there exist continuous linear forms f_n such that $\| f_n \| = 1$ and $f_n(x_n) = 1$. Set $S_n x = f_n(x)x_n$.

12. (i) See *Exercise 8*.
    (ii) See *Exercise VI.8.9*.
    (vi) $T^{-1} - \mu^{-1}I = \mu^{-1}(\mu I - T)T^{-1}$.
    (vii) See *Exercise VI.6.12*.
    (viii) See *Exercise VI.6.13*.
    (ix) See Subsection 3 in § 9 of [7], or Theorem 4.7.4 of [4].
    (x) Suppose μ is not an AP-value. By *Exercise 8*, $T - \mu I$ is bounded below, hence $T - \mu I$ is invertible by part (iv) of *Exercise VI.8.14*.
    (xi) If $\mu \in s(T)$, μ is an AP-value by part (x), hence $|\mu| = 1$ by *Exercise 3*.
    (xii) *Exercise 1.4* and parts (ii), (ix).

13. Let x_n be an orthonormal basis for $\mathfrak{K}$, and choose a sequence $\mu_n \in \Lambda$ such that every $\mu \in \Lambda$ is the limit of a subsequence of μ_n (see *Exercises II.8.3* and *III.6.6*). Define $Tx_n = \mu_n x_n$. Every $\mu \in \Lambda$ is an AP-value for T by the argument in *Example 2*. If λ is not in Λ, there is an $\epsilon > 0$ such that $|\mu_n - \lambda| \geq \epsilon$ for all n. Clearly $(T - \lambda I)^*(T - \lambda I) \geq \epsilon^2 I$, hence λ is not an AP-value for T, by *Exercise 8*. Indeed, $T - \lambda I$ is invertible by part (iv) of *Exercise VI.8.14*, hence λ is not in $s(T)$.

CHAPTER VIII

§ 1. 2. T is an operator by *Example IV.7.6*.
   5. See *Theorem 4* and *Example 3*.
   6. (i) If $\| x_n \| = 1$ and T^*Tx_n is convergent, then Tx_n is Cauchy by the calculation

$$\| T(x_m - x_n) \|^2 = (T^*T(x_m - x_n) \mid x_m - x_n)$$
$$\leq 2 \| T^*Tx_m - T^*Tx_n \|.$$

   See Subsection 10 of § 5 of [7].
   (ii) $(T^*)^*T^* = TT^*$ is CC by *Theorem 4*.
   7. (i) See *Example 3*.
   (ii) See *Exercise VI.8.12*, *Exercise 6*, and part (i).
   8. (ii) Let $\mathfrak{N}$ be the n-dimensional linear subspace generated by the y_k, and define a linear mapping $T: \mathfrak{N} \to \mathfrak{K}$ such that $Ty_k = z_k$ (see *Theorem IV.1.3*). T is continuous. Define $T = 0$ on $\mathfrak{N}^\perp$, and extend T to $\mathfrak{K}$ via the relation $\mathfrak{K} = \mathfrak{N} \oplus \mathfrak{N}^\perp$. Then, T is a finite-dimensional operator.

9. (i) See *Theorem IV.9.3*.

   (ii) See *Exercise V.8.13*.

   (iii) See *Example 3* and *Exercise 2*.

   (iv) See *Exercise V.8.15*.

10. (ii) It suffices to consider an operator with one-dimensional range, say $Tx = (x|x_1)z$; one can assume $\|x_1\| = 1$. Let $\mathfrak{N}$ be the null space of T; $\mathfrak{N}$ is a separable Hilbert space (see *Exercise III.6.5*), hence has an orthonormal basis $x_2, x_3, \cdots$. Then, $x_1, x_2, x_3, \cdots$ is an orthonormal basis for $\mathfrak{K}$, and $\sum_1^\infty \|Tx_k\|^2 = \|Tx_1\|^2$.

11. Let $R \in \mathit{g}$, $R \neq 0$. If z is a vector such that $Rz \neq \theta$, and A is the operator $Ax = (x|z)z$, clearly $T = RA$ is an operator with one-dimensional range, and $T \in \mathit{g}$. One has $Tx = (x|z)y$, where $y = Rz$. Suppose S is any other operator with one-dimensional range; by *Exercise VI.7.14*, $Sx = (x|z_1)y_1$ for suitable vectors y_1, z_1. By *Exercise 8*, there exist operators B and C such that $Bz = z_1$ and $Cy = y_1$. Then $S = CTB^*$, hence $S \in \mathit{g}$. Thus, g contains every operator with one-dimensional range. See the proof of *Theorem 3*.

12. If $\|Tx_n\| \geq n$, Tx_n cannot have a convergent subsequence.

13. (i) See *Theorems 1* and *2*.

   (ii) See *Theorem 4*.

   (iii) See the proof of *Theorem 5*.

   (v) See *Exercise IV.7.12*.

   (vi) If $\mathcal{E}$ is infinite-dimensional, one can construct an infinite sequence x_n such that $\|x_n\| = 1$ and $\|x_m - x_n\| \geq \frac{1}{2}$ whenever $m \neq n$; see item V in Subsection 1 of §4 of [7].

14. If $\mathcal{E}$ has dimension n, let $S: \mathbb{C}^n \to \mathcal{E}$ be any vector space isomorphism; S and S^{-1} are continuous by *Exercise IV.7.12*, and $TS: \mathbb{C}^n \to \mathcal{F}$ is continuous by *Example IV.7.6*. If $x_n \in \mathcal{E}$ and $\|x_n\| \leq 1$, $S^{-1}x_n$ has a convergent subsequence (by the complete continuity of $I: \mathbb{C}^n \to \mathbb{C}^n$), hence so does $(TS)(S^{-1}x_n)$.

15. (i) If $\|x\| = 1$, $z_n \in \mathfrak{N}$, and $z_n \to x$, then $\|z_n\| \to 1$; set $y_n = \|z_n\|^{-1}z_n$.

   (ii) If $x_n \in \mathcal{E}$ and $\|x_n\| \leq 1$, choose $y_n \in \mathfrak{N}$ with $\|y_n\| = \|x_n\|$ and $\|y_n - x_n\| < 1/n$.

16. See Theorem 2.13.5 of [4].

§ 2.   1. Let T_n be the unique operator such that $T_n x_k = \sum_{j=1}^{n} \alpha_{jk} x_j$ for all k. Then, T_n is finite-dimensional and $\| T_m - T_n \| \to 0$.

  2. Observe that $\sum_{j,k} |\alpha_{jk}|^2 < \infty$, and quote *Exercise 1*.

§ 3.   1. (i) See *Theorem 3*.

    (ii) By Theorem 26A of [6], there exists a scalar μ in the spectrum of T such that $|\mu| = \| T \|$. By part (x) of *Exercise VII.3.12*, μ is an AP-value. Quote *Theorem VII.3.1*.

  4. Let μ be a scalar in the spectrum of T with $|\mu|$ as large as possible (see part (ix) of *Exercise VII.3.12*). Let λ_n be any sequence of scalars such that $|\lambda_n| > |\mu|$ and $\lambda_n \to \mu$. Defining $R_n = T - \lambda_n I$ and $R = T - \mu I$, one has $\| R_n - R \| \to 0$; the R_n are invertible, and R isn't. We assert that μ is an AP-value for T. Assume to the contrary; by *Exercise VII.3.10* there exists an $\epsilon > 0$ such that $\| RS \| \geq \epsilon$ whenever $\| S \| = 1$. Then, $\| RS \| \geq \epsilon \| S \|$ for every operator S. Fix any index m such that $\| R_m - R \| < \epsilon/2$. For every operator S, $\epsilon \| S \| \leq \| RS \| = \| (R - R_m)S + R_m S \| \leq \| (R - R_m)S \| + \| R_m S \| \leq \| R - R_m \| \| S \| + \| R_m S \| \leq \epsilon/2 \| S \| + \| R_m S \|$. In particular, for $S = R_m^{-1}$, one has $\epsilon \| R_m^{-1} \| \leq \epsilon/2 \| R_m^{-1} \| + 1$, hence $\epsilon/2 \leq \| R_m^{-1} \|^{-1}$. Then $\| R_m - R \| < \epsilon/2 \leq \| R_m^{-1} \|^{-1}$. It follows that R is invertible (see the proof of Theorem 4.3.2 of [4]), a contradiction. See also the Corollary of Theorem 4.11.1 of [4].

  5. See § 55 of [2].

  6. See Theorem 5.5-C of [10].

  7. For any operator T, $\lim \| T^n \|^{1/n} = \text{LUB} \{ |\mu| : \mu \in s(T) \}$, where $s(T)$ is the spectrum of T (see Theorem 4.7.3 of [4]), hence the equivalence of (b) and (c) is clear.

    (b) implies (a) by part (i) of *Exercise VII.3.12*, and *Exercise 4*.

    (a) implies (b) is implicit in the hint given for *Exercise 4*. It should be mentioned that the usual definition of "generalized nilpotent" is condition (c). If T is normal, it can be shown that $\lim \| T^n \|^{1/n} = \| T \|$ (see Theorem 4.12.1 of [4]).

  8. Since S has no proper values, by *Theorem 2* it cannot have a non-zero AP-value. Incidentally, $\| S x_k \| = 1/k \to 0$ shows that 0 is an AP-value.

§ 4.   2. See the Corollary of *Theorem 1.5* for the "if" part. Conversely if T is CC, then T^* is CC by *Exercise 1.6;* consider the Cartesian form $T = A + iB$.

3. (i) See the hint to *Exercise VII.2.3.*
   (ii) Show that $(T - S)(T - S)^* \leq (T - S)^*(T - S)$.
   (iii) Parts (i) and (ii).

4. See *Theorem 2.*

6. (iii) The reference for this is given in the hint to *Exercise VI.8.15.*

8. This is clear if $T_k = 0$ for all k. Assume otherwise, say $T_1 \neq 0$. Let μ be a non-zero proper value for T_1, and consider $\mathfrak{N} = \mathfrak{N}_{T_1}(\mu)$. $\mathfrak{N}$ is invariant under each T_k. Since moreover $T_k^*T_1 = T_1 T_k^*$, $\mathfrak{N}$ reduces each T_k.

   Among the finite-dimensional linear subspaces, different from $\{\theta\}$, which reduce every T_k, let $\mathfrak{M}$ be one of smallest possible dimension. Let $R_k = T_k/\mathfrak{M}$. It suffices to show that every R_k is a scalar operator. Assume to the contrary, say, that R_j is not scalar. Let λ be a proper value of R_j. By assumption, $\mathfrak{N}_{R_j}(\lambda) \neq \mathfrak{M}$. But, the earlier argument shows that $\mathfrak{N}_{R_j}(\lambda)$ reduces each R_k, hence each T_k (because already $\mathfrak{M}$ reduces each T_k); this contradicts the minimality of the dimension of $\mathfrak{M}$.

9. See Theorem 5.5-G of [10].

10. See the Remark preceding Theorem 2.13.4 of [4].

Index